The Illustrated Encyclopedia of
ANIMALS

Marshall Cavendish

Academic Advisors:
Doctor Ray Hall,
Lecturer in Geography,
Queen Mary College, University of London.

Doctor P. F. Rawson, B.Sc., Ph.D., F.G.S.,
Queen Mary College, University of London.

Editors:
Michael Bisacre
Richard Carlisle
Deborah Robertson
John Ruck

Published by Marshall Cavendish Books Limited
58 Old Compton Street,
London W1V 5PA.

© Marshall Cavendish Limited 1975—84

Printed and bound in Italy by New Interlitho SpA.

ISBN 0 86307 200 3

Contents

The
World of Animals

The Animal Kingdom

Probably the best known division in the animal kingdom is that between the animals which have backbones, the vertebrates, and those which do not, the invertebrates. The vertebrates claim a larger share of human attention since man himself is a vertebrate—it is easier for us to relate to animals that are built more or less on the same body plan. Also, the vertebrates are the largest of animals.

Whatever the invertebrates may lack in size is more than compensated for in numbers. They are so numerous that their combined weight, or *biomass*, is far greater than that of the vertebrates. As proof of this, it is only necessary to think of the structure of a typical food chain and its associated pyramid of numbers. The organisms at each level of the pyramid, which form the food of those at the level above, must have a greater biomass than their predators. For example, on the African plains the breeding population of antelopes and zebra must have a greater biomass than the population of lions which it supports.

The invertebrates also dominate the animal world in numbers of species. As zoologists tend to disagree about the details of classification their estimates vary, but well over a million species of living animals are known and only about 40,000 of these are species of vertebrates. All the others are invertebrates, including three-quarters of a million arthropods, a group which might be judged the most successful of all. Insects are arthropods and just one group of insects, the beetles, outnumber the living species of vertebrates by over 7 to 1, for almost 300,000 species of beetles are known.

Animal groups

The animal kingdom is made up of 24 or 25 major subdivisions, or *phyla*. The members of a particular phylum will all have certain features in common at one time or another in their life histories, even though they may look very different as adults. It would be hard to imagine two more different animals than men and sea squirts, yet we both belong to the same phylum, the *Chordata*. The tadpole-like larva of the sea squirt has the three typical chordate features: a *notochord* running dorsally along the body, gill slits in the pharynx and a nerve chord lying centrally above the notochord. These features are also observed in the human embryo, but, except for the nerve chord, they do not last for long.

The construction of a family tree to show the relationships between the various phyla and the order of their evolution is bound to be somewhat speculative—evolution is a slow process and has taken place over many millions of years. The family relationships and ancestry of a particular animal may be established by a number of methods. Firstly it must be compared in all stages of development with other animals. If there is a strong similarity between, say, the larvae of two animals this may indicate a close family relationship. On the other hand it may simply mean that the two

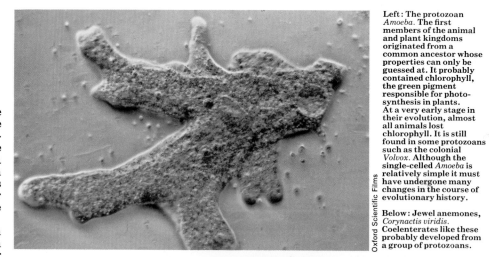

Left: The protozoan *Amoeba*. The first members of the animal and plant kingdoms originated from a common ancestor whose properties can only be guessed at. It probably contained chlorophyll, the green pigment responsible for photosynthesis in plants. At a very early stage in their evolution, almost all animals lost chlorophyll. It is still found in some protozoans such as the colonial *Volvox*. Although the single-celled *Amoeba* is relatively simple it must have undergone many changes in the course of evolutionary history.

Below: Jewel anemones, *Corynactis viridis*. Coelenterates like these probably developed from a group of protozoans.

Oxford Scientific Films

Below: An earthworm, *Lumbricus terrestris*. In common with other annelids, the earthworm has a segmented body. Although most of the segments are alike, some are specialized for particular functions. The saddle-like bulge (the clitellum) visible in the picture plays an important role in reproduction.

Stephen Dalton/NHPA

Heather Angel

Left: An African grasshopper in mid-air. Along with crustaceans and spiders, insects belong to the enormous phylum *Arthropoda*. Although arthropods have segmented bodies like annelids, specialization is much more extreme. The third thoracic segment, for example, carries powerful legs, and wings.

W. Perrie/NHPA

Below: An edible snail, *Helix pomatia*. Unlike annelids and arthropods, molluscs are not segmented, and it therefore seems likely that they branched off from the evolutionary tree before segmentation arose. There is, however, a striking similarity between the trochophore larvae of molluscs and those of annelids.

Jean Paul Thomas/Jacana

A lioness with zebra kill, in South West Africa. The vigilance of the zebra herd forces lions to make combined rushes, or lie in ambush for their prey.

grasshopper

butterfly

beetle

wasp

louse

flea

centipede

man

chimpanzee

peripatus

scorpion

spider

woodlouse

silverfish

mite

bluebottle

land snail

jaguar

earthworm

lobster

squid

sea snail

sea slug

syncarida

nautilus

sea butterfly

ragworm

copepod

rotifer

cockle

bryozoa

leech

barnacle

nematode worm

chiton

brachiopod

deuterostomia

stony coral

protostomia

tapeworm

turbellaria

gastrula

jellyfish

graptolite (extinct)

blastula

hydrozoan

morula

tabulata (extinct)

simple cell

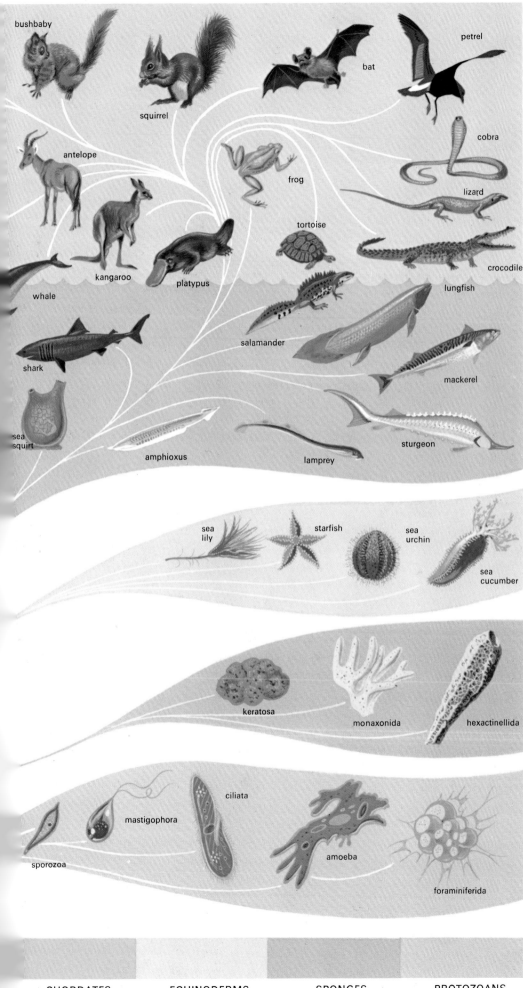

larvae have adapted in the same way to similar living conditions. It is always important to look at all the evidence rather than a single clue. Further indications of an animal's ancestry can sometimes be found in its development from egg to adult, particularly in the way the cells divide and the way the mouth and anus are formed.

Fortunately we do not have to rely only on what we can glean from living species, for fossil remains provide direct evidence of animals which lived in prehistoric times. Indeed fossils provide the most satisfactory evidence of an animal's ancestry. Usually the most ancient fossils are found in the lower rock strata and the most recent ones in the upper strata.

Some of the best fossil lineages are provided by the molluscs. Snails with backwardly coiled shells, straight-shelled cephalopods (related to the present day nautilus) and bivalves were already common in the Ordovician seas of 450 million years ago, and since that time molluscs have been a dominant group in the sea. At one time the sea was populated by great numbers of these early molluscs called *ammonites*, and today their relatives the squids and cuttlefish are important open sea creatures. Sea urchins and starfish have a good fossil history but some other groups, notably the arthropods, are not so well represented and it is more difficult to understand their relationships with the other invertebrates.

Early characteristics
Two important features, observed in almost all animals, probably arose at a very early stage in evolutionary history: bilateral symmetry and the presence of a mesoderm layer between the inner and outer body walls. The former condition may have come about as an adaptation to feeding on the seabed. The development of the mesoderm layer paved the way for the appearance of an internal body cavity surrounding the gut, a necessary preliminary to the development of more specialized organs. The way in which the mesoderm is formed in an embryo or larva provides an important distinction between animals on the two main lines of animal evolution, known as the arthropod and the chordate lines.

The development of the body cavity was a significant improvement in the body plan. Muscles could press against such a fluid-filled cavity to push the animal through the mud without interfering with the operation of the mouth or any other activities of the gut. Organs could become bigger and more complex in an internal body cavity. Several worms evolved with body cavities that fulfilled these functions but they were not identical in structure. The earthworm's body cavity is called a *coelom*. Its ancestors probably had an open cavity so the animal was just two long tubes, one inside the other. The earthworm, however, is segmented and so the coelom is divided up. The animal

Left: An evolutionary tree of the animal kingdom. The scheme begins with a simple cell, the supposed ancestor of plants as well as animals. The single-celled animals, the protozoans, probably developed directly from this. Cell division led to more complex structures: the morula, blastula and gastrula.

In the last of these an inner wall of cells is present and the animal has developed radial symmetry. It is likely that the ancestors of the coelenterates and the sponges developed from animals modelled on the gastrula plan as did the forerunners of the chordate and arthropod lines. Most extinct animals are not shown.

CHORDATES   ECHINODERMS   SPONGES   PROTOZOANS

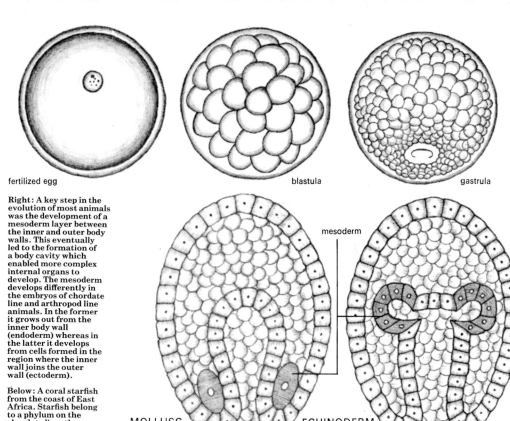

fertilized egg

blastula

gastrula

moves with one of its pointed ends going first, so the segments at this end become modified so as to become a sort of reconnaissance party, with the main outward-looking sense organs and an important nerve centre. In other words, a simple head develops.

In the arthropods the process has gone further and the head is distinct. So distinct, in fact, that its original segmented nature has been modified almost beyond recognition. Vertebrates, too, are segmented but in a different way. The segmentation can be seen in the repetition of the vertebrate and the spinal nerves.

The arthropod body plan

In the arthropod body plan segmentation is retained and the exoskeleton appears for the first time. In evolving an external skeleton the arthropods have produced an outstandingly effective answer to a number of problems. The arthropod skeleton provides support for the body, protection from enemies and, often, protection against the loss of such important substances as water. As compared with the internal vertebrate skeleton the arthropod skeleton is not only more useful in these ways, but also stronger. As any engineer knows, a hollow tube is stronger than a solid rod of the same material and equivalent weight.

The external skeleton is a major factor in the success of the arthropods, but it also imposes severe limitations upon them. It limits their size and, because an external skeleton cannot grow as easily as an internal one, arthropods must moult as they grow. Moulting is a hazardous process. For a short while, until its new, larger skeleton expands and hardens, the moulting arthropod is defenceless.

Another factor which limits arthropod size is the manner in which they supply oxygen to their internal tissues. In some arthropod groups, including the insects, tracheae—tiny branching tubes—carry air to all parts of the body. Air moves through the tracheae at least in part by diffusion, a process which is inadequate to supply oxygen to the middle of a large organism. The bulkiest insect, the Goliath beetle, uses muscular pumping to help ventilate the tracheae, but even so it is less than 15 cm (6 in) long when fully grown.

Appearing before the vertebrates on the chordate line of evolution are the echinoderms. One reason they appear on this branch of the plan is that, in the embryo, the mesoderm layer develops in the same way as in the chordates.

Vertebrates

By far the most important chordates are the vertebrates—animals with backbones. The first vertebrates probably appeared about 450 million years ago. They were fish which looked rather like an armoured version of the present-day lamprey and they had neither jaws nor pairs of fins. They used the gill slits in the pharynx to strain food from the water. From these early vertebrates fish called *placoderms* developed, which had both jaws and paired pectoral and pelvic fins and sometimes a series of smaller fins between these. The placoderms gave rise to the cartilagenous fish such as sharks. These and the bony fish were able to colonise freshwater and marine habitats as successfully as the molluscs and arthropods. Their shape, pattern and colour was

6

Right: A key step in the evolution of most animals was the development of a mesoderm layer between the inner and outer body walls. This eventually led to the formation of a body cavity which enabled more complex internal organs to develop. The mesoderm develops differently in the embryos of chordate line and arthropod line animals. In the former it grows out from the inner body wall (endoderm) whereas in the latter it develops from cells formed in the region where the inner wall joins the outer wall (ectoderm).

Below: A coral starfish from the coast of East Africa. Starfish belong to a phylum on the chordate line, the *Echinodermata*.

mesoderm

MOLLUSC EMBRYO

ECHINODERM EMBRYO

David C. Houston/Bruce Coleman

Heather Angel

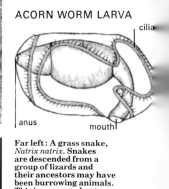

ACORN WORM LARVA

cilia

anus

mouth

Far left: A grass snake, *Natrix natrix*. Snakes are descended from a group of lizards and their ancestors may have been burrowing animals. This is suggested not only by the loss of limbs but also by the structure of their eyes and ears. The remnants of hind legs can still be seen in some snakes such as boas and pythons.

Left: A puffin, *Fratercula arctica*, with two newly caught fish. Like the mammals, birds are descended from reptiles. They developed very rapidly at the end of the Mesozoic era about 65 million years ago. Their success was no doubt helped by the rapid spread of insects and flowering plants at that time. These provided a plentiful supply of food.

Heather Angel

Bruce Coleman

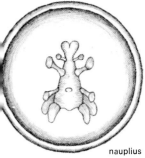

nauplius

larva

Left: The development of a lobster from egg to larva. One way to learn about an animal's ancestry is to study the growth of its embryo. In the case of a lobster there is a three-limbed nauplius stage which is characteristic of all crustaceans, even of the sedentary barnacles which do not outwardly look like crustaceans.

Right: Sea squirts, *Ciona intestinalis*. These are one of the few groups of invertebrate animals to belong to the phylum *Chordata*, which includes all the vertebrates. The relationship between an adult sea squirt and the other chordates is not at all obvious, but chordate features are clearly seen in a sea squirt's tadpole-like larva.

Below: A grayling, *Thymallus thymallus*. Present day fish developed from jawless ancestors which were the first vertebrate animals. The fish's body is supported by its backbone but is able to flex from side to side. It is movements of this sort that propel the fish through the water.

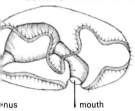

ECHINODERM LARVA

anus   mouth

Left: Although there is hardly any resemblance between an adult chordate and an adult echinoderm, the larvae shown here are very much alike. Acorn worms belong to a phylum which is closely related to the chordates. This sort of similarity often helps to establish relationships between otherwise quite different animals.

Above: A brightly coloured toad, *Bufo periglenes*. Amphibians have changed considerably since they first ventured from the sea about 350 million years ago, but most of them still must return to the water to breed. Amphibians have adapted to many habitats. Some frogs have toe pads for climbing trees.

Below: Cheetahs, *Acinonyx jubata*, are the fastest mammals. They can keep up a speed of about 100 kph (62 mph) over a distance of 600 m (660 yd). Like birds, mammals are warm-blooded and this enables them to lead more active lives than other animals like reptiles whose blood temperature varies with the surroundings.

modified to suit the conditions they colonised, but their success depended in each case on a body plan with an internal supporting skeleton.

The bony fish fell into two groups—those whose bones and muscles remained within the body wall and those whose bones and muscles extended into the fins. A group of these latter 'lobe-finned' fish were probably the first vertebrates to venture on to land: they became the first amphibians. The lobe fins were gradually transformed into legs.

The early amphibians would have been able to feed on a variety of invertebrates which had preceded them on to land, indeed it may have been the presence of this new food source that first attracted them from the water. Amphibians could not, however, stray far from water. They needed a moist environment to keep down the loss of water from their bodies by evaporation and they could not breed in the absence of water. Their larvae were aquatic.

A group of amphibians gave rise to the reptiles which were much better equipped for life on land. A waterproof outer layer of the skin eliminated the problem of water loss and they were able to colonise dry areas of the land. Extra membranes in the reptiles' eggs kept the embryo bathed in fluid and allowed it to develop on dry land.

The Mesozoic era, with the coming of the giant dinosaurs, was the heyday of the reptiles. One such animal, the brontosaurus, must have weighed about 20 tonnes, reaching a length of 18 m (60 ft). It was the largest land animal that has ever lived. By the end of the Mesozoic era, about 65 million years ago, the reptiles were on the decline and the dinosaurs had become extinct.

From two groups of the many reptiles that once existed, the birds and the mammals evolved. Some reptilian features, such as the scaly skin on their legs, are still evident in birds. Both birds and mammals differ from reptiles in one fundamental respect: they are warm-blooded. In order to lead an active life the conversion of food into energy must proceed at an adequate rate in the animal's body. The biochemical reactions involved, like most chemical reactions, are very dependent on temperature—if the temperature is too low they will proceed relatively slowly. Thus reptiles, being cold-blooded, cannot keep moving for long periods even though they can move very swiftly for a short time; at night, when their body temperature is low, they are very sluggish. Birds and mammals, on the other hand, have both developed mechanisms for keeping the body temperature at a suitable constant level and so are capable of sustained periods of activity.

In mammals there are three main structural departures from the reptilian body plan. Firstly, the limbs are rotated so that they become located underneath the body rather than projecting from the sides. This is a much improved arrangement for an animal that lives on land, for much less effort is required to support the body weight—it is transmitted directly through straightened legs to the ground. Secondly, the jaws of mammals are much simpler than those of reptiles and thirdly, the teeth of mammals are divided into three basic types, incisors, canines and molars, while the teeth of a reptile are all very much alike.

The Invertebrates

Corals, when formed into reefs, seem not to be animals at all. Reef building corals are found north and south of the equator as far as the 25th line of latitude. Each begins as a larva, later changing into a polyp. (see p.132).

Protozoa

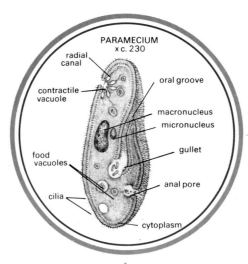

PARAMECIUM
x c. 230

radial canal

contractile vacuole

oral groove

macronucleus

micronucleus

food vacuoles

gullet

anal pore

cilia

cytoplasm

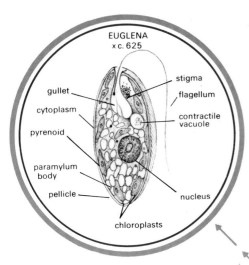

EUGLENA
x c. 625

gullet

stigma

cytoplasm

flagellum

pyrenoid

contractile vacuole

paramylum body

pellicle

nucleus

chloroplasts

The Protozoa, 'first animals', are a group of minute, single-celled organisms forming the lowest major division or phylum of the Animal Kingdom. The rest of the Animal Kingdom is composed of multicellular organisms, the Metazoa.

Although there are more protozoa in the world than all other animals put together, their activities generally pass unobserved because they are so small. The majority are smaller than 1mm in diameter and are invisible to the unaided eye. Many have to be measured in microns—1micron, μ (mu) = 0.001mm—and can only be seen under a microscope.

The fascinating life of the Protozoa was first seen and studied by Anton van Leeuwenhoek, a seventeenth century Dutch microscopist. About 45,000 distinct forms, or species, both living and extinct have since been identified. These can be divided into four sections, or classes, according to their different methods of locomotion—the Sarcodina, including the amoeba; the flagellates or Mastigophora; the ciliates or Ciliophora; and the spore formers or Sporozoa.

Occasionally numbers increase to such an extent that the protozoa can be seen by the naked eye. A common flagellate, *Euglena,* forms a green scum on the top of stagnant ponds, for example, as large numbers are attracted to the light at the surface. In the Caribbean and off the coast of California, periodic surges in the population of another flagellate, *Gonyaulax,* colour the sea red by day and make it brightly luminescent by night. During these 'red tides', the concentration of toxic waste materials produced by *Gonyaulax* becomes lethal to other marine life. Thousands of fish and shellfish are killed, with serious economic consequences for the local fishermen.

Habitat and ecology

Protozoa are widely distributed throughout the world, living everywhere and anywhere there is fresh or salt water, from the polar regions to hot springs. Since they are microscopic, they are able to exploit situations that are inaccessible to

Left: *Euglena* is a bright green flagellate often found in the green scum floating on the surface of stagnant ponds. The light sensitive red eyespot on the gullet guides it to the strong sunlight it needs to build its own food from simple chemicals. It bores its way quickly through the water by the spiralling motion of its flagellum.

Above: *Paramecium* is covered by short, motile 'hairs' or cilia which are used for movement and feeding. It is always very active, busily swimming around in search of good feeding grounds and living conditions. It is also one of the speediest protozoa and has been recorded covering about 600 times its own length in a minute.

Structurally a protozoan resembles a single cell, the basic unit from which all plants and animals are made. Three dimensional diagrams of cross sections of a 'model' cell and the various types of protozoa show how each is basically a blob of colourless, gelatinous cytoplasm contained by a cell membrane. In the protozoa the cytoplasm is often divided into a clear, outer ectoplasm and a granular, inner endoplasm. The cell membrane allows simple chemicals to enter and leave the cell yet stops complex proteins in the cytoplasm from escaping. Small units or organelles suspended in the cytoplasm do all the work of the cell under the direction of the nucleus. The

mitochondria are the energy generators of the living cell. The endoplasmic reticulum, a convoluted network of double membranes weaving through the cytoplasm, may serve as a transport system. It also supports some ribosomes, the cell's protein-making factories. These proteins may be stored in the Golgi apparatus. The protozoa have made modifications to the basic cell format. Structures such as cilia, flagella, contractile and food vacuoles, shells and skeletons equip them for life as independent organisms capable of movement, feeding, respiration, secretion, excretion and reproduction, and sensitive to changes in their environment.

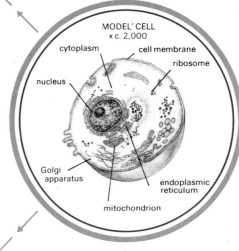

MODEL' CELL
x c. 2,000

cytoplasm

cell membrane

ribosome

nucleus

Golgi apparatus

endoplasmic reticulum

mitochondrion

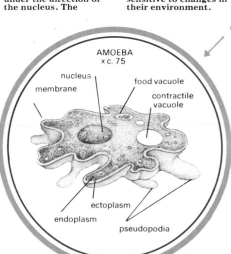

AMOEBA
x c. 75

nucleus

food vacuole

membrane

contractile vacuole

ectoplasm

endoplasm

pseudopodia

Left: The small drop of water on this leaf could contain about 280 amoebas.

Left: *Amoeba* is a pliable mass of animated jelly or cytoplasm surrounded by an elastic skin or membrane which is always changing shape as it moves. One of its favourite haunts is among the rotting weed at the bottom of a pond where it creeps around hunting for the other protozoa, small plants and bacteria which it eats with a voracious appetite.

Below: The sporozoite is the infective stage of the malarial parasite, *Plasmodium.* When a mosquito bites a man, sporozoites are injected into the bloodstream. They travel to the liver and divide. The parasites then invade the red blood cells and digest the blood pigment, producing toxic wastes that may cause the fever associated with malaria.

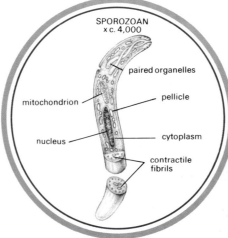

SPOROZOAN
x c. 4,000

paired organelles

mitochondrion

pellicle

nucleus

cytoplasm

contractile fibrils

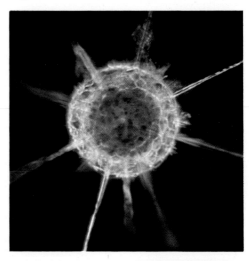

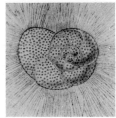

Above: The beautifully delicate glassy skeleton of a radiolarian consists of a holey, central sphere which contains the cytoplasm of an amoeba-like body. The small, thin spikes radiating from the centre bear extremely fine pseudopodia for catching and carrying food. These radial spines also protect the animal.

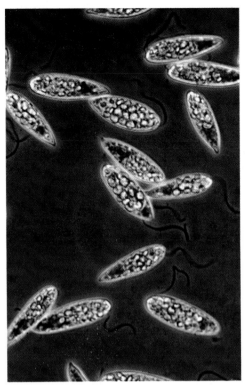

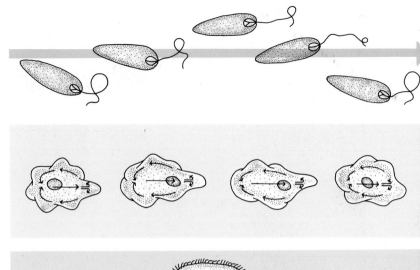

Left and right: *Euglena* and other flagellates move by thrashing the water with their fine, whip-like flagella. In each lash a spiralling wave travels up from the base of the flagellum to its tip. As it unwinds, it spins the flagellate forwards around a spiral course so that the same point on the body always faces the centre.

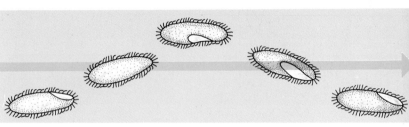

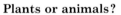

Right: The amoeba glides forwards by pushing out temporary extensions of the cytoplasm called pseudopodia. The rest of the body then advances by flowing into the pseudopod. It is thought that the endoplasm flows up the centre to the tip of the pseudopod and then back down the sides.

Right: The motion of the cilia is similar to rowing. Each beat has a power stroke and a recovery stroke. Individual beats are coordinated, passing along the body in waves like wheat bending in a breeze. *Paramecium* spins as it corkscrews through the water because its cilia are spirally arranged and beat slightly obliquely.

larger animals. Many are found living in the thin film of water surrounding each soil particle and between the grains of sand on a beach. They are also easily dispersed by water currents, wind and rain. Soil dwellers are often transported in the mud that clings to an animal's feet. To avoid drying up in times of drought, some protozoa such as the amoebae secrete tough, protective envelopes around themselves to form a *cyst* and survive in this dormant state until favourable conditions prevail again.

Other protozoa have become adapted to a parasitic way of life, living in or on the bodies of plants and other animals. These species represent a serious health hazard, especially in the tropics where protozoa are responsible for such diseases as malaria, African sleeping sickness, Chaga's disease and amoebic dysentery.

Protozoa occur at all levels in a community. Some are producers, manufacturing their own food from simple chemicals and light energy like plants; the rest are consumers, either herbivores eating plants or carnivores eating other animals. Since protozoa are present in such vast numbers in marine and fresh water planktons—suspensions of tiny plants (phytoplankton) and animals (zooplankton) floating in the water—they form important links in many food chains. In the summer along the coast of California, the mussel, *Mytilus,* eats such large quantities of *Gonyaulax* that its flesh is tainted with the protozoan's poison. Although harmless to the mussel, it can cause food poisoning in man if mussels are eaten during the summer months.

Plants or animals?
Some flagellates such as *Euglena* and *Volvox* have plant and animal characteristics. Like plants they are green because they have chloroplasts containing the green light-trapping pigment chlorophyll in their cytoplasm. Yet like animals these flagellates are able to move freely.

The existence of these plant-like flagellates causes some confusion about their correct classification. Generally the Protozoa is regarded as an intermediate group in which a sufficient majority is classically animal in form and habit to warrant their position in the Animal Kingdom. The relatively few plant-like forms included in the Protozoa indicate a continuous evolution from plant to animal forms of life.

Movement
There are three methods of locomotion among the Protozoa. The amoeba flows slowly forwards by projecting temporary extensions of the cytoplasm called pseudopodia or 'false feet'. The flagellates move more swiftly by whipping their flagella through the water. The ciliates, the speediest protozoa, swim by beating their cilia against the water. *Paramecium* has been observed covering about 2.5mm per second, or approximately 600 times its own length in a minute.

Feeding
All animals need food as a source of energy and to provide the raw materials for growth, repair and reproduction. Protozoa have two main methods of nutrition. The phytoflagellates such as *Euglena* are autotrophic, producing their own food, as do plants, in a process called photosynthesis. They absorb simple chemicals—water, carbon dioxide and mineral salts—from the surrounding water and build them into more complex sugars using energy from sunlight trapped by the chloroplasts. Oxygen is given off as a byproduct. Excess sugar is converted to starch by a structure called a pyrenoid associated with each chloroplast and then stored as an energy reserve in the

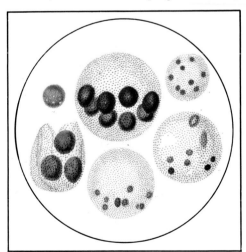

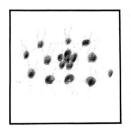

Left: The Foraminifera secrete multichambered shells with tiny pores through which pseudopodia project for feeding. The White Cliffs of Dover on the south coast of England are built of limestone composed of billions of foraminiferan shells. These were deposited in the sea floor sediment millions of years ago.

Above left and left: Each *Volvox* colony consists of thousands of microscopic green flagellates embedded in a jelly-like sphere. Individuals are linked by protoplasmic threads and show amazing coordination of their flagella. Daughter colonies are released by the rupture of the parent wall.

Above: Clusters of *Vorticella,* a sedentary ciliate, are often found clinging to the weed in fresh water ponds. During feeding the bell-shaped body is extended on a long, thin stalk to trap food particles. If the water is disturbed, the stalk contracts suddenly like a rapidly recoiling spring.

11

Below: *Amoeba* is adept at capturing *Paramecium*. When *Paramecium* swims imprudently close, the marauding amoeba changes course to intercept it. As it draws nearer to its prey, *Amoeba* extends pseudopodia over, under and around *Paramecium*, embracing it in a food vacuole.

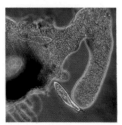

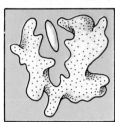

Contractile vacuole fully distended

Contractile vacuoles

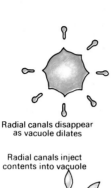

Radial canals disappear as vacuole dilates

Radial canals inject contents into vacuole

Central vacuole almost empty; radial canals full

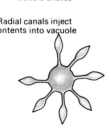

Contractile vacuole emptying; radial canals filling

Radial canals swell as vacuole continues to empty

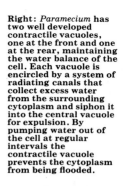

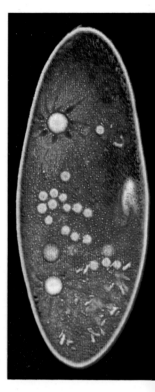

Left: Under the microscope the contractile vacuoles of a paramecium can be seen filling and emptying alternately with a pulsating rhythm. As the main vacuole empties, the radial canals begin to swell with water flowing in from the surrounding cytoplasm. Then the contents of the canals drain into the contractile vacuole, gradually dilating it. When fully distended, the central reservoir suddenly collapses, discharging its contents through a temporary pore in the cell membrane.

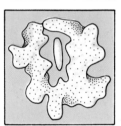

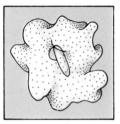

Right: *Stentor* is a large ciliate that can alter its shape dramatically by means of long, elastic fibres in its cytoplasm, from a 'horn' for feeding to a 'megaphone' if threatened. When in danger of being choked by debris a stationary stentor will first try to dodge the deluge by bending from side to side. Then it will reverse the ciliary beat in an attempt to blow the storm away. If this fails it will swim off to a more hospitable location.

Below right: Sometimes *Stentor* looks green because it harbours a green algae, *Zoochlorella*. They share a symbiotic relationship, in which *Stentor* provides shelter while the algae offer extra food and oxygen.

Below: When feeding, *Stentor* anchors itself to a base with its holdfast and beats the elaborate system of fused cilia around its mouth. This creates a swirling water current that wafts food particles into the mouth. They are carried down to the end of the gullet where they are incorporated into food vacuoles.

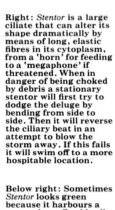

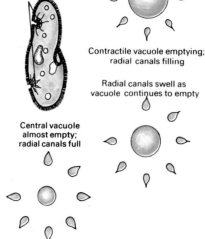

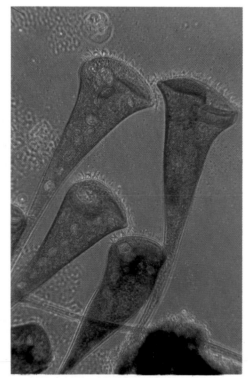

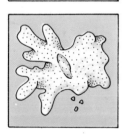

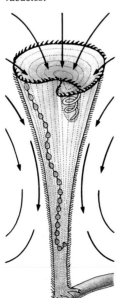

Above: The paramecium may struggle in the food vacuole at first but it becomes quieter when the oxygen supply is used up. The paramecium silhouette grows less distinct as the food particle is gradually decomposed by digestive enzymes. Indigestible remnants are simply left behind as the amoeba advances.

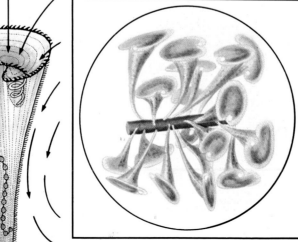

paramylum granules in the cytoplasm.

Photosynthesis becomes impossible in weed-choked ponds where little sunlight penetrates to any depth. Under these conditions, *Euglena* may resort to a saprophytic form of nutrition, obtaining the simple organic materials it needs to sustain itself from the decaying vegetation in the water.

The majority of protozoa, however, are heterotrophic, relying on their skills as predators to capture their food, and their ability to digest it. Clusters of *Paramecium*, for example, can often be found hunting around a decaying morsel of flesh or vegetation where there is a high density of the bacteria that form their staple diet. As the paramecium moves through the water, the special cilia lining the oral groove suck a current of water and food particles into the gullet. They are then incorporated with a small drop of water into a food vacuole, or bubble, in the cell interior.

Digestive enzymes are secreted from the cytoplasm into the vacuole to break down the food particles into simpler units—sugars and amino acids (the building blocks of proteins). These are then absorbed into the cytoplasm. As digestion proceeds the food vacuole moves slowly around the body along a defined path in the cytoplasm. This leads to the anal pore where the indigestible portion of the meal is expelled.

Water control and excretion

Many protozoa, especially those such as *Amoeba* and *Paramecium* living in fresh water, have a special structure in their cytoplasm known as a contractile vacuole which helps to regulate the water balance of the cell. The cytoplasm of the protozoa is vulnerable to flooding as water flows along a natural gradient from the weak environmental solution to the more concentrated cytoplasm in a process called osmosis. The contractile vacuole prevents the cell from bursting by pumping water out at regular intervals.

It is possible that some soluble waste products are also eliminated from the cell

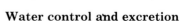

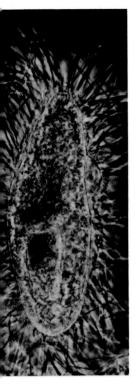

Left: This shaggy paramecium has recently released its trichocysts. These long, spear-tipped filaments are thought to act as defensive weapons. When attacked by a predator, *Paramecium* fires a barrage of trichocysts at it, forcing it away.

Right: Paramecium usually multiplies asexually by binary fission. Sometimes this cycle is interrupted by a sexual phase called conjugation. Two paramecia of different 'sexes' align lengthwise. Upon contact each micronucleus divides twice. Three of the new micronuclei disappear as the fourth undergoes a further division. One product of this division from each individual migrates through the fused oral grooves to unite with the stationary nucleus of the partner to form a zygote. This then divides three times while the old macronuclei disappear. Four micronuclei develop into new macronuclei and are distributed into four new cells by further cell divisions.

BINARY FISSION

cytoplasm divides

two new daughter cells

micronucleus
macronucleus

nuclei divide

full grown Paramecium

CONJUGATION

second cell division

micronuclei divide

first cell division

micronuclei divide again

4 micronuclei become macronuclei

exchange of micronuclei

macronucleus disappears

via the contractile vacuole. Protozoa have no special organs of excretion for getting rid of undigested food or harmful waste products from the body. Soluble waste materials are usually excreted by free diffusion through the cell membrane. Solid materials are either ejected through a temporary pore in the cell membrane or left behind as the animal moves forwards.

Growth and reproduction

Growth and reproduction in protozoa are closely linked. In many cases when an individual reaches a certain critical size it simply divides into two new cells, each containing half the nucleus and half the cytoplasm of the parent cell. This asexual division of the parent cell into two daughter cells is called binary fission. It may occur as often as eight times a day in well nourished protozoa, resulting in very rapid increase in numbers. Sometimes, the asexual cycle in *Paramecium,* for example, is interrupted by a sexual phase called conjugation.

Parasitic Sporozoa, including the malarial parasite, *Plasmodium,* carry out another form of asexual division called schizogony. This is a form of multiple budding in which four to many thousands of new individuals develop as buds on the surface of the parent. Eventually the buds break off and are distributed around the body as spores.

Behaviour

Protozoa are sensitive to many kinds of changes in their environment—light intensity, temperature gradients, chemical and mechanical barriers—and respond to each stimulus with an appropriate sequence of movements or secretions. Both reception and response seem to be general properties of the cytoplasm. An amoeba, for example, has no nervous system but cringes from bright lights and high temperatures. The only receptor system that has been identified in protozoa is the light sensitive eyespot or stigma of certain flagellates. The red eyespot of *Euglena* directs it towards the strong light sources for photosynthesis. As it moves forwards, its front end sways from side to side, testing the direction of the light.

Most patterns of behaviour are related in some way to the stimulus. Paramecia, for example, are incredibly active little creatures, constantly swimming about in search of food. Any obstacle, extreme temperature change or obnoxious chemical in the path of the paramecium elicits an avoiding reaction. By momentarily reversing the direction of the ciliary stroke it beats a hasty retreat, changing direction slightly as it goes. It then proceeds on a new tack. If it still collides with the obstruction it will continue the 'advance and retreat' policy until it successfully navigates a path around the obstacle. Such adaptive behaviour improves the individual's chances of survival.

Because most of the protozoa do not have shells or skeletons they do not survive well in the fossil record of what animals living hundreds of millions of years ago were like. Consequently, while it is tempting to take the 'first animals' title to its logical conclusion and assume that all other multicellular animals evolved from the simpler single-celled animals, there is no firm evidence to support this. It is only possible to say that the Protozoa are the simplest of living animals.

Despite the apparent simplicity of their structure and organization, however, the protozoa are remarkably successful animals, both in terms of numbers and in the variety of places in which they live. Within the limitations of one cell, the Protozoa have achieved an incredible diversity of form and habits.

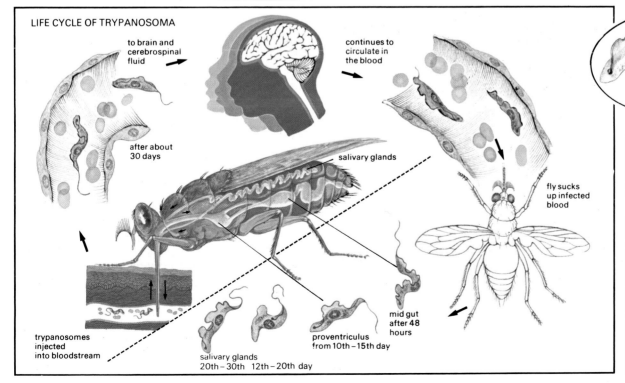

LIFE CYCLE OF TRYPANOSOMA

to brain and cerebrospinal fluid

continues to circulate in the blood

after about 30 days

salivary glands

fly sucks up infected blood

trypanosomes injected into bloodstream

salivary glands 20th–30th

12th–20th day

proventriculus from 10th–15th day

mid gut after 48 hours

TRYPANOSOME x c. 2,500

flagellum

undulating membrane

pellicle

Above: *Trypanosoma* is a long, slender parasitic flagellate living in the human bloodstream where it causes Africa sleeping sickness. The flagellum is held in an undulating membrane.

Left: Trypanosomes are transmitted by the tsetse fly. If a fly bites an infected man it sucks up some trypanosomes in its blood meal. These multiply in the fly's gut and migrate to the salivary glands. When the fly feeds again, some trypanosomes are injected into the wound with the saliva. They reproduce rapidly in the bloodstream and finally invade the fluid around the brain, producing a characteristic lethargy, coma and ultimately death.

13

Sponges and Corals

Corals, sea anemones and jellyfish are members of a primitive group of animals called Coelenterates. Most of them live in the sea—*Hydra* is an exception as it lives in fresh water. Coelenterates have three major characteristics in common: a simple three-layered body-wall; a single body cavity with only one opening or mouth which is an entrance for food, water and oxygen and the exit for wastes and water; and stinging tentacles.

Corals are best known for the massive 'rocky' reefs they build in the tropics. The Great Barrier Reef of Australia is the largest coral reef in the world. It stretches as a giant natural breakwater for 2,012 km (1,260 miles) down the east coast from north of Queensland to just south of the tropic of Capricorn. Occasionally the tip of the reef breaks the surface of the warm, blue Pacific Ocean in a scattering of coral islands and treacherous reef flats. In some places the reef is as much as 457 m (1,500 ft) thick. Yet almost unbelievably the whole of this huge underwater mountain chain has been designed and built by countless billions of industrious little animals called *coral polyps*, each of which is little bigger than a match head.

Each tiny, stony coral polyp looks like a miniature sea anemone sitting in its own private fortress. Small stationary animals like the coral polyp are particularly vulnerable to attack by hungry predators. In order to protect themselves, the stony corals construct hard, chalky skeletons around their bodies into which they can retreat very rapidly in times of danger. It is these white skeletons of the living and, more importantly, the dead coral that form the intricate limestone framework of the reef.

The majority of reef-building corals form large colonies. In some, like the rounded brain coral, the walls of the skeletons merge, creating an intriguing maze of ridges and valleys that meander across the surface of the boulder like the convolutions of the human brain. Others, such as the staghorn coral, are more delicate, with fine branches that create dramatic silhouettes in the water.

In many coral colonies, the neighbouring polyps are only semi-detached. Individuals are linked through holes in the skeletal walls and by body flaps that spread as a thin film across the surface of the colony. Food is shared between polyps via these connections.

Reef corals are typically shy, nocturnal feeders. During the day, polyps are withdrawn into their skeletal cups and the coral looks disappointingly lifeless. But at night, the whole reef comes magically to life. All the coral polyps stretch out their tentacles, probing the waters like fields of hungry flowers. Any small animals that accidentally collide with them are paralysed and trapped by means of powerful stinging cells called *nematocysts*.

While stony corals are the main reef architects and masons, other animals and plants also contribute 'bricks and mortar' to the reef structure. The most important of these are the 'stinging' corals—relatives of the true stony corals that also build heavy, limy skeletons—and the encrusting seaweeds. These stony seaweeds cement loose coral sand, empty snail shells and other rubble into the crevices between the individual coral colonies, binding them permanently together in the massive reef platform.

Growth of the reef

Reef-forming corals are very selective about where they live. They can only grow in shallow, tropical seas where the temperature of the water never falls below 20°C. It is only in these warmer waters that the coral polyps can extract calcium from the sea water and deposit it as chalk, or calcium carbonate, in their skeletons at a faster rate than the waves wash it away again.

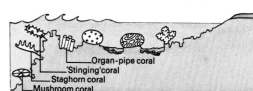

reef edge — reef platform — coral

Organ-pipe coral
'Stinging' coral
Staghorn coral
Mushroom coral

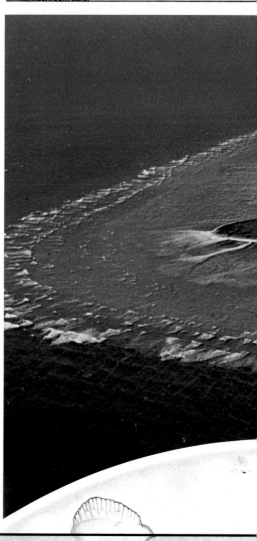

Valerie Taylor, Ardea

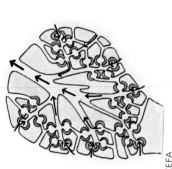

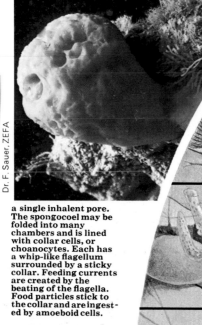

Dr. F. Sauer, ZEFA

Above: Sponges in the phylum *Porifera* are the most primitive multicellular animals. They are aquatic, predominantly marine and sedentary. The surface is penetrated with many inhalent pores through which water laden with small food particles passes into a central cavity, or spongocoel. It leaves by a single inhalent pore. The spongocoel may be folded into many chambers and is lined with collar cells, or choanocytes. Each has a whip-like flagellum surrounded by a sticky collar. Feeding currents are created by the beating of the flagella. Food particles stick to the collar and are ingested by amoeboid cells.

Portuguese man-of-war

Sea slug · Sea anemone · Butterfly fish · Tiger cowrie

Fan worm · Sea cucumber · Damsel fish · Sea squirt · Bailer

Sponges · Zooplankton

Feather star

Phytoplankton

Clam

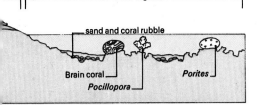

shallow lagoon

sand and coral rubble

Brain coral
Pocillopora
Porites

Silver gull

SECONDARY CARNIVORES

Moray eel
Tusk fish
Sea snail
Crown of thorns starfish
Giant triton

PRIMARY CARNIVORES

Blue starfish
Reef octopus

HERBIVORES

Green turtle
Sea urchin
Parrot fish
Crab
Sea hare

PLANTS

Seaweed

Heather Angel

Left: A slice through a coral reef reveals the zonation of coral growth. The richest growth occurs on the reef cliff. Only the heaviest corals can survive the surf breaking over the reef edge. More delicate forms thrive in the calmer waters of the lagoon.

Left: One Tree Island is a coral island on the Great Barrier Reef. The darker areas of the surrounding reef platform are regions of living coral; the paler patches are coral sand and rubble.

Right: The reef-building stony corals only flourish in shallow tropical seas where the water is always warmer than 20°C.

Above: The pretty little Devonshire cup coral is a hardy, solitary specimen which lives on the rocky shores around Britain. A bird's eye view shows its central split of a mouth surrounded by a perfect ring of tentacles. The bright spots on the tentacles are the stinging cells that stun the prey.

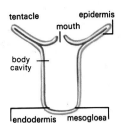

tentacle
epidermis
mouth
body cavity
endodermis
mesogloea

Left and right: The Coelenterates have two body plans. The stationary polyp of the corals and sea anemones is a squat, hollow column topped with tentacles. The free-swimming, bell-shaped jellyfish medusa is basically a squashed upside down polyp with an over-developed middle layer of jelly.

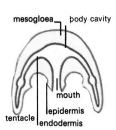

mesogloea
body cavity
mouth
tentacle
epidermis
endodermis

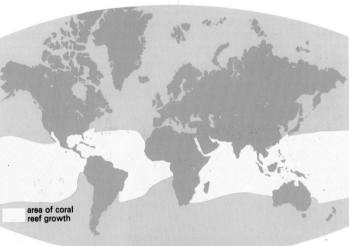

area of coral reef growth

Below: A cut-away section of a stony coral polyp shows it sitting in its chalky skeleton. The body flaps link up with neighbouring polyps for food sharing.

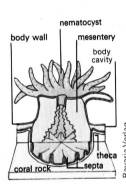

nematocyst
body wall
mesentery
body cavity
coral rock
theca
septa

Bavaria Verlag

Left: The vacant skeletal cups of a dead stony coral colony clearly show the thin radial ridges, or septa.

Below left: A branching 'soft' coral colony grows on the terraces of a reef cliff. 'Soft' corals can live in deeper water than the stony reef-building corals because they do not need sunlight for skeleton formation.

Below: A single 'soft' coral polyp stretches out its eight feathery tentacles for feeding. The individual polyps that build the branches of the colony are linked by a mass of flesh called coenenchyme. The whole colony is stiffened by a hard rod.

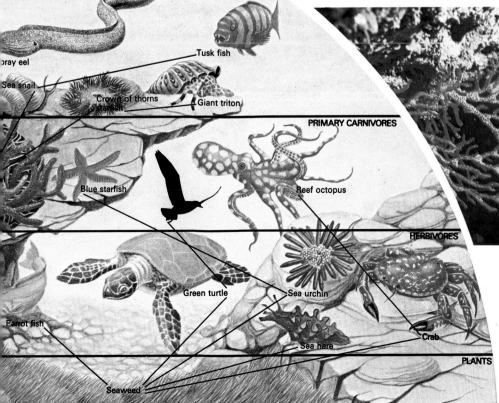

Walt Deas, Seaphot

mouth
tentacle
pinnule
mesentery
pharynx
reproductive organ
body cavity
coenenchyme
axial rod

Left: A coral reef is like a giant, living kaleidoscope, home for teeming millions of brightly coloured animals and plants that find food and shelter in or around its numerous nooks and crannies. Docile sponges, garish sea slugs and venomous snails live side by side on the reef while rainbow blurs of little fish dart in and out among the coral. A tangled web of 'eat and be eaten' interactions is played out between the members of the complex reef community on a magnificent stage of living coral. Each line on the chart points up from the prey to its predator in the next level of the community.

15

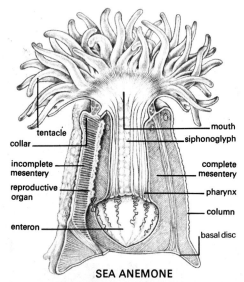

SEA ANEMONE

(diagram labels) tentacle · collar · incomplete mesentery · reproductive organ · enteron · mouth · siphonoglyph · complete mesentery · pharynx · column · basal disc

Top: A sea anemone is divided up internally by soft partitions called mesenteries. These greatly increase the surface area for the absorption of food and oxygen.

Above: The colourful Catherine-wheel of a dahlia anemone's crown of tentacles is a very efficient food trap.

Below: Glistening beadlet sea anemones cling tenaciously to the side of a rock pool at low tide. The column is contracted into a tight little button with the tentacles tucked away inside to protect them from water loss and damage until the tide comes in again. Then the tentacles can expand for feeding.

Right: A clown fish peeps out from between the tentacles of a sea anemone where it lives, apparently immune to their stings. In return for shelter, the gaily painted little fish probably cleans up the crumbs of waste the sea anemone spits out and may also lure other unwary fish within range of the tentacles.

This does not mean, however, that corals cannot exist in colder seas. The hardy, solitary Devonshire cup coral, *Carophyllia,* for example, is found in British waters at temperatures as low as 3°C, although clearly it cannot participate in reef formation under these conditions.

Corals also only thrive in crystal-clear water. Too much sediment in the water, around the mouth of a river, for example, would smother the tiny coral polyps as it settled. Lots of silt also makes the water murky, which inhibits reef formation by blocking the sunlight.

Sunlight is a critical factor in stony coral growth because of a crucial association between the coral and some minute plants called *Zooxanthella* which live within the cells of the coral tissue. Algal growth stimulates skeleton production, probably by speeding up the chemical process of extracting calcium from the sea water. It may also increase the metabolic efficiency of the coral polyp by using its waste products. The living region of the reef is therefore restricted to the upper reef levels—usually the top 61 m (200 ft) of water—where enough light penetrates to enable algal growth to proceed at an efficient rate.

These small plant 'guests' in the coral tissue contribute to the pastel yellow, brown and green colours of some reef-forming corals. The brighter reds and oranges are created by pigment cells in the body wall. This explains why the corals lose their attractive colours when they die and the living tissue disintegrates. All that remains is the bleached, brittle skeleton, which is itself quickly covered with a 'mossy' film of seaweed growth and becomes a dull, greenish colour.

Building a reef is a mammoth task—coral reefs generally grow very slowly. The corals spread by producing vast numbers of minute 'hairy' larvae called *planulae.* These tiny scouts swim around exploring the reef until they find a hard surface, such as a piece of dead coral, upon which to settle. The sedentary planula then gradually changes into a small polyp, developing a whorl of small bumps or juvenile tentacles around its mouth and the rudiments of a skeleton at its base.

This pioneering young polyp is the founder member of a new coral colony. A miniature polyp sprouts from the side of its column. Gradually as the bud grows bigger it starts to separate from its parent, although they never become completely detached. Budding continues and the colony expands. Thus the reef is built up, layer upon layer, with the skeletons of the ancestors supporting the present generation of living coral.

Life on the reef

Some of the most spectacular reef residents are relatives of the stony corals—the 'soft' corals, sea anemones and jellyfish. These colourful and sometimes bizarre looking creatures are less sensitive about the temperature of the water in which they live than their skeleton-forming cousins. Consequently they are familiar to rock-pool explorers and beach combers around the coasts of North America, Europe and Africa.

'Soft' corals invariably live in colonies, creating fragile, branching formations like bendy sea firs, sea feather and sea whips. In fact the 'soft' corals are not

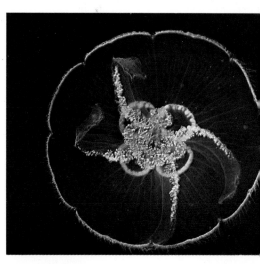

The tiny transparent moon jellyfish, *Aurelia,* floats around the oceans of the world. Viewed from below, the four oral arms around the mouth are clearly visible. Food raining down on to the top of the bell is swept to the edge where it is 'licked' off by the oral arms and carried to the mouth.

AURELIA

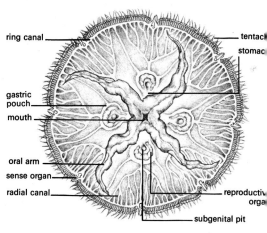

(diagram labels) ring canal · gastric pouch · mouth · oral arm · sense organ · radial canal · tentacle · stomach · reproductive organ · subgenital pit

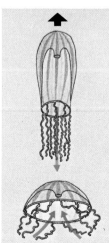

Above: Jellyfish are jet propelled. By gently lifting the sides of the bell water is sucked up underneath. When the bell contracts a jet of water is squirted downwards, forcing the jellyfish up into the food-rich surface waters. As soon as the umbrella stops opening and closing, the jellyfish begins to sink.

Below: *Haliclystus* is an unusual, stationary jellyfish. Unlike its free-swimming relatives it lives hanging down by a short stalk from a piece of weed like a tiny orange bell. Each of the eight lobes of the bell is trimmed with a spray of knobbed tentacles which are used for defence and for catching food.

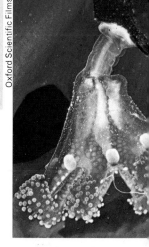

16

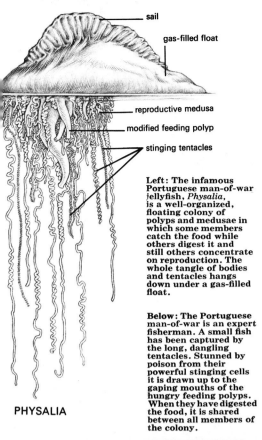

sail

gas-filled float

reproductive medusa

modified feeding polyp

stinging tentacles

PHYSALIA

Left: The infamous Portuguese man-of-war jellyfish, *Physalia*, is a well-organized, floating colony of polyps and medusae in which some members catch the food while others digest it and still others concentrate on reproduction. The whole tangle of bodies and tentacles hangs down under a gas-filled float.

Below: The Portuguese man-of-war is an expert fisherman. A small fish has been captured by the long, dangling tentacles. Stunned by poison from their powerful stinging cells it is drawn up to the gaping mouths of the hungry feeding polyps. When they have digested the food, it is shared between all members of the colony.

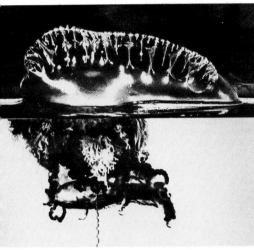

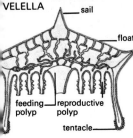

VELELLA

sail

float

feeding polyp

reproductive polyp

tentacle

Above and left: *Velella* is a small colonial jellyfish. Its saucer-shaped float is filled with air chambers for great buoyancy and topped with a high crest to catch the wind as it drifts on top of the sea. This float supports one central feeding polyp surrounded by reproductive polyps and stinging tentacles

really soft at all, but rather leathery to the touch. They are often called 'false' corals because unlike the stony corals they do not build heavy cases around their bodies. Instead they rely on an internal network of coloured rods, spikes or spines to support the mass of soft tissue.

Fortunately, 'soft' corals do not lose their vivid red, orange, yellow and blue colours when they die because this colour is largely part of the skeleton and not of the living tissue. The skeletal rods of the red precious coral, for example, which grows in the Mediterranean and around the Japanese Islands, have been used since Greek times for making jewellery.

The sea anemones are structurally very similar to stony coral polyps, except that they are much bigger and lack a skeleton. One monster sea anemone, the giant barrier reef anemone, can grow as big as 0.9 m (3 ft) in diameter. Most of them also exist independently rather than forming colonies. They spend most of their time anchored to rocks and dead coral by their basal discs, or buried in the sand with their tentacles waving freely in the water, waiting to trap and paralyse passing small fish.

Coelenterates on the move

Although they look permanently anchored on the rocks, most sea anemones are perfectly capable of moving at least short distances, usually by shuffling slowly along on their bases. Some sea anemones will even ride on the back of a hermit crab's shell, an arrangement which seems to work to their mutual benefit. The crab gains camouflage and protection from the sea anemone's stinging tentacles. In return the sea anemone probably collects food floating up as the crab picks over the debris on the reef floor, looking for edible particles.

Sea anemones often reproduce asexually by splitting in half down the middle. They also multiply sexually by producing planulae larvae in much the same way as the coral polyps do.

In complete contrast to the sedate corals and sea anemones, the jellyfish are free to float around the oceans of the world at the whim of winds, tides and currents. Two distinct types of jellyfish frequent the reef—the true, medusoid jellyfish and the colonial jellyfish. The true, free-swimming, umbrella-shaped jellyfish float around in the water, occasionally flapping the sides of the umbrella to lift themselves back into the food-rich pastures at the surface.

Such jellyfish have a complicated lifecycle. Reproductive organs in the mature medusoid jellyfish produce eggs and sperms. The fertilized egg develops into a planula larva that settles and forms a polyp-like larval stage. In spring this polyp undergoes a weird type of segmentation called *strobilation* in which the column of the polyp divides up into a stack of discs. Each disc gradually develops eight radial arms and eventually swims off as a small jellyfish bell.

Jellyfish are notorious for the painful sting they can inflict on unsuspecting swimmers who accidentally brush against the stinging cells on their trailing tentacles. Fortunately, jellyfish stings are rarely fatal to a healthy man. The box jellies, or sea wasps, which appear from time to time around the Australian coast, are an exception however. They are particularly dangerous because the cubes of

Above: A pale forest of *Obelia* grows on a piece of seaweed. The inset shows a detail of a feeding polyp.

Below: Each *Obelia* colony consists of a main stem which grows up from an anchoring 'root' system with feeding and reproductive polyps branching off at intervals.

OBELIA

tentacle

mouth

bud

sperm

egg

medusa

reproductive polyp

medusa bud

planula

feeding polyp

planula settles

horny covering

young *Obelia*

Above: In the life cycle of *Obelia*, a tiny medusa buds from the colony and swims off. Its egg, fertilized by a sperm from another medusa, grows into a 'hairy' planula larva which scouts about until it finds a rock or seaweed on which it lands. Then it becomes a small polyp that forms a new *Obelia* colony by budding.

Below: In the colonies of the oaten-pipes hydroid, *Tubularia*, the feeding polyps are perched on top of long stalks. Each one is surrounded by a cluster of reproductive medusae cascading down between the snaking tentacles. *Tubularia* often grows on rocks and seaweed around the coasts of Britain and America.

17

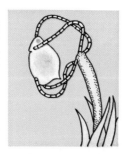

Above left: *Hydra* cartwheels along by repeatedly arching its bendy body over, then flipping its column over its tentacles and swinging back into an upright position again.

Left: *Hydra* lives in fresh water ponds attached to pieces of weed, wood or a stone.

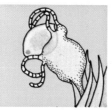

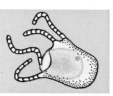

jelly are practically transparent and therefore very difficult to see in the water. Their powerful stings cause painful local inflammation and can even be fatal.

The equally infamous Portuguese man-of-war is another stinging visitor to the coral reef. Normally they bob like large, purple-tinged air bubbles on the surface of the water with their tentacles hanging down to trap small reef fish. Sometimes during storms they are washed ashore and left stranded high and dry on the beach, like crumpled plastic bottles.

Threats to the reef

A coral reef behaves like some huge, self-repairing mountain range. Any factor that damages the thin outer 'skin' of living coral exposes the inner, dead regions of the reef to wave action and erosion. Actively budding coral polyps are able to keep pace with a limited amount of damage. If the damaged area is extensive, however, coral regrowth by budding to cover the injury is too slow to prevent serious reef disintegration.

Fortunately, such serious damage has apparently occurred rarely in the long history of the Great Barrier Reef. There is increasing concern, however, about the effect of marine pollution by industrial waste and crude oil spillage on coral growth. Such toxic wastes may either kill the coral polyp by choking or poisoning it, or kill the microscopic animals on which the coral feeds, thus starving it to death.

Another imminent threat to the reef is the amount of dredging, blasting and drilling for valuable deposits of limestone, sand and oil which takes place on or near the reef. The thousands of tourists who visit the reef each year also unwittingly crush large numbers of coral polyps and skeletons as they trample over the reef platform, collecting coral souvenirs.

The most serious attack on the Great Barrier Reef—and other reefs in the Red Sea, the Indian and Pacific Oceans—has occurred in the spiky shape of the crown of thorns starfish, *Acanthaster planci.* This predator is normally found only in very small numbers, feeding at night on coral polyps, particularly those of the important stony corals. Under normal circumstances, coral growth keeps pace with predation. Since the early 1960s, however, there has been a population explosion of *Acanthaster* which has left acres of the reef stripped of living coral and disintegrating.

The reason for this comparatively sudden increase in numbers—whether it is a natural population cycle or triggered off in some way by man upsetting the balance of nature on the reef—is not clear. It has been suggested, for example, that the large scale removal of the only real predator on *Acanthaster,* the giant triton snail, by collectors of its beautiful shell may be one cause.

Urgent control measures are being taken to protect the reef from the onslaught of starfish and man. The crown of thorns starfish has been 'outlawed' and biologists are also experimenting with means of birth control for the starfish, and a careful watch is being kept on the exploitation of the reef's natural resources. In future, strict conservation of the Great Barrier Reef province as a wildlife reserve should help to ensure the survival of one of the great natural wonders of the world.

HYDRA

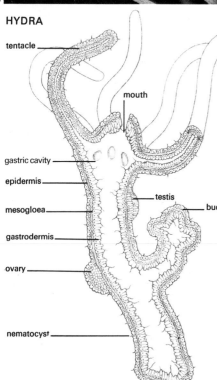

tentacle

mouth

gastric cavity

epidermis

mesogloea

gastrodermis

ovary

testis

bud

nematocyst

basal disc

Right: The waving tentacles of *Hydra* are a death trap for many water fleas. Each one is armed with a battery of stinging cells, or nematocysts. Their poisonous threads kill or paralyse the prey when it swims against them. Then the stretchy tentacles bend over, stuffing the food into the mouth.

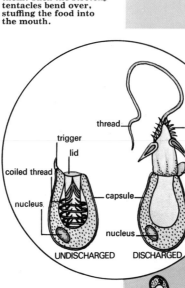

thread

bristle

trigger

lid

barb

coiled thread

lid

capsule

nucleus

nucleus

UNDISCHARGED   DISCHARGED

Above: *Hydra* reproduces sexually and asexually. In the autumn, ovaries or testes develop as small bumps on the side of the column. The fertilized egg drops to the bottom of the pond where it overwinters in the mud protected by a thick coat. In spring, a tiny *Hydra* hatches which will multiply in summer.

Right: Nematocysts are *Hydra's* deadly weapons. An undischarged nematocyst consists of a tightly-coiled thread wound into a capsule in the tentacle wall. When the prey swims against the tentacles, it triggers a rapid firing of nematocysts, probably by causing a sudden increase in the water pressure of the capsule.

In some nematocysts, the thread is barbed and the tip rotates like a drill as it is ejected. This pierces the prey and injects a lethal poison. In others, the thread is sticky and winds about the prey like a lasso, thus ensnaring it. Each nematocyst is only fired once and then replaced.

Roundworms

The roundworms, or nematodes, can be regarded as one of the most successful groups in the animal kingdom, whether success is measured by numbers or by adaptability. One scientist remarked that if all other matter was swept away the outlines of mountains, valleys, lakes, seas and rivers would still be dimly recognizable from a film of nematodes. Even the position of most plants and animals would be indicated by little piles of them.

Large numbers of nematodes are present in all parts of the world, from the polar seas to hot springs, from arid deserts to ocean depths. Several million organisms are present in every square metre of the top few centimetres of the ocean bed. Some nematodes live in very peculiar habitats—there is even a species which has been found only in German beer mats.

One of the most remarkable features of the group is that all forms have the same basic body pattern, whether they are the microscopic free-living nematodes found in soil or water, or the parasitic worms found in plants or animals, which can measure up to 30 cm (1 ft). All nematodes also have the same basic life cycle: egg, four larval stages, and adult form.

Parasitic worms

There is at least one plant-parasitic nematode that will attack almost every crop whether in the field, the orchard, the back garden or the greenhouse. Because of their microscopic size their existence is often not recognized, yet about ten percent of crops grown are eaten by nematodes. In Britain alone it is estimated that more than two million pounds worth of potatoes are lost annually to the ravages of the potato eelworm. Other nematodes are a major cause of illness in domestic animals and in man. The most common is that well-known nuisance the threadworm which, according to one source, is the second most common organism infecting man after the common cold virus. Threadworms are present in the gut in about one third of all children in England and often cause irritation in the anal region.

Hookworms are more actively harmful than most nematodes and are a serious cause of anaemia, particularly in tropical countries. The daily volume of blood lost by sufferers throughout the world is calculated to be about 8,200,000 litres (1,800,000 gallons). The young stages live in soil and actively burrow through the skin of the feet, while the adults live in the small intestine, biting off portions and sucking blood. Once common in the southern United States and in Western Australia, hookworms have become less common since the wearing of shoes became general.

Some parasitic nematodes have a simple life history with only one host. Their eggs are passed out on to the soil where they, or larvae which develop from them, may be eaten by a new host. Others have a second or *intermediate* host in which the young stages develop. All have evolved mechanisms for overcoming the hazards of transmission from one host to another. For instance in the potato eelworm, *Heterodera rostochiensis,* the female be-

Left: A nemertine worm. These animals are less complex than roundworms but more developed than flatworms. They all have a long, straight intestine with a mouth at one end and an anus at the other end. The long, thin, retractable tube on the right is used to catch prey, for example protozoa.

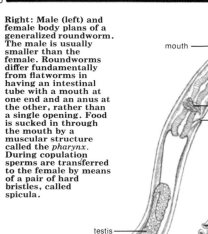

Right: Male (left) and female body plans of a generalized roundworm. The male is usually smaller than the female. Roundworms differ fundamentally from flatworms in having an intestinal tube with a mouth at one end and an anus at the other, rather than a single opening. Food is sucked in through the mouth by a muscular structure called the *pharynx*. During copulation sperms are transferred to the female by means of a pair of hard bristles, called spicula.

mouth
pharynx
nerve ring
excretory pore
intestine
anterior ovary
vulva
uterus
posterior ovary
testis
ejaculatory duct
spiculum
anus
rectal gland
adhesive foot glands

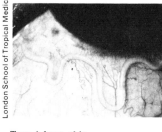

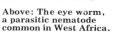

Top: A long, thin nematode worm of the family *Mermthoidea* emerges from its dead host. These worms spend their early life as parasites of invertebrates such as the spider, but the adults are free-living.

Above: The eye worm, a parasitic nematode common in West Africa.

Below: The life cycle of the human parasite *Ascaris*. The eggs passed out in the faeces hatch in the small intestines of the new host within a few hours of ingestion, and then embark on a 'tour' of the host body. They enter the bloodstream and are carried to the liver, heart and then the lungs where further growth occurs. The worms finally pass into the throat and are carried to the intestine where they mature fully.

Right: Roundworms of the family *Ascaris* taken from the bile ducts of a young pig. Although almost indistinguishable from the parasite of man, *Ascaris lumbricoides* (below), these worms do not normally develop to maturity in a human host. Similarly the human parasite will not infect pigs.

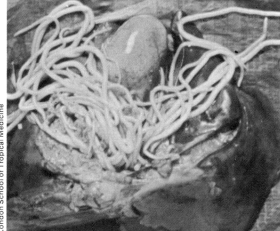

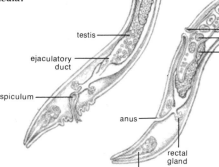

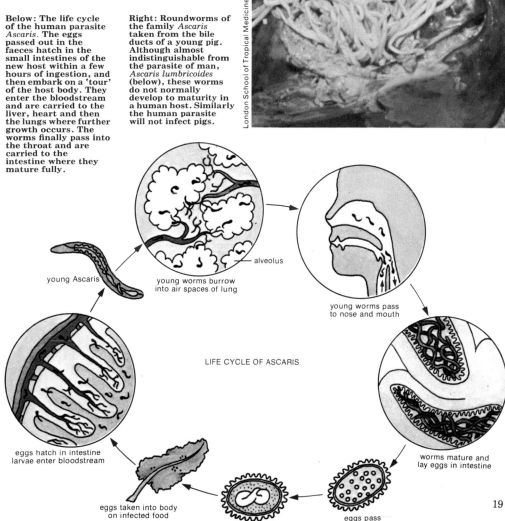

LIFE CYCLE OF ASCARIS

young Ascaris

young worms burrow into air spaces of lung

alveolus

young worms pass to nose and mouth

eggs hatch in intestine larvae enter bloodstream

worms mature and lay eggs in intestine

eggs taken into body on infected food

larva forms inside egg

eggs pass out in faeces

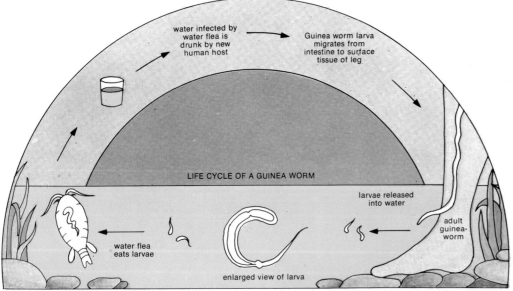

water infected by water flea is drunk by new human host

Guinea worm larva migrates from intestine to surface tissue of leg

LIFE CYCLE OF A GUINEA WORM

larvae released into water

adult guinea-worm

water flea eats larvae

enlarged view of larva

The guinea worm has long been one of the more uncomfortable features of life in India and Africa. The engraving on the left shows an adult worm, which can measure more than a foot (30 cm) in length, being removed from the leg of a sufferer by winding it out on a stick. This process is painful and only successful when precautions are taken against infection. When an infected limb is bathed in water, larvae are released through an ulcer formed on the skin by the adult worm. The larvae are eaten by water fleas, *cyclops* (right), and when infected water is drunk the larvae pass to new human hosts where they develop to maturity.

London School of Tropical Medicine

Bruce Coleman

Heather Angel

Above: Hairworms of the species *Gordius*. These animals are found in ponds and ditches all over the world, and the adult worms are free-living. The larvae, however, are parasites of insects and they emerge fully grown when the insect approaches or falls into a stream or pond.

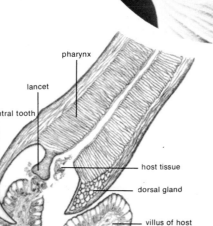

pharynx

lancet

ventral tooth

host tissue

dorsal gland

villus of host

International Journal for Parasitology

Above: The head of a hookworm, *Necator americanus*, showing the cutting surfaces or 'teeth' on each side of the mouth. These worms infect the intestines of both men and pigs. They are most common in hot countries, causing anaemia in the host.

Left: A human hookworm grips on to a projection called a *villus* in the wall of the intestine. The *lancet* erodes the intestinal wall so that the worm can feed on the blood and tissue fluids of the human host.

comes full of eggs and dies in potato roots left in the soil but her body wall remains as a protective cyst. The larvae inside the eggs hatch only when stimulated by a secretion from another crop of potatoes and may survive in a dormant state for many years, making them very difficult to eradicate.

Each female of the common roundworm in pigs and man, *Ascaris lumbricoides,* produces up to 200,000 eggs every day—the weight of all the eggs produced annually in China has been computed at more than 16,000 tonnes. The eggs are passed out of the host body in the faeces and must be ingested by a new host before development can continue, so despite the vast numbers produced the chances of any one egg finding a comfortable maternity home in the human body are infinitesimal.

A striking adaption of life history to environmental conditions is shown by a bizarre parasite of man, the guinea worm, *Dracunculus medinensis*. The adult female worms measure over 30 cm (1 ft) and live beneath the skin, usually in the legs. When mature the female causes a blister to form, bursts when an infected limb is paddled in water. This is the signal for the head of the worm to burst and release thousands of minute wriggling larvae into the water. The portion of the worm still projecting from the ulcer then dries up and more larvae are released only when the limb is plunged into water again. In this way the parasite is able to exist in desert areas where oases essential for its transmission are few and far between.

The larvae resemble free-living nematodes and only when eaten by water fleas, *Cyclops*, do they develop further. Water fleas are tiny crustaceans which live in ponds or the open wells often used as sources of drinking water in areas of the Middle East, Africa and India, and the parasite enters the body of man when an infected water flea is swallowed.

An even more specialized life cycle is shown by the *filariae*, tissue dwelling nematodes living in all the land dwelling groups of vertebrates. As their intermediate hosts, filariae have biting insects which pick up the larvae from the blood when feeding; the parasites are thus spared the hazards of exposing their eggs or larvae to the outside world. A heavy infestation of these nematodes can cause elephantiasis in man because the circulatory system is blocked by the worms.

Body structure

Nematodes all have a cylindrical body shape, pointed at either end and with few protruberances, apart from extensions at the tail end of some male parasitic forms used to clasp the females in copulation. This uniformity of structure can be explained to some extent by the great internal pressure of the fluid filling the body cavity. This is higher than in any other group in the animal kingdom and may reach one and a half times atmospheric pressure. If the body wall of a nematode is punctured the contents are expelled with considerable force. The high internal pressure has also resulted in a simple undulating mode of locomotion which is particularly suitable for moving through a sticky medium and partly explains their great success as animal parasites.

Nematodes have an outer impermeable *cuticle* which has three layers of fibres arranged in a spiral trellis pattern. The

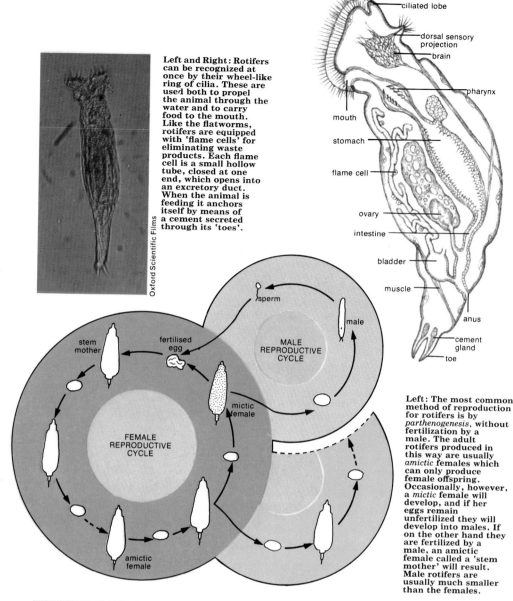

ciliated lobe
dorsal sensory projection
brain
pharynx
mouth
stomach
flame cell
ovary
intestine
bladder
muscle
anus
cement gland
toe

sperm
male
MALE REPRODUCTIVE CYCLE
fertilised egg
stem mother
mictic female
FEMALE REPRODUCTIVE CYCLE
amictic female

Left and Right: Rotifers can be recognized at once by their wheel-like ring of cilia. These are used both to propel the animal through the water and to carry food to the mouth. Like the flatworms, rotifers are equipped with 'flame cells' for eliminating waste products. Each flame cell is a small hollow tube, closed at one end, which opens into an excretory duct. When the animal is feeding it anchors itself by means of a cement secreted through its 'toes'.

Oxford Scientific Films

Left: The most common method of reproduction for rotifers is by *parthenogenesis*, without fertilization by a male. The adult rotifers produced in this way are usually *amictic* females which can only produce female offspring. Occasionally, however, a *mictic* female will develop, and if her eggs remain unfertilized they will develop into males. If on the other hand they are fertilized by a male, an amictic female called a 'stem mother' will result. Male rotifers are usually much smaller than the females.

Above: The small white cysts of the potato eelworm. The eggs inside each cyst will only hatch when a new potato crop is planted to act as host for the larvae.

Left: A plant parasite feeds on a fungus. This roundworm, a female, has the typical nematode shape, a cylindrical body pointed at each end. The mouth is at the top left and the anus close to the tail at the bottom right.

Right: The gall-like swellings on the roots of this plant are caused by the root knot nematode. Melons, tomatoes, cotton and even orchard trees may be attacked by this parasite.

Ministry of Agriculture and Fisheries

C. C. Doncaster, Rothamsted Experimental Station

Ministry of Agriculture and Fisheries

fibres in each layer are arranged in two sets that diagonally cross over each other, enclosing minute diamond shapes. They can be compared to 'lazy tongs', the contraction of the longitudinal muscles making the worm shorter and fatter and the internal fluid pressure making it longer and thinner when the muscles relax.

A specialization present in the mouth cavity of some plant-parasitic nematodes is a spear which can be protruded like a miniature hypodermic needle to penetrate the cellulose wall of plant cells and suck up the contents. Some animal-parasitic forms have a large mouth cavity with cuticular 'teeth' for cutting off portions from the gut wall of their host.

Related animals

There are other little-known groups of animals which are near or distant cousins of the nematodes. The spiny-headed worms, or *acanthocephalans,* are all parasitic, mostly in the guts of birds or fish. They have no digestive tract, food being absorbed through minute canals in the thick wrinkled body wall, but all have a fearsome looking proboscis (a long muscular projection) which is armed with rows of hooks and can be withdrawn into the body. The hooks provide a firm anchorage to the gut wall of the host. These worms are very much adapted to a parasitic mode of life as the only free-living stage in the whole life cycle are the eggs, which are passed out in faeces and eaten by an intermediate host, usually an insect.

The hairworms, or *nematomorphs,* are a small group of freshwater animals which are not hermaphrodite but exist in separate sexes. While the adults are free-living the young live parasitically in insects such as grasshoppers or dragonflies. If the host insect falls into water the young hairworm will emerge. It is remarkable that the fully developed juvenile in the insect may be many times the length of its host. The long threadlike adult, which may be up to one metre or yard long but only 3mm (0.12 in) wide, swims like a miniature snake in the water. A typical example is *Gordius,* so named because the loosely tangled masses of adults in water are reminiscent of the Gordian knot of mythology. Its unexpected appearance in cattle troughs after an insect had fallen in led to the belief that it developed from horse hairs.

Rotifers and *gastrotrichs* are common all over the world but because of their microscopic size are rarely recognized. The rotifers or 'wheel animals' live in water and soil, and their most characteristic feature is the unique organ at the front of the body which in some forms looks like a rotating wheel. It has many hair-like structures, *cilia,* which by their beating can either form a whirlpool drawing particles into the rotifer's mouth or can act like a propeller, driving the animal forward. Rotifers of one species or another are present in almost every wet or damp spot and there are even forms which can withstand complete drying and extreme temperatures—above boiling point or below −200°C (−328°F)—for many years. The gastrotrichs are a related group of m1scroscopic worm-like organisms without a wheel organ. They are found in seas, lakes and ponds, often anchored to stones by means of adhesive glands at the tail end of the body.

Crustaceans

Crustaceans range from the microscopic transparent organisms that form a major part of plankton in the sea, to the much larger and more familiar shrimps, crabs and lobsters. It is a large class of animals and, indeed, although most crustaceans live in the sea, there are many freshwater and land-dwelling varieties as well. Wood-lice, for example, are found under stones and rotting wood in most back gardens, and the 'water flea', *Daphnia*, is present in most ponds and lakes.

The crustaceans belong to the *Arthropoda* (a name which means 'jointed legged'), the largest and most successful of the animal groups. Out of a total of over one million known animal species, more than three-quarters are arthropods. As well as crustaceans, the group encompasses four other major animal classes: the centipedes, the millipedes, the arachnids (spiders) and, the largest class of all, the insects.

Before considering the particular features of the crustaceans, it is worth looking at the general characteristics of the arthropods. Firstly, almost all have segmented bodies like the annelids, but in the higher arthropods the various segments are markedly different from each other and serve specialized functions. Secondly, as anyone who has eaten crab or lobster will know, they have a hollow shell-like skeleton, called the *exoskeleton*, which acts as a framework for the body. Unlike the skeleton of a vertebrate animal, the arthropod exoskeleton encloses the soft parts of the body, and the various sections are moved by means of internal muscles.

The exoskeleton is formed by the outer layer of the body, called the *cuticle*, which is made up of a substance called *chitin* and protein. It is segmentally hardened to act as a skeleton. Once the cuticle has been formed, it cannot increase in size and so arthropods have to moult in order to grow. Useful calcium salts and other material are withdrawn from the old cuticle while the new soft, larger cuticle forms underneath. The animal takes in water or air, swells up and splits the old cuticle along the lines of weakness. It then takes in still more water or air and increases further in size before the new cuticle hardens.

Most crustaceans are aquatic, and they can grow much larger than terrestrial arthropods. This is probably because the buoyancy of the water permits a larger body weight to be supported when the cuticle is soft, just after moulting, and the animal is lacking its skeletal support. Like other arthropods, the body is segmented and can be divided into three regions: the head, the thorax and the abdomen. In some crustaceans, however, the head and thorax are joined to form a single *cephalothorax* region covered by a large shield of cuticle called the *carapace*.

Again, like other arthropods, crustaceans show a basic arrangement of a pair of limbs per segment and, unlike the insects and arachnids, retain these limbs in most species. The adaptations of these limbs are often exquisite and they are rewarding subjects to study. The basic equipment is a pair of antennae, which are primarily sensory but sometimes serve

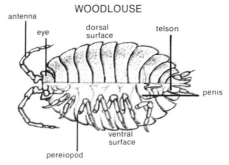

WOODLOUSE

antenna — eye — dorsal surface — telson — penis — ventral surface — pereiopod

Above: A body plan of a woodlouse, split to show the upper and lower body surfaces.

Below: The under surface of a pill woodlouse showing the brood pouch with young. These crustaceans are well adapted to life on land; their bodies are shaped to resist drying by evaporation.

Right: Common woodlice on the underside of a piece of tree bark. These animals are usually found in damp places because their gill-like breathing organs must be kept moist. Woodlice are the most common land crustaceans. They are found all over the world and feed on rotting vegetation.

Heather Angel

J. A. Grant/Natural Science Photos

COMMON CRUSTACEANS

Fairy shrimp *Anostraca branchipus*

Water flea *Daphnia*

scud *Hyalella*

Cyclops

Crayfish *Fluviatius*

Woodlouse *Porcellio scaber*

fresh water

terre

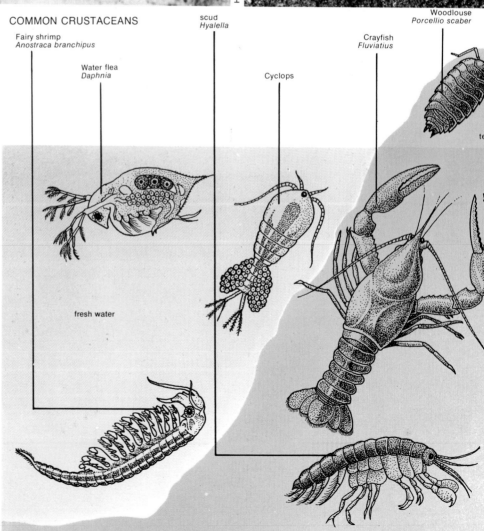

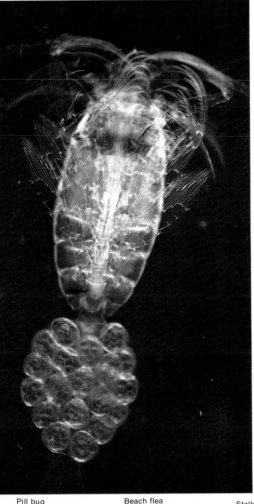

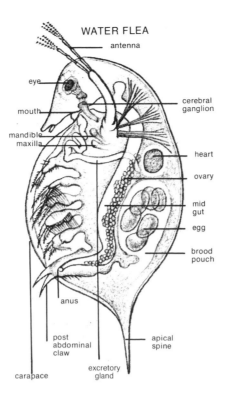

WATER FLEA

- antenna
- eye
- mouth
- mandible
- maxilla
- cerebral ganglion
- heart
- ovary
- mid gut
- egg
- brood pouch
- anus
- post abdominal claw
- apical spine
- excretory gland
- carapace

Jacana

Left: A marine copepod with a bulging egg sac. The copepods are the most important of all crustaceans since they are a major constituent of the plankton which provides food for many sea creatures. The plankton consists of all sorts of small animals and plants carried along by sea currents.

Above: A body plan of the water flea *Daphnia*. These animals belong to the branchiopods, a group of freshwater crustaceans. They are about 1.6 mm across and live in ponds and ditches. A carapace formed of two plates encloses most of the body. They swim by jerking the large branched antennae.

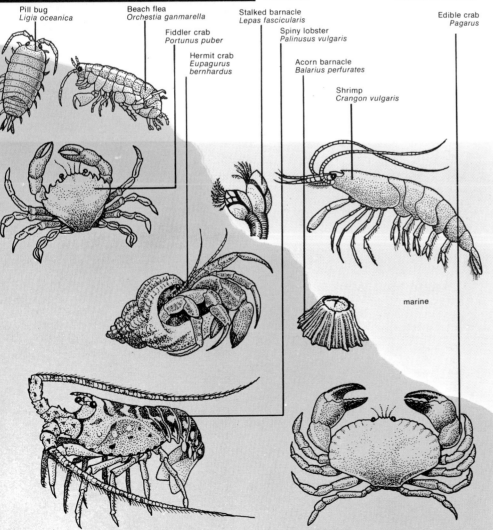

Pill bug
Ligia oceanica

Beach flea
Orchestia ganmarella

Fiddler crab
Portunus puber

Hermit crab
Eupagurus bernhardus

Stalked barnacle
Lepas fascicularis

Spiny lobster
Palinusus vulgaris

Acorn barnacle
Balarius perfurates

Shrimp
Crangon vulgaris

Edible crab
Pagarus

marine

other purposes as well, a pair of chewing mandibles and two pairs of limbs, called *maxillipeds*, for transferring food to the mouth. These are followed by other limbs for feeding, respiration, swimming, walking and reproduction.

The crustacean groups

The primitive *Branchiopoda* (the name means 'gill legs') are a group of freshwater crustaceans which exhibit many features typical of the class. They have leaf-like limbs used for feeding and often for swimming and respiration as well. Like most crustaceans, these animals are filter feeders; as the legs swing forwards, water is sucked in between them and food particles are filtered off on fringing hairs. As the legs swing back stiffly to propel the animals through the water, a small leakage washes the food from the hairs forwards to the mouth. Here the particles are stuck together with a sticky fluid and manipulated into the mouth by the mouthpart limbs. Some branchiopods have stouter, more bristly limbs that are used to stir up detritus lying on the pond bottom or to scrape algae off pond weeds.

Smaller animals of the group, like *Daphnia* and its close relatives, live in ponds while others are successful planktonic species in large lakes. The branchiopods succeed in avoiding competition with other animals by appearing early in the spring with the bloom of algae and then declining again.

Crustaceans move through water in many different ways. For example, many row themselves along by their limbs. In the primitive brine shrimps and fairy shrimps all the limbs beat fore and aft in what is called *metachronal rhythm*—each one slightly ahead of the one behind. The limbs are straight on the back stroke and flexed on the recovery stroke so as to propel the animal along. At the same time food is collected by the limbs.

Crustaceans, being essentially aquatic animals, use gills carried on limbs for respiration. In small species the general body surface may be used, or, in the branchiopods, the thin-walled limbs themselves. These thin-walled regions usually have special respiratory currents directed over them.

The nervous system and sense organs of crustaceans are typically arthropodan —sensory hairs for mechanical and chemical sensation, simple and compound eyes for light perception and vision. Some advanced species may recognize their prey visually. Many planktonic species migrate vertically each day; they swim down during the daylight hours and rise to the surface at night covering distances of as much as 600 ft (200 m). This is thought to be important in increasing the feeding range of the animals.

The sexes are separate in most crustaceans, and some structure for transferring sperm to the female is present in most males. Fertilized eggs typically develop into a series of larvae, often planktonic in the case of non-planktonic adults, thus avoiding competition with the adult population and aiding dispersal of the species. The first larval stage is called the *nauplius* and this has an oval body carrying three pairs of limbs. The nauplius larval stage is a fundamental characteristic of crustaceans; animals which are very different when adult (barnacles and copepods, for example) often have remarkably similar nauplius larvae. Even when 23

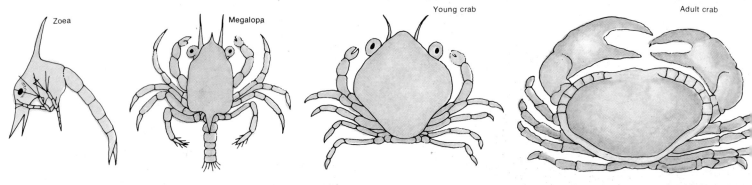

Zoea   Megalopa   Young crab   Adult crab

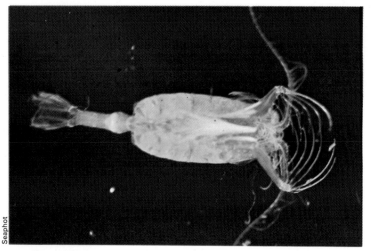

Seaphot

Above and left: Plankton is composed of a variety of small animals and plants. Among the crustacean members are the copepods (left) and newly hatched larvae of crabs (top left). These young larvae are called zoeae. The series of pictures above shows the other stages in the development of the edible crab, *Cancer pagurus*. The zoea is free-swimming, and about three or four weeks after hatching it changes into a megalopa larva which sinks to the sea floor. This becomes a young crab with a shell width of about 2.5 mm after a few more days. An adult crab can measure as much as 30 cm (1 ft) across.

Dr. F. Sauer/Bavaria

Far right: The European crayfish, *Astacus astacus*. This animal only lives in very clean water and is therefore susceptible to pollution. It is not surprising that these creatures are becoming less common.

Right: A diagram showing the internal organs of a lobster. The stomach is divided into two sections separated by a strainer. Food is ground up in the cardiac stomach and then passes to the pyloric stomach where it is mixed with the digestive fluids.

Below: A marine shrimp *Stenopus hispidus*.

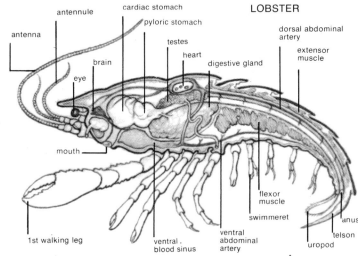

LOBSTER

antenna — antennule — cardiac stomach — pyloric stomach — dorsal abdominal artery — extensor muscle — testes — heart — digestive gland — brain — eye — mouth — 1st walking leg — ventral blood sinus — ventral abdominal artery — flexor muscle — swimmeret — uropod — telson — anus

Bavaria

the eggs hatch into a different larval form, as in the case of the crayfish, there is often evidence of a nauplius-like embryonic stage in the egg before hatching.

Resistant, heavily-shelled eggs are produced by many branchiopods. Brine shrimp eggs have been experimentally exposed to severe drying and temperatures of 100°C and still remain viable. Some animals like *Daphnia* produce eggs early in the season which do not require fertilization by a male and so the population can increase rapidly. In the summer and autumn they produce fertilized, resistant eggs to survive the rigours of winter.

Crustaceans in the food chain

The *Copepoda* are a group of small crustaceans which occur in immense numbers in marine and freshwater plankton. They are of enormous importance to all marine life, because they are one of the first links in the food chain. It has been estimated that there are more marine copepods than all other animals put together, and they constitute the world's largest stock of animal protein. (Plankton is basic to the feeding of animals like herring, sardines, whales and basking sharks; a whale can reach maturity and a weight of between 60 and 70 tonnes within two years just by straining plankton from the sea.) Not all copepods, however, are planktonic; *Cyclops*, for example, is a familiar form found in ponds and ditches.

Like the branchiopods, most copepods are filter feeders but they use different methods. Vortices generated by swimming bring particles towards the animal and these are then collected by the bristly mouthparts which create their own feeding current by rapid vibration.

Many copepods have evolved towards parasitism, and some are highly adapted for this way of life. Less modified forms are external parasites such as the fish lice which are flattened and have clawed limbs for clinging to the host. A more advanced state is seen in animals like the gill maggot, *Chondrochanthus*. With its loss of limbs, it hardly resembles a copepod apart from the sucking mouthparts embedded in the blood-rich gill tissue of the fish host.

Most crustaceans have several methods of travelling, although one may be dominant. In the copepods, the limbs near the head are rotated rather than rowed, and this creates a vortex on either side of the animal, driving it slowly forward. This type of movement is closely

P. Morris/Ardea

Above: A slipper lobster, *Scyllarus*. These animals are easily distinguished by their flattened second antennae.

Left: A hermit crab occupies the shell of a whelk. As the crab grows, it periodically replaces its home with a new, larger one.

Heather Angel

Right: The top two diagrams show the difference between the skeleton of a vertebrate animal and the exoskeleton of an arthropod. The bottom diagram shows the structure of the cuticle of an arthropod. The waxy outer layer prevents water from penetrating the layers underneath.

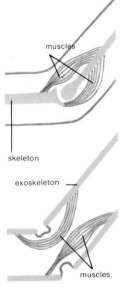

muscles

skeleton

exoskeleton

muscles

Left: A male and female masked crab, *Corystes cassivelaunus*. The smaller animal is the female.

Right: A painted crayfish, *Panulirus longipes*. This animal is only about 7.5 cm (3 in) long, but it shows many of the features common to both lobsters and crayfish. The body is divided into two distinct regions; the cephalothorax and the segmented abdomen. The cephalothorax has a single shield-like covering, the carapace, while each of the five abdominal segments has its own covering, called a somite. The abdomen ends in a fan-like tail called the telson.

Heather Angel

Ron Taylor/Ardea

waxy layer

rigid chitinous layer

flexible chitinous layer

epidermis

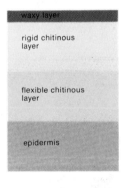

Below: The nauplius larva of *Sacculina carcini*. The adult is shaped like a sack and is parasitic on crabs, extracting nourishment by means of 'roots' growing into the host's body. A nauplius larva with three pairs of limbs is characteristic of many very different crustaceans.

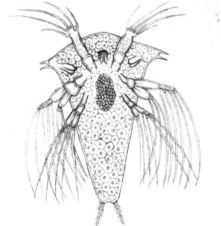

linked to the way the animal feeds, but the forked trunk limbs may also be used in rowing fashion for more rapid movement.

Barnacles

If one considers the barnacle zone of a rocky shore, it is as if a coat of living tissue had been painted on the rocks, so numerous and so close together are they packed. The barnacles, or *Cirripedia*, are also filter feeders, but as adults they remain attached to rocks, relying on the sea to bring food to them. Enclosed in their shells they can resist drying at low tide but open up to feed when the tide is in. This way of life is one commonly adopted by many different animals, from sponges to sea squirts.

The barnacles have been aptly described as lying on their backs, kicking food into their mouths. They are highly modified animals, with six pairs of curved hairy legs called *cirri* which are repeatedly thrust out of the shell cavity in subtly different ways, to form an effective net with which to catch suspended food.

Another group of crustaceans are the *Ostracoda*, tiny animals which mostly live in freshwater habitats. They do not have an obviously segmented body, but are recognized as crustaceans by their jointed limbs and, in many of them, the characteristic nauplius larva.

Lobsters, crabs and shrimps

These, the best known crustaceans, belong to the great group called the *Malacostraca*. Among them, the essential model is a shrimp-like swimming animal, but this has been modified to form bottom-living and burrowing animals as well. All the familiar forms of crab, crayfish and lobster are bottom-living forms. Terrestrial or semi-terrestrial woodlice (or sow bugs) have evolved here as well. A carapace joining the head to the thorax and enclosing this region is especially characteristic of the *Malacostraca*, although not peculiar to them. While the more primitive members of the group are filter feeders, specialization of limbs allows feeding upon larger prey or food masses. The characteristic pincers for manipulation of food become developed in this group.

In prawns and shrimps, the limbs on the abdomen, called *swimmerets*, row the animal along. In bottom-living forms, like crayfish and lobsters, the swimmerets are small and incapable of propelling the animal; they are nevertheless important in making a pouch for their brood and

Heather Angel

Left: The common prawn, *Leander serratus.* **Like their crayfish cousins, shrimps and prawns can move very rapidly backwards to escape from danger, by flexing their powerful abdominal muscles. Shrimps and prawns are common in many parts of the world. They are usually found in shallow coastal waters.**

Right: A vividly marked painted shrimp, *Hymenocera picta.* **These animals feed on starfish which they attack with their pincers. Bright colours and bizarre markings to warn off predators are particularly common in animals which live in tropical marine environments.**

COMMON PRAWN

1st and 2nd pereiopods — antennule — artery to head — antenna — heart — gills — ventral abdominal artery — dorsal abdominal artery

Heather Angel

Left and below: A stretch of the Welsh coastline showing the barnacle line along the rocks. Barnacles like the acorn barnacles (below) cling to the rocks. They close up when above the water line at low tide, but when submerged they extend their thoracic limbs to search for food.

Above: The body plan of a prawn. The walking legs are modified thoracic limbs and are called pereiopods. The limbs on the abdomen are called swimmerets or pleopods and they are used to propel the animal through the water. The gills are situated underneath the carapace where they are protected.

Heather Angel

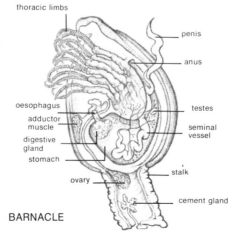

BARNACLE

thoracic limbs — penis — anus — oesophagus — adductor muscle — digestive gland — stomach — testes — seminal vessel — stalk — ovary — cement gland

Heather Angel

Above: Goose barnacles, with their limbs extended for gathering food. These animals get their name from the ancient belief that they were the young of barnacle geese. The supposed marine origin of these birds once allowed them to be eaten during religious fasts when meat was banned.

Right: A body plan of a barnacle. These animals live attached to rocks by means of a cement gland. They are hermaphrodite, having reproductive organs of both sexes. Early zoologists thought these animals were molluscs, like oysters, but their first larval stage is clearly a crustacean nauplius.

may be retained solely for this purpose as in crabs.

The legs on the thorax of *Malacostraca* are relatively strong, often unforked, and used for walking. Though slender in animals like prawns, which can swim well, these walking legs are very strong in species like lobsters, crawfish and crabs, or in semi-terrestrial or terrestrial forms like sand hoppers and woodlice.

The swimming crabs are bottom-living animals, with small swimmerets and abdomens, that have acquired an ability to swim. The last pair of walking legs of swimming crabs are flattened so that they can be used as paddles to propel the animal.

Many crustaceans make use of the abdomen for swimming, most commonly as an escape mechanism. In animals like the freshwater crayfish the last pair of swimmerets are broad and form a tail fan with the end of the abdomen. When the abdomen is suddenly bent under the body this shoots the animal backwards through the water. Anyone who has tried to pick up a crayfish will be well aware of this effective mechanism.

Many of these animals collect food particles by rotary movements of parts of the thoracic limbs, as in the *Euphausids* (the 'krill' that whalebone whales feed on). Alternatively, some animals like the fiddler crabs may collect food from mud or from sand grains picked up and carefully searched by the mouthparts. Most of the larger *Malacostraca*, however, are predators and scavengers, feeding on relatively lethargic prey.

The gills in advanced *Malacostraca* are protected by a downgrowth of the carapace, and water is drawn through the gill chamber by specially modified limbs. Species living in muddy or tidal conditions may have the openings of the gill chamber guarded by hairs; indeed, in a crab they are hard to detect. The blood is circulated by a heart after oxygenation in the gills, the usual respiratory pigment being haemocyanin.

The crustaceans are of great zoological interest as well as being economically important. They provide food vital to life in the sea and, to a lesser extent, are a source of food for man. On the negative side, some copepods transmit human parasites like the guinea worm of the tropics, and barnacles have long been a problem for shipping. Another crustacean pest is *Limnoria lignorum*, a tiny marine animal which bores into wood. If present in large enough numbers these animals can destroy wooden jetties and wharves.

Slugs and Snails

Snails and slugs are molluscs belonging to the class *Gastropoda*. This is the most successful of the mollusc classes, containing as it does some 35,000 living species most of which are marine. The sea shore limpets and winkles, the land dwelling snails and slugs, and the fresh water pond snails are well known to all while many of the beautiful marine forms are familiar only to specialists.

From their outward appearance it is hard to imagine that molluscs could have anything in common with the segmented worms *(annelids)*, but the two groups are quite closely related. The likeness is only clearly apparent in the embryonic and larval stages; the early embryos of the two groups are almost identical and the larvae, called *trochophores,* are very similar to each other. Molluscs, however, do not have the segmented structure of the annelids; it is thought that they must have branched off from the evolutionary tree just before the annelids, the first group to show segmentation.

The gastropods most commonly encountered are the garden slugs and snails. These are very abundant; many hundreds of slugs can be removed each night from a half acre garden without markedly affecting the total slug population. Although the common terrestrial slugs and snails are often rather drab, other members of the class can be vividly coloured. These include the yellow, pink and brown periwinkles found on rocky sea shores, green sea hares, iridescent blue winkles and ormers, and blood-red freshwater snails. In contrast to many of their terrestrial cousins, the sea slugs exhibit an astonishing variety of colours and markings.

Although gastropods do not generally form an important part of the human diet, several species can be eaten. Indeed, the gastronomic possibilities of the species *Helix pomatia,* the 'edible' snail, are directly responsible for its presence in Britain; it was introduced by the Romans who obviously considered it a delicacy. In certain regions of Africa the large land snail, *Achatina,* is an important source of food, and various marine species such as the periwinkle, *Littorina littorea,* found on European shores, and the conch, *Strombus gigas,* common in the West Indies are also eaten.

The shells of certain snails have long been admired for their iridescent colouring, and they are nowadays collected by the ton for use in the jewellery trade. *Trochus* shells, for example, are widely used in Japan to make decorative buttons.

The body of a gastropod is divided into three parts: the head, the foot and the *visceral mass* which contains most of the internal organs. This arrangement is typical of molluscs. In snails, the visceral mass is covered by a single coiled shell, often of great complexity and beauty. Coiling is an ancient gastropod feature, probably associated with making the visceral mass more compact. As well as being coiled, the visceral mass is twisted during development of the *veliger,* one of the larval stages of a gastropod. To begin

Heather Angel

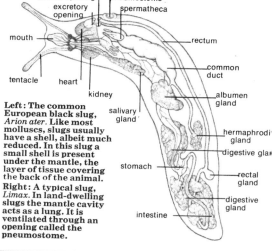

Left: The common European black slug, *Arion ater.* Like most molluscs, slugs usually have a shell, albeit much reduced. In this slug a small shell is present under the mantle, the layer of tissue covering the back of the animal.
Right: A typical slug, *Limax.* In land-dwelling slugs the mantle cavity acts as a lung. It is ventilated through an opening called the pneumostome.

Anthony Bannister/NHPA

Left: A giant land snail, *Achatina maculata.* These animals are found throughout most of southern Africa, and in some places they are an important source of food. This one is about seven inches (18 cm) long.

Below: A series of diagrams to show how a snail moves along. Bands of contracted longitudinal muscle are lifted up and moved forwards while the regions in between are held to the ground by a mucous slime. This results in the 'waves' o contraction which are observed to move along the foot of the animal. Snails can typically move at a speed of about 2 inches (5 cm) per minute.

Right: The mating of two Roman snails. *Helix pomatia.* Although these animals are hermaphrodites, mating is essential because they cannot fertilize their own eggs. During copulation sperms are passed from each animal to the other by means of a penis. A 'love dart' made of a substance containing lime is discharged by each snail into its mate at the culmination of courtship. This unusual behaviour is thought to stimulate effective mating of the animals.

NHPA

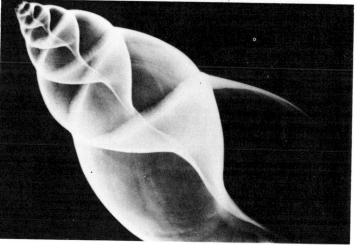

P. Morris/Ardea

Below and left: The shell of the giant African snail *Achatina.* The picture on the left is an X-ray photograph.

Heather Angel

Heather Angel

Left: Giant pond snails, *Limnaea stagnalis*. These gastropods are *pulmonates,* which means they have a lung cavity, rather than gills, and breathe air. A string of eggs surrounded by transparent gelatinous material have been laid on the shell of the nearer animal by another snail.

Right: A body plan of a land-dwelling snail. Blood is supplied to the various organs through an aorta leading from the heart. The aorta has two branches, one supplying the head and foot, the other supplying the visceral mass. The blood is oxygenated directly by air in the lung.

Left: Two views of a shell of the freshwater snail *Helisoma trivolvis*. The shell of a living snail is lined with a layer called the mantle which thickens into a collar where it joins the foot of the animal. Most of the shell is formed by a secretion from this mantle collar.

Right: A whirlpool ramshorn snail, *Planorbis vortex*. These snails are found in ponds and lakes. They can withstand a high level of pollution because, unlike other gastropods, they have haemoglobin in their blood. This improves respiration, making lower oxygen levels acceptable.

with, the veliger is symmetrical so that one side matches the other and it has a foot, a head with a mouth, and a digestive tube leading through the visceral mass to the anus at the back.

During development the visceral mass twists round through 180° while the head and foot of the animal remain stationary so that the anus comes to be positioned above the head of the animal. The string of faeces coming from under the front of the shell of a snail is outwardly visible evidence of this twisting. Possibly as a result of the coiling and twisting processes, the organs on one side of the body do not develop fully. Usually it is the organs on the right side of the adult (the left side of the larva) which are reduced.

While many gastropod species remain twisted throughout their lives some untwist later, but usually some sign of their earlier twisted condition remains. No one is sure what advantage twisting gives gastropods or their larvae, and it is strange that the most characteristic feature of the group should remain so little understood.

Gastropod groups

Gastropods show a wide range of form and adaptation to different ways of life, and they are divided into three groups: the *prosobranchs,* the *opisthobranchs* and the *pulmonates*. The prosobranchs have gills at the front of the body and well developed shells. They are mostly marine and exhibit the characteristic twisting as in winkles and top shells. The opisthobranchs have gills at the back of the body, reduced shells and a more streamlined shape. Like the prosobranchs they are marine, but the gills are less well developed or even

absent, and the twisting is less marked or lost. Examples include the sea hares and sea slugs. Finally, the pulmonates are land or freshwater species without gills. They breath air in a lung cavity and show the characteristic twisting of the visceral mass. Garden slugs and snails fall into this class.

In most molluscs the foot is highly muscular and this is certainly true of the gastropods which are active animals, albeit slow moving. If a snail's foot is observed while the animal is moving on a piece of glass, about eight darker bands moving forward can be seen. These are bands of contracted longitudinal muscle lifted up and moved forwards before being put down, while the regions in between are held down by mucus secreted from a gland at the front of the body. Variations of this musculature allow greater mobility or speed, or dogged adherence to resist wave action or predators. In contrast, forms such as the sea butterflies 'fly' under water using lateral flaps of the foot in a most graceful way. Swimming forms of this sort show great reduction of the shell which may even be absent altogether and a general lightening of the body.

Some gastropods, such as limpets, are adapted to withdraw under their shell by means of a shell muscle and cling to rocks, while others, like winkles, retreat entirely within the shell and close the opening with a plate, the *operculum,* carried on the back of the foot. This is especially important in shore-dwelling species as it prevents them from drying out at low tide as well as helping them to resist predators. In land snails a horny cover sealing the shell entrance may be formed, especially when the animal hiber-

nates, to isolate the animals from the hostile outside world. Their ability to resist drying out has been an important factor in the successful adaptation of many gastropods to a terrestrial existence.

Feeding

Primitive gastropods show the basic method common to many molluscs of more or less continuous feeding. The food-collecting structure, the *radula,* is a continuously growing flexible strip bearing rows of teeth which is moved over the ground to collect particles of food. It is flanked by horny jaws and moved by a muscular region of the gut called the *buccal mass*. Particles of food are drawn in a mucus string to the stomach by the *style,* a secreted rod which is rotated by hair-like structures called *cilia*. The food is sorted out by cilia in the stomach, fine particles being carried into a large digestive gland where digestion and absorption takes place. The intestine leads from the stomach to the rectum which discharges into the *mantle cavity,* a region located above the head of the animal under the shell which also houses the gills. This kind of general arrangement is seen in ormers and slit limpets, but evolution has also developed the feeding mechanism and gut in a number of other directions.

In limpets and many winkles the radula has fewer but stouter teeth for rasping algae from rocks and is very long to compensate for rapid wear. As food is not mixed and feeding is intermittent, the stomach lacks the continuously winding style and the complex sorting areas and simply forms a storage region. Forms such as the slipper limpet and chinaman's hat collect fine food particles in mucus on an

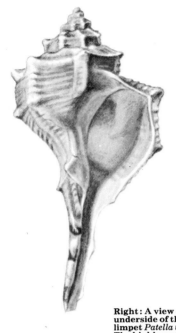

Left: The shell of the marine snail *Murex* found along the shores of the Mediterranean. In the time of the Phoenicians many thousands of these snails were killed annually for the purple dye they produce. Huge deposits of such shells have been found at Tyre, Sidon and other former Phoenician cities.

Right: Coloured varieties of *Nucella lapillus,* the dog whelk, lying on an Atlantic shore. Like *Murex,* these snails produce a purple dye which was once extracted and used. Egg capsules, each containing as many as 1,000 eggs, can also be seen in the picture.

D. P. Wilson

Right: A view of the underside of the limpet *Patella vulgata.* The highly muscular foot, the tentacles and, between the tentacles, the mouth can clearly be seen. The large foot allows the animal to cling tightly to rocks on the sea shore, thus preventing it from becoming dislodged by the action of the waves.

Left: A shell of the marine limpet *Acmaea.*

Far right: A body plan of the marine limpet *Acmaea.* Water circulates under the shell to supply oxygen to the gills and to carry away waste products.

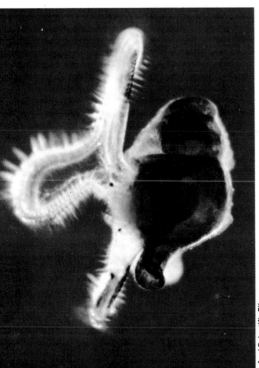

Alison Wilson

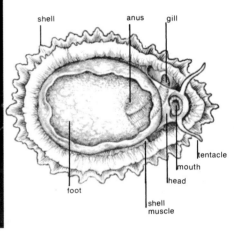

shell — anus — gill — tentacle — mouth — head — foot — shell muscle

Left: The veliger larva of a gastropod. This stage of development is intermediate between the first larval stage, called the trochophore, and the adult snail. The veliger is free-swimming, propelling itself through the water with the hair-like cilia plainly visible in the picture.

Right: A violet snail, *Janthina globosa,* floats on a raft of air bubbles. These snails are found along the east coast of Africa.

Below: Stages in the development of a veliger larva. To begin with the veliger (left) is symmetrical with one side of the animal matching the other. The shell is very small and the foot has hardly begun to develop. In its most advanced stage (right) the veliger has a well developed shell and foot and the visceral mass has become twisted so that the anus comes to lie above the animal's head.

Oxford Scientific Films

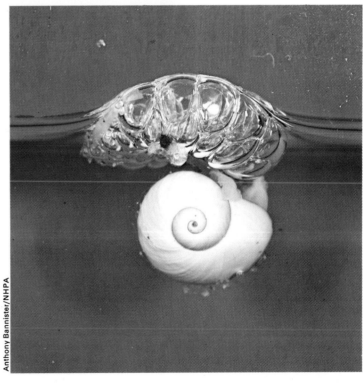

Anthony Bannister/NHPA

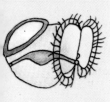

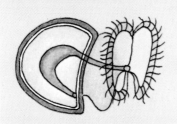

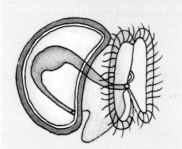

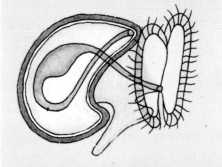

Right: A sea slug crawling on an African coral reef. The remarkably vivid colours and the strange shapes of the sea slugs serve as a camouflage to protect them against predators. In deeper water where there is less light, these animals lose much of their brilliant colour.

Anthony Bannister/NHPA

enlarged gill. A string of food and mucus is then pulled into the mouth by the simple radula and buccal mass, but the stomach and style are well developed to deal with the continuous supply of particles.

In herbivores, like the snails and seaweed-feeding forms such as the sea hare, the radula has rows of small teeth for breaking up the food which is bitten off in pieces by the jaws. Many gastropods have become carnivores, and in such forms the radula is short with reduced rows of sharp teeth. Salivary glands become large and secrete enzymes capable of digesting proteins, while the forward gut region may be developed so that the buccal mass can be brought to the tip of an elongated proboscis. Such a proboscis is often developed as a 'drill' for penetrating the shells of bivalve molluscs such as mussels or oysters. The shells are neatly drilled by the radula, with the help of acid secretions in some species, so allowing entry of the proboscis. Drilled bivalve shells can often be picked up in large numbers on sandy shores at low tide. Less specialized carnivorous gastropods feed on stationary animals such as sponges and coelenterates.

Some sea slugs which feed on coelenterates show a most extraordinary adaptation. While most of the victim's body tissue is digested in the normal way, stinging capsules, called *nematocysts*, remain intact and eventually find their way to projections called *cerata* in the slug's body surface. Here they mature and come into action if the animal is attacked for example by a predator. Associated with this remarkable mechanism is the bright colouration of these sea slugs which presumably acts as a warning to predators.

Right: A series of diagrams of *Limacina*, a shelled sea butterfly, to show how it moves through the water. The animal has two wing-like parapodia which push it along.

Below: A sea butterfly, *Cavolinia*, found along the coast of the Atlantic ocean.

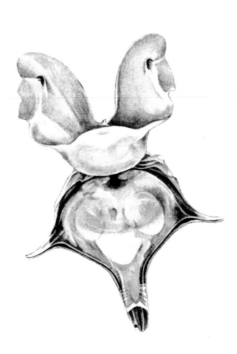

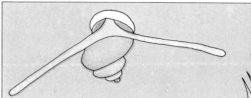

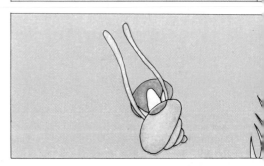

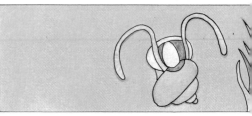

Left: A sea slug, *Cyerce nigra*. The shield-like structures covering the animal are modified gills, called cerata, and contain outgrowths of the liver.

Above: A sea slug, *Chromodoris coi*. The sea slugs belong to the *opisthobranch* group of gastropods.

Below: A sea hare, *Aplysia punctata*. In the background is sea lettuce, *Ulva*, which is eaten by sea hares. The animal swims along by means of two flap-like parapodia, one on each side of the body.

Bottom: Another species of sea hare, *Aplysia sowerbyi*.

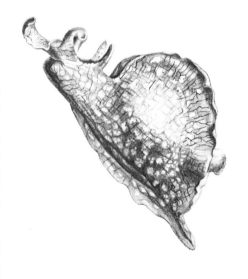

Most terrestrial snails and slugs are herbivorous, but some prey on animals such as earthworms. Perhaps the most advanced carnivores are the marine cone shells. Here the radular teeth are reduced to a single pair in each row. They are very large and pointed, and have a groove that carries a nerve poison secreted by the salivary glands. A single radular tooth is suddenly struck into the prey, rapidly paralysing it with the salivary poison. One Australian species of this group has even proved fatal to man.

Respiration

The mantle cavity of all molluscs is vitally important, but in the gastropods with their diversity of form and habits, it shows much variation. It is most important as a respiratory area protecting the delicate gills. In the primitive ormers and their relatives, water is brought in over the two gills and then out through a series of apertures along the mid-line of the shell, carrying away with it waste products from the anus and the kidney ducts. This irrigation is brought about entirely by the action of cilia. In more advanced gastropods the gill and kidney of the right hand side are lost and water can flow in an efficient U-shaped path, in at the left hand side, across the single gill and out at the right hand side. The mantle cavity opens at the front of the animal as a result of the twisting process, and the flow of water through it may be assisted by the animal's forward movement. In the sea slugs and their relatives respiration takes place through the general body surface or by means of secondary gills. The pulmonates such as garden slugs have a single small opening called a *pneumostome* leading into

the mantle cavity which acts as a lung; the anus, kidney and genital ducts open outside the mantle cavity.

In all gastropods the heart drains blood from the respiratory surface and distributes it by means of arteries throughout the body from where it drains into the main body cavity. Haemocyanin is the respiratory pigment and its general efficiency is low, but this is unimportant in view of the low level of activity of the animals. Unlike haemoglobin, the red iron-containing respiratory pigment of human blood, haemocyanin is very faintly blue and contains copper.

In reproducing their kind, gastropods show remarkable diversity. In the most primitive species, reproductive cells, or *gametes*, are shed through the mantle cavity into the sea where fertilization takes place and the larvae develop. During their life some gastropods show a change of sex. In a group of slipper limpets, *Crepidula farnicata,* sitting one on top of the other it is observed that the sexes range from a young male on top, through hermaphrodites to the largest female on the bottom. Most gastropods have very complex hermaphrodite reproductive systems that allow internal fertilization, and they may produce hard shelled eggs or even live young. This is another factor that has been important in colonising difficult non-marine habitats.

With terrestrial life and hermaphroditism a complex courtship is often seen. Common garden snails for example indulge in a remarkable courtship which culminates in the shooting of lime-containing 'love darts' into each other, followed by copulation and the mutual exchange of sperm.

31

Octopuses, Squid and Oysters

There are more than 80,000 living and 35,000 fossil species of the molluscs. As a large and successful group of the animal kingdom, they inhabit a wide range of ecological niches, and are found on land, in freshwater and in the sea.

The group can be divided into seven classes, three of which contain fairly common animals. The mussels, oysters, cockles, clams, scallops and razor shells belong to the Bivalvia class and are typically rather slow-moving creatures, often found buried in sand or mud on the sea bed or firmly attached to rocks. In contrast, squid, cuttlefish and octopus are active swimmers belonging to the class Cephalopoda. This class contains the largest known invertebrate animal, the deep sea squid, *Architeuthis*, which can reach a length of more than 15 metres (50 ft). The class Gastropoda contains the slugs, snails and limpets. Somewhat less familiar are the 'coat of mail' shells or chitons of the class Placophora, and the specialized, often worm-like and burrowing, deep water species in the class Scaphopoda.

The final class, Monoplacophora, contains the primitive *Neopilina* which looks rather like a limpet and was first discovered in 1952, dredged up from deep water off the Pacific coast of Mexico.

Molluscs and Man

A number of molluscs, particularly bivalves, are of economic importance, usually as a source of food. Oyster cultivation has been recorded from Roman times, and the presence of quantities of oyster, mussel and scallop shells in archeological excavations emphasizes the importance of shell-fish in the diet of prehistoric man. British oyster beds were once the largest in Europe, but have greatly declined in extent and productivity over the last century. The accidental introduction of oyster predators such as the American oyster drill (a marine snail) as well as the arrival of competitors for food or space such as the American slipper limpet, *Crepidula*, and the barnacle, *Elminius*, have all contributed to the decline of the British oyster beds. On top of this, there has been over-fishing, pollution and, in 1962-63, a particularly severe winter. Most commercial beds today are stocked with the faster growing but gastronomically inferior Portuguese oyster, *Crassostrea angulata*. This warmer water species rarely breeds in Britain, and so young oysters are imported from abroad for sowing in British beds.

Also of considerable economic importance, albeit adverse, are the shipworms, *Teredo*. These are specialized bivalves that can bore into wood using their shells and feed off the wood cellulose. They can cause extensive damage to wooden jetties and piers.

Mollusc characteristics

All the mollusc classes, despite apparently having a great diversity of structure, have certain basic molluscan features in common. One of the most obvious is the possession of a hard external shell for the

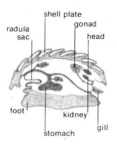

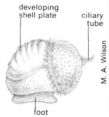

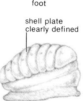

Above: The top diagram shows the positions of the main organs of a chiton. The eight shell plates are secreted by the mantle which covers the upper part of the body. Chitons breathe by means of gills which lie on both sides of the animal between the mantle and the foot. The centre diagram shows a free-swimming chiton larva with the shell plates just beginning to develop. The ring of cilia around the middle of the animal enables it to move through the water. The bottom diagram shows a later stage of development. The cilia have been lost, and the foot and the shell plates are much more clearly defined.

M. A. Wilson

Left and below: Chitons or 'coat-of-mail' shells are perhaps the most typical of all molluscs. They have a soft body, a muscular foot and a hard covering shell. They are found on rocks along the seashore where they feed on algae and other vegetable matter. In some chitons like the one on the left, *Acanthochitona crinita*, the fleshy mantle grows over the outer edge of the shell and carries nine pairs of tufts of bristles. These bristles are extremely sensitive to touch. Chitons are most active at night, returning during the day to a particular home location. If disturbed they cling tightly to the rock.

Jane Burton/Bruce Coalman

Jacana

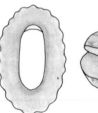

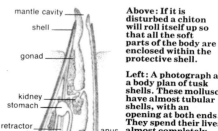

Above: If it is disturbed a chiton will roll itself up so that all the soft parts of the body are enclosed within the protective shell.

Left: A photograph and a body plan of tusk shells. These molluscs have almost tubular shells, with an opening at both ends. They spend their lives almost completely buried in the sand with only the top of the shell projecting. Currents of water flowing in and out of the upper shell opening permit respiration and the excretion of waste products. The head has a large number of sense organs, called *captacula*, which help in capturing prey.

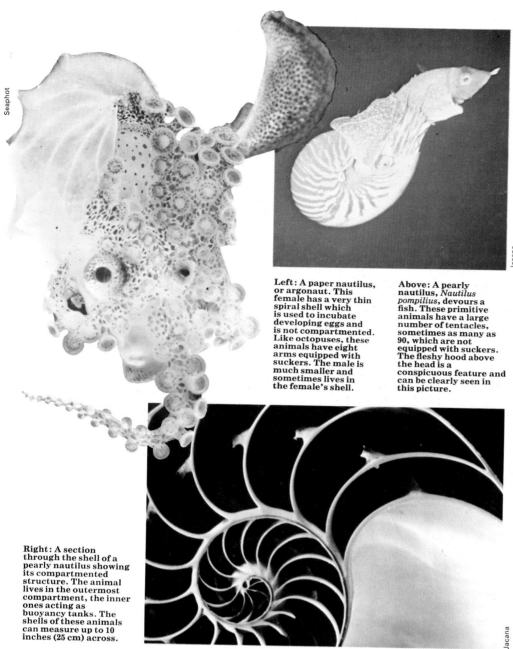

Left: A paper nautilus, or argonaut. This female has a very thin spiral shell which is used to incubate developing eggs and is not compartmented. Like octopuses, these animals have eight arms equipped with suckers. The male is much smaller and sometimes lives in the female's shell.

Above: A pearly nautilus, *Nautilus pompilius*, devours a fish. These primitive animals have a large number of tentacles, sometimes as many as 90, which are not equipped with suckers. The fleshy hood above the head is a conspicuous feature and can be clearly seen in this picture.

Right: A section through the shell of a pearly nautilus showing its compartmented structure. The animal lives in the outermost compartment, the inner ones acting as buoyancy tanks. The shells of these animals can measure up to 10 inches (25 cm) across.

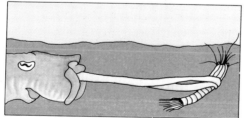

Above and left: The common cuttlefish, *Sepia officinalis*, is another member of the mollusc family. These creatures catch their prey by shooting out a pair of tentacles at the unsuspecting victim. The tentacles are usually retracted in a cavity underneath the eyes and are not normally visible. The shell of the cuttlefish, called the cuttlebone, is covered by the mantle and is often given to cage birds as a source of calcium. When attacked, the animal releases an inky fluid which contains the brown pigment *sepia* used by artists. Most of the time cuttlefish remain partly buried on the sandy ocean floor, lying in wait for prey.

protection of the soft body (the Latin word *mollis* means soft). The shell is of particular importance to biologists as it helps to identify the species. The innermost layer of the shell, the nacreous layer, is iridescent and is the commercially valuable mother of pearl. It is composed of flat horizontal plates of aragonite crystals, one of the crystalline forms of calcium carbonate. Outside the nacreous layer are two further layers. The middle layer is again composed of calcium carbonate crystals, but here they are arranged perpendicularly to the shell surface. The outermost layer, called the *periostracum*, is a thin horny covering which prevents the two calcium carbonate layers from being attacked if the water is acidic.

In the common sea mussel, *Mytilus edulis*, and other bivalves the shell takes the form of two plates or 'valves' almost completely enclosing the body and held firmly together by strong *adductor* muscles. The valves are joined at their upper edge by an elastic ligament 'hinge', and controlled relaxation of the adductors causes the valves to open. Shells can reach gigantic proportions. For example, the giant clam, *Tridacna*, living in shallow warm water on the coral reefs of the Indian and Pacific Oceans, has a shell over a metre across, weighing up to a quarter of a tonne (250 kg).

Cephalopods like the squids usually have a very small shell. In the squid, *Loligo*, and the cuttlefish, *Sepia*, the shell is internal, forming the 'pen' and 'cuttlebone' respectively. In the octopus, however, it is completely absent. Fossil cephalopods such as *Belemnites* and *Ammonites* have a large, chambered shell and such a condition is still seen in the pearly nautilus, a primitive member of the group found in the surface waters of the south-west Pacific. The shell is spirally coiled and new chambers are added as the nautilus grows; the animal lives in the largest, most recently formed chamber. The other chambers are kept filled with a gas to neutralize the animal's weight in the water, like the buoyancy tanks of a submarine, so that the nautilus can move up and down through the water at will.

The papery nautilus or argonaut is only distantly related to the pearly nautilus. Here only the female produces a shell which is paper-thin and fragile. It is held by two racquet-shaped arms and is used as an incubation chamber for the developing eggs. Sometimes, however, the much smaller, shell-less male has been known to inhabit it.

The chitons, a small group of marine molluscs, have a somewhat flattened body covered by a shell of eight overlapping plates. A well developed foot enables the chiton to attach itself, limpet-like, to rocks in the inter-tidal zone. If detached it can curl itself up like a wood louse because of the freedom of movement between the shell plates, and in this way it protects itself from possible injury by wave action. It is a herbivore, rasping seaweed from rocks with a well developed 'tongue', the *radula*, which acts like a chain saw.

Structure

The molluscan body is divided into three parts: head, foot and visceral mass. The head is particularly obvious in cephalopods where in addition to the mouth there is a pair of eyes comparable with those of the vertebrates, having an iris diaphragm, a movable lens and a curved retina. This gives the cephalopods the ability to discriminate colour and fine detail. In bivalves, probably because they lead a much less active life, the head region is absent. The foot, however, is well developed, being muscular and plough-like in shape, and can be protruded between the two valves for digging or burrowing. In mussels the foot has a gland which produces a mass of extremely tough protein threads, the *byssus*. These are used to attach the animal to rocks in the intertidal zone, so overcoming wave action. The cephalopod foot has become modified to form a circle of eight or ten arms—an octopus has eight, squid and cuttlefish ten—surrounding the head and also a funnel which connects the mantle cavity with the exterior. In squids two of the arms are particularly long and prehensile and can be retracted. They are known as the tentacles and are used for catching prey.

The visceral mass contains the main body organs and is surrounded by a thick flap of rather muscular tissue known as the *mantle*, the edge of which produces the major part of the shell. The mantle forms a skirt around the visceral mass, being attached to it only at the top. The cavity so formed between the mantle and the body is known as the *mantle cavity* into which open the anus, the kidney and reproductive ducts. Contained within the cavity are the respiratory organs, the gills or *ctenidia*.

Since many bivalves lie buried at considerable depths, the gills are supplied with water by means of two extendable tubes or *siphons*: an inhalant siphon which conducts oxygenated water and food into the mantle cavity from above the surface, and an exhalant siphon which removes the partially deoxygenated water together with any waste products. The mussel possesses a pair of gills each of which has undergone folding to produce a large surface area for respiration and also food collection. Small planktonic organisms and organic debris entering the mantle cavity are sieved off by cilia on the gills, trapped in long strings of mucus, and transported by other cilia to the mouth.

A rotating rod, the crystalline *style*, is present in the stomach. It acts as a capstan, winding in the long mucus strands, but it also releases enzymes vital for digestion. Large particles that could clog the filtering apparatus are removed by ciliary rejection currents and periodically the shell valves are clapped together. The increase in mantle cavity pressure shoots the debris out through the inhalant siphon.

In cephalopods the gills are supplied with water by muscular activity. The mantle muscles relax, increasing the volume of the mantle cavity, and water enters between the mantle and the base of the funnel. The modules then rapidly contract, causing the water to be violently expelled through the funnel. By pointing the funnel in different directions cephalopods, particularly the very active ones like squids, can move at considerable speed in any direction by a water-jet propulsion mechanism. Normally, however, a squid swims forwards by undulating the fins on either side of its body. In times of danger a black pigment, *melanin*, can be liberated into the water, producing a 'smoke screen' to confuse predators.

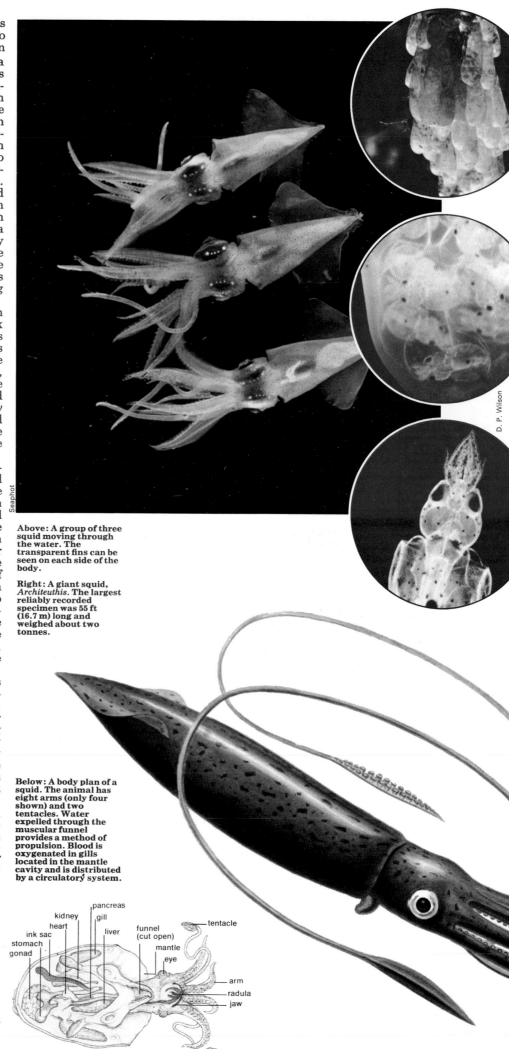

Seaphot

D. P. Wilson

Above: A group of three squid moving through the water. The transparent fins can be seen on each side of the body.

Right: A giant squid, *Architeuthis*. The largest reliably recorded specimen was 55 ft (16.7 m) long and weighed about two tonnes.

Below: A body plan of a squid. The animal has eight arms (only four shown) and two tentacles. Water expelled through the muscular funnel provides a method of propulsion. Blood is oxygenated in gills located in the mantle cavity and is distributed by a circulatory system.

pancreas
kidney
heart
gill
ink sac
stomach
gonad
liver
funnel (cut open)
tentacle
mantle
eye
arm
radula
jaw

Left: A series of pictures to show the development of the dwarf squid, *Alloteuthis subulata.* Each of the transparent egg capsules shown in the top picture contains many eggs. The centre picture is a close-up of one of the capsules showing the embryos in the eggs in a fairly advanced state of development. The bottom picture shows a newly hatched young squid. The two eyes and the heart are plainly visible.

Right: A young deep water squid. A squid has ten arms provided with suckers. Two of the arms are elongated to form tentacles for catching prey such as fish.

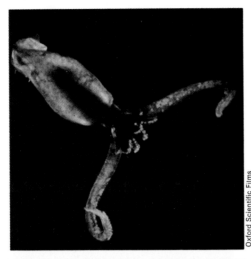

Oxford Scientific Films

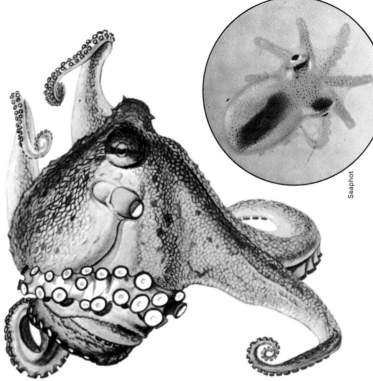

Seaphot

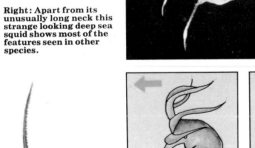

Heather Angel

Above: A close-up of the suckers of the squid *Loligo forbesi.* The tiny hooks on the rim of each sucker help to grip the prey. Both the arms and tentacles have suckers.

Right: Apart from its unusually long neck this strange looking deep sea squid shows most of the features seen in other species.

Seaphot

Above: The common octopus, *Octopus vulgaris,* and (inset) a newly hatched octopus. These animals do not have a larval stage: the young hatch directly from the egg capsules. Unlike most other molluscs, octopuses have no trace of a shell, not even an internal one.

Right: A lesser octopus, *Eledone cirrosa,* with a captured shore crab. The octopus is biting through the shell of the crab with its beak. Octopuses exhibit considerable skill and perseverence in hunting their prey, sometimes even following crabs on to dry land.

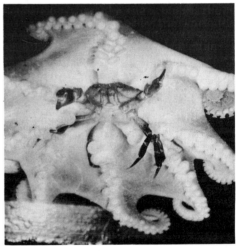

D. P. Wilson

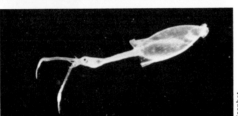

Above and right: The three diagrams above show how an octopus escapes from an enemy. On being disturbed the animal moves rapidly 'backwards', helped by a jet of water from its funnel. The opening of the funnel is clearly visible in the photograph of *Octopus vulgaris* on the right.

P. Morris/Ardea

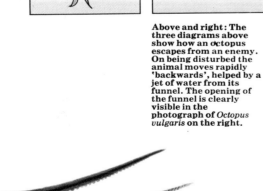

35

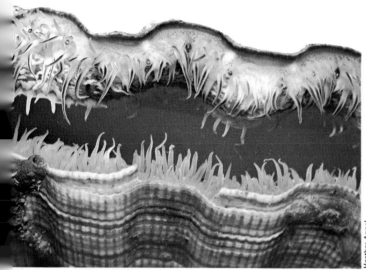

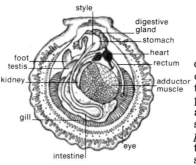

Above: A body plan of a scallop. Blood is circulated through blood vessels by the heart and is oxygenated in the gills. The gills are covered with cilia which maintain a current of water through the valve plates. This carries food particles to the animal's mouth.

Above: A close-up of the giant scallop, *Pecten maximus*. The edge of the mantle carries numerous tentacles as well as a series of eyes which look rather like pearls. The eyes are fairly well developed and can detect motion, so helping the animal to escape from its predators.

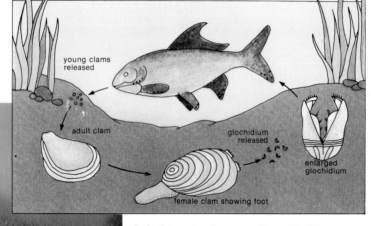

Left: A queen scallop, *Chlamys opercularis*, escapes from one of its predators, the common starfish, by clapping together its valve plates. Although these animals can swim they are often found anchored to rocks by means of *byssus* threads. Queen scallops are common in the Mediterranean.

Above: The life cycle of the freshwater clam. Fertilized eggs develop into larvae called *glochidia* in the gills of the female clam. These are released into the water and attach themselves to the gills or fin of a fish. Here they develop into young clams which then leave their host.

Left, right and below: Three different bivalve molluscs. On the left is a spiny cockle, *Acanthocardia echinata*, with its foot protruding from between the two valve plates. Right is a mussel, *Mytilus edulis*, lying open in sea water, and below is an American spiny oyster, *Spondylus*.

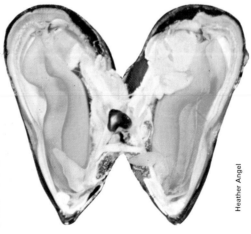

Right: The formation of a pearl by an oyster. This is a protective mechanism to prevent parasites such as fluke larvae from harming the animal. The outer layer of the mantle, the *epithelium*, secretes layers of pearly substance around the parasite to isolate it.

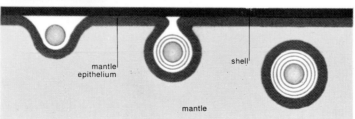

Cephalopods are carnivorous, feeding on fish and the larger crustacea. Food is captured by the long tentacles which, like the arms, are equipped with numerous powerful suckers. Living food is killed by a pair of strong beak-like jaws. The salivary glands produce enzymes called *proteases* which allow food to be partially digested before it reaches the stomach. In species like *Loligo*, the salivary glands also produce a powerful poison.

As might be expected from their active way of life, the cephalopods have a very well developed nervous system. The brain possesses higher intelligence centers so that sensory information can be memorized and used to modify behaviour. Leading from the brain are giant nerve fibres capable of rapidly transmitting impulses at up to 20 metres per second. This allows the animal to contract all the mantle muscles almost instantaneously.

Many deep sea squids are luminescent. Often the light-producing organs are highly complex, having lens tissue and reflector cells as well as the light-generating cells themselves. It may be that these cells enable the squid to pick out its prey in the darkness.

Reproduction

The bivalves usually reproduce by releasing enormous numbers of eggs and sperm into the water. External fertilization results in the development of ciliated larvae called *trochophores*. The trochophore, together with the next larval stage, the *veliger*, floats in the plankton and distributes the species before settling on a suitable surface and developing into an adult. In the freshwater swan mussel, *Anodonta*, and the European flat oyster, *Ostrea edulis*, however, fertilization is internal: sperms are released into the water and then carried into the mantle cavity to fertilize the eggs. In *Ostrea* clouds of veligers are liberated about eight days after fertilization.

It has been estimated that *Ostrea* can incubate up to a million eggs at a time, but even this number is small compared with the reproductive potential of the American oyster, *Crassostrea virginica*, where eggs are released in masses of 100 million at a time. Oyster veligers settle down after between one and two and a half weeks, but they are capable of swimming off again if they find the surface unsuitable. Eventually, however, the veliger cements itself to a surface, ideally a flat rock. This is done with a secretion from a cement gland in the foot which is a modification of the byssal gland found in mussels. At this stage the young oysters are about 1.2 mm (0.047 inch) across and are known as *spat*.

In cephalopods, fertilization usually follows an elaborate courtship often involving complex colour changes. The eggs are generally fertilized internally, one of the arms of the male, the *hectocotylus*, being specialized for transferring packets of sperm, known as *spermatophores*, into the female mantle cavity. Squids lay their eggs in clusters on the sea bed where they are left to develop. Eventually the eggs hatch directly into young squid. Unlike most other cephalopods, however, the octopus exhibits very little preliminary courtship behaviour, but the female takes great care of the eggs, flushing them with water and cleaning them with the tips of her arms.

The octopus, a creature
often underestimated.
Its senses are developed
enough to recognize
an impressive range of
objects by sight.

Insects

The insects are undoubtedly the largest and one of the most successful groups of animals. There are more than 750,000 species inhabiting a vast range of habitats on land and in water. The only environment that insects have failed to colonize to any great extent is the sea; they are completely absent from deep sea water. In the air, on the other hand, they are present up to heights of 2,000 metres (6,600 ft), forming an aerial 'plankton' on which many birds depend for food.

Insects owe their success to a number of features, perhaps the most important of which is the development of a waterproof layer on the outside of their hardened cuticle. This has liberated them from the restrictive damp environments of the onychophorans, centipedes and millipedes and, coupled with the development of flight, has enabled them to escape more easily from predators and to explore and colonize new habitats. Another important feature of the insect success story is their tremendous reproductive potential.

Insects are built on the basic arthropod design. The body is divided into three quite distinct regions. A head of six joined segments bears the feeding and sensory apparatus and is connected by a very short 'neck' to a thoracic region of three segments which bear the wings and three pairs of walking legs. The third region is an abdomen of eleven segments, either with no limbs at all or with small specialized limbs for purposes other than walking.

Wingless insects

Not all insects have wings, and they are thus divided into two groups: the wingless *Apterygota* and the winged *Pterygota*. The former contains those groups like the springtails, *Collembola*, and the bristletails, *Thysanura*. In these species some of the other features typical of insects are also poorly developed.

The springtails are small cosmopolitan, insects with a unique forked jumping organ at the bottom end of a short abdomen of five or six segments. They have a 'spring' fastened to the end of the abdomen by a 'catch' which when released allows the spring to move suddenly downwards, striking the ground and throwing the insect into the air. Since their cuticle is not waterproofed they only thrive in damp environments, in leaf mould, soil and rotting wood. It has been estimated that in an acre of English meadowland there may be as many as 250,000,000 rounded green springtails, *Sminthurus viridis*.

Bristletails derive their name from three bristle-like projections at the end of the abdomen and their long bristle-like antennae. They are about 2 cm (0.8 in) long and their legs are well developed for swift running. Although they are found throughout the world, they also are restricted to damp environments. The best known bristletails are the silverfish, *Lepisma*, and the firebrat, *Thermobia domestica*. The silverfish is so called since the division of the body into three parts is not obvious, giving a fish-like form and the body of the adult is covered with silvery scales which easily rub off. They are frequently found in larders, cup-

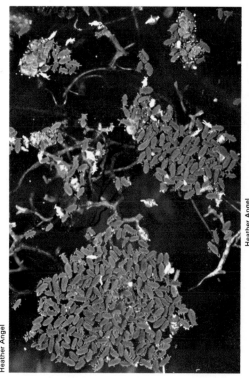

Heather Angel

Heather Angel

Left: Springtails, *Podura aquatica*, clustering on the surface of a pond. Springtails are primitive wingless insects which are usually very small. They have a spring mechanism formed from a pair of abdominal limbs. On each side of the head there is a group of simple eyes rather than the compound eye of most insects.

Above: Well camouflaged bristletails, *Petrobius maritimus*, on a stone. These animals get their name from the three jointed filaments at the tail end of the abdomen. Like the springtails, bristletails are primitive insects and cannot fly. They are usually found among rotting wood or leaves and under stones.

Below: The mating of two damselflies. The male grasps the female's thorax with claspers at the end of his abdomen. Like most insects damselflies have two pairs of wings carried on the second and third thoracic segments. Damselflies carry their wings parallel to their abdomens when they are not in flight.

Right: A close-up of the head of a dragonfly, *Aeshna cyanea*, showing the enormous compound eyes. They are composed of almost 30,000 separate light-sensitive units and cover most of the head. Compound eyes are found in most insects although in some (infants, for example) they may be composed of as few as 50 units.

Anthony Bannister/NHPA

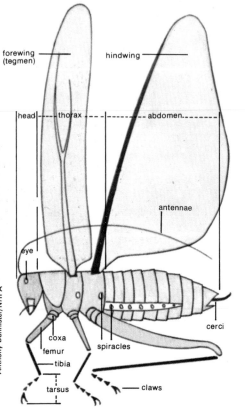

38

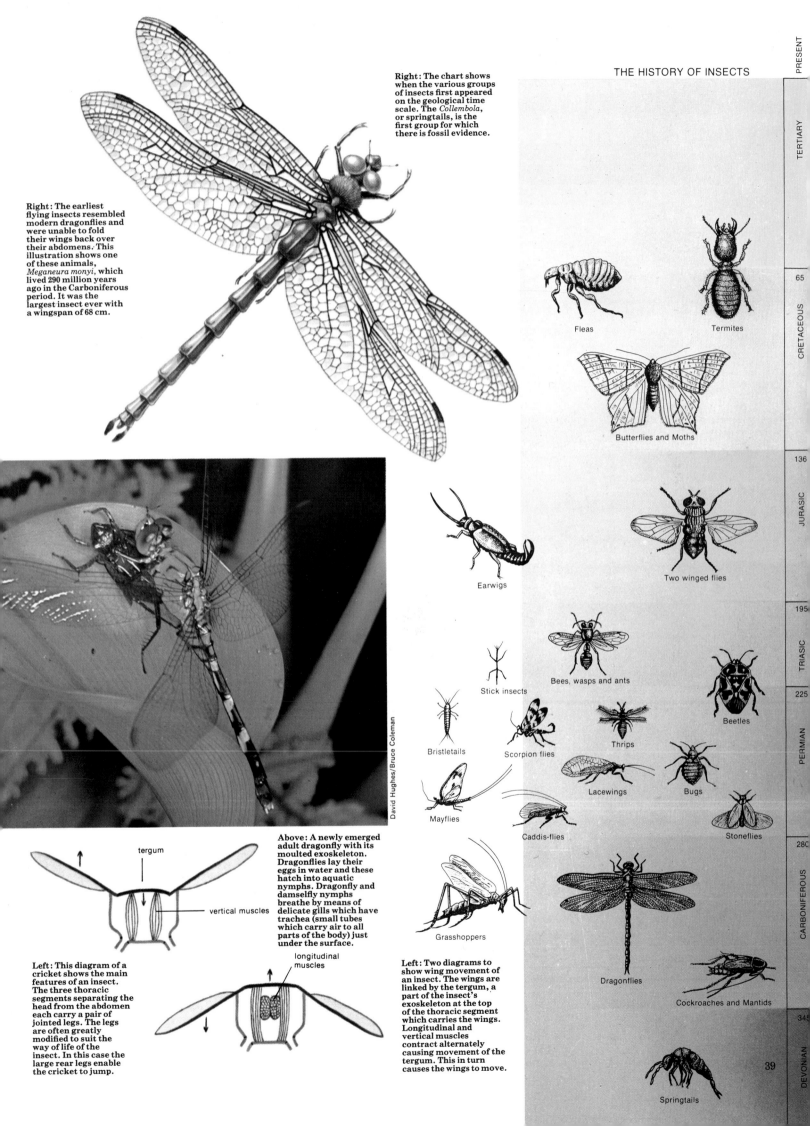

Right: The earliest flying insects resembled modern dragonflies and were unable to fold their wings back over their abdomens. This illustration shows one of these animals, *Meganeura monyi*, which lived 290 million years ago in the Carboniferous period. It was the largest insect ever with a wingspan of 68 cm.

Right: The chart shows when the various groups of insects first appeared on the geological time scale. The *Collembola*, or springtails, is the first group for which there is fossil evidence.

David Hughes/Bruce Coleman

tergum

vertical muscles

Left: This diagram of a cricket shows the main features of an insect. The three thoracic segments separating the head from the abdomen each carry a pair of jointed legs. The legs are often greatly modified to suit the way of life of the insect. In this case the large rear legs enable the cricket to jump.

longitudinal muscles

Above: A newly emerged adult dragonfly with its moulted exoskeleton. Dragonflies lay their eggs in water and these hatch into aquatic nymphs. Dragonfly and damselfly nymphs breathe by means of delicate gills which have trachea (small tubes which carry air to all parts of the body) just under the surface.

Left: Two diagrams to show wing movement of an insect. The wings are linked by the tergum, a part of the insect's exoskeleton at the top of the thoracic segment which carries the wings. Longitudinal and vertical muscles contract alternately causing movement of the tergum. This in turn causes the wings to move.

Fleas

Termites

Butterflies and Moths

Earwigs

Two winged flies

Stick insects

Bees, wasps and ants

Bristletails

Scorpion flies

Thrips

Beetles

Mayflies

Lacewings

Bugs

Caddis-flies

Stoneflies

Grasshoppers

Dragonflies

Cockroaches and Mantids

Springtails

PRESENT

TERTIARY

65

CRETACEOUS

136

JURASIC

195

TRIASIC

225

PERMIAN

280

CARBONIFEROUS

34

DEVONIAN

39

boards and behind skirting boards of houses and in books where they can cause damage to the binding material. Firebrats occur in large numbers around fireplaces, boilers and bakery ovens.

It is probable that the winged insects arose from a bristletail-like stock 400 million years ago in the Devonian era. The first winged insects could not fold back their wings over their abdomen when at rest. These insects are known as the *Palaeoptera* and are represented by the present day dragonflies and damselflies (the *Odonata*) and mayflies (the *Ephemeroptera*).

Dragonflies, damselflies and mayflies

Dragonflies, or 'devils daring needles' as they are sometimes known, derive their name from their long, brilliantly coloured scaly body. They are completely harmless to man although males patrolling their territory can be a nuisance when they try to drive away human intruders. They are among the largest living insects; a Borneo dragonfly, *Tetracanthagyna plagiata*, has a wing span of 18cm (7.1 in) and a length of about 13 cm (5.1 in). A 300 million year old fossil dragonfly from the Carboniferous era had a wing span of about 68cm (26.8 in) making it the largest known insect. The *Odonata* have two pairs of large wings with a complex system of veins supporting the wing membrane. Although the wings are only capable of simple up and down movements, dragonflies can travel at speeds estimated at up to 96 kph (60 mph) which makes them one of the fastest flying insects. Damselflies, however, have a much slower, fluttering flight which, with their more slender body, easily distinguishes them from dragonflies.

Both dragonflies and damselflies mate near water, and the males are distinguished from females by their colour. In some damselflies there is even a form of courtship. The method of mating is unique among insects. The male transfers sperm from the opening of the male glands at the end of the abdomen to an accessory organ near the front of the abdomen. He then alights on the back of a female and holds her head (male damselflies hold the female's thorax) with a pair of claspers at the end of his abdomen. The female curls her abdomen round so that her posterior reproductive opening is in contact with the male accessory organ and sperm is transferred.

Damselflies and some dragonflies insert their eggs into the stems of water plants and some dragonflies bury them in sand or gravel at the water's edge. Most dragonflies, however, shed the eggs directly into the water while flying over it with the tip of their abdomen under the surface. The eggs hatch into nymphs which, like the adults, are carnivorous. Young fish, other aquatic insects and tadpoles are caught by a unique method. The lower lip, the *labium*, is enlarged and is rapidly extended to seize the prey in its pincer-like hooks. The labium is then retracted bringing the victim within reach of the jaws.

Damselflies spend at least a year and dragonflies two years as nymphs. In this time they form a very important source of food for fresh-water fish. After this they climb up a water plant into the air and undergo a final moult to become winged adults which live for only a few summer months.

Left: An adult mayfly, *Ephemera danica*. The larvae of these insects are aquatic and breathe by means of gills.

Below: A diagram to show how the song of a male cricket is produced. One of the front wings has a series of ridges near its base while the other front wing carries a projection coupled to a membrane. When the wings are rubbed together the projection is drawn across the ridges so generating the characteristic song which is amplified by the membrane.

Right: The head of a bush cricket. These insects have mouthparts which are designed for biting and chewing.

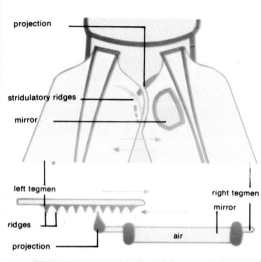

projection

stridulatory ridges

mirror

left tegmen

right tegmen

mirror

ridges

projection

air

Below: The nymph of a stonefly. These animals are aquatic and only live in clean water. Their presence therefore means a low level of pollution. They breathe by means of gills. The adult flies have two pairs of large membranous wings but are poor fliers and usually prefer to run from place to place.

Right: A lubber grasshopper, *Phymateus purpurascens*, displaying the vivid colours of its hind wings.

Far right: The bizarre toad grasshopper is wingless and normally well camouflaged against its background. It is found in the dry and semi-desert regions of Southern Africa.

Below: Locusts often migrate in enormous numbers either on the ground as bands of nymphs, called hoppers, or as flying insects. Locusts may either be in a migratory or a solitary phase and during these phases differ both in structure and physiology. A solitary locust is identical to a grasshopper.

Right: A front leg (above) and back leg (below) of a grasshopper. Insect legs have four main sections: the coxa which connects the leg to the thorax; the femur which in the back leg of a grasshopper is enlarged to contain the muscles needed for jumping; the tibia, and the tarsus which terminates in claws.

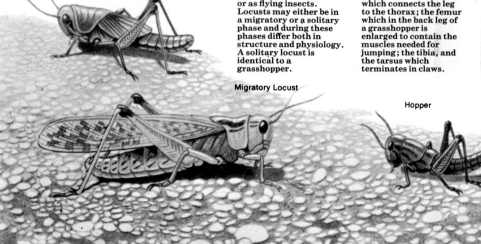

Grasshopper

Migratory Locust

Hopper

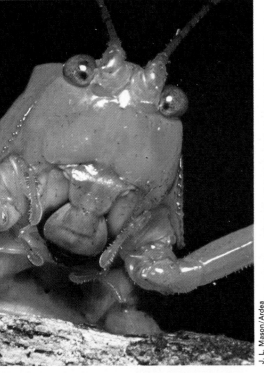

J. L. Mason/Ardea

Bruce Coleman

Anthony Bannister/NHPA

The group known as *Ephemeroptera* to which the mayflies belong, is so called because of the 'ephemeral' life of the adult fly. It usually lives only long enough to reproduce. This may take a few hours or at the most a few days after the transition from an aquatic nymph stage that may last for up to four years. The adult has two pairs of finely veined wings; the first pair is larger than the hind pair which may be absent in some species. The legs are small and weak; the abdomen ends in three, or sometimes two, long filaments or *cerci*. The antennae are greatly reduced but the compound eyes are very well developed, suggesting great dependence on sight. This also seems to be the case in the free-swimming nymphs which orientate themselves by the direction from which light reaches their eyes. If illuminated from below they will swim upside down. The nymphs breathe by means of gills along each side of the abdomen and are herbivorous. The mouth parts of the adult, however, are rudimentary and the adult is incapable of feeding. The front part of the gut can be filled with air to reduce the body weight and make flight easier.

The aquatic nymph of a mayfly first changes into a terrestrial *subimago* stage whose wings are dulled by a covering of extremely fine hairs. After a few hours this stage moults to the true adult, or *imago*, stage. The emergence of adults is synchronized so that great numbers appear together, the males gathering in large dancing swarms which attract the females. The male dies immediately after mating and the female soon after dropping her eggs into the water. Adult mayflies are a favourite food of fish, especially trout, and artificial flies are made by anglers as lures to catch them. The subimagos are called 'dun' and the adults 'spinners'.

From the original *Palaeoptera* there also arose insects, probably in the early Carboniferous era, which were able to fold their wings over the abdomen when at rest. They are called the *Neoptera* and were able to explore such new environments as areas of dense foliage, to hide under stones and logs, and even to burrow. The early *Neoptera* were probably similar to the present day stoneflies and give rise to the group containing the grasshoppers and crickets, the *Orthoptera*. In this group the immature forms are known as nymphs and generally resemble the adult form except in size and degree of wing development. They gradually change into the adult imago stage through a series of up to twenty moults. They also inhabit the same general environment as the adult and eat the same type of food. Insects with this development are *exopterygote* insects.

A second more specialized evolutionary line from the early neopteran stock led to the flies, butterflies, bees and beetles where the young, known as *larvae*, do not resemble the adult and usually occupy a very different environment, feeding on different foods. After a number of moults the larvae pass through a quiescent *pupal* phase where extensive alteration of larval tissue precedes the emergence of a winged adult. These are the *endopterygote* insects to which about 80 per cent of present-day insects belong.

Grasshoppers, crickets and cockroaches

The *Orthoptera* include such insects as grasshoppers, katydids, crickets, cock- 41

Above: A desert locust just after moulting. Locusts are a type of grasshopper and sometimes migrate in swarms causing enormous damage to the surrounding countryside and crops. A medium sized swarm may contain 1,000,000,000 insects and consume as much as 3,000 tonnes of vegetable material in a single day.

Below: Front and side views of the head of a grasshopper. The animal has three simple eyes (ocelli) as well as the two large compound eyes. The mouthparts, designed for biting and chewing, are equipped with two pairs of sensory organs, or palps, which help the insect to distinguish one sort of food from another.

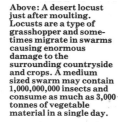

Below: A section through a grasshopper showing the internal organs. Food absorption occurs in the middle region of the gut and excretion is through small tubes called malpighian tubules. The insect extracts almost all the water from any food it eats and this enables it to live in hot, dry regions.

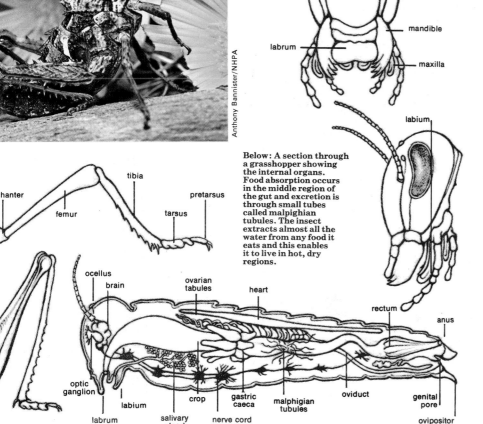

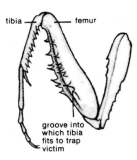

tibia — femur

groove into which tibia fits to trap victim

Right and above: A praying mantis and a diagram of one of its forelegs. The leg is specially adapted for seizing prey. The prey is grasped between the femur and the tibia which have spiny inside edges for the purpose. The innermost section of the leg, the coxa, is much larger than that of a grasshopper.

Below: A well camouflaged praying mantis eating a fly. These insects lie in wait for their prey, seizing the victim very rapidly when it strays within reach of the forelegs. These insects get their name from the way they carry their forelegs (see the picture on the right) which looks rather like an attitude of prayer.

Jacana

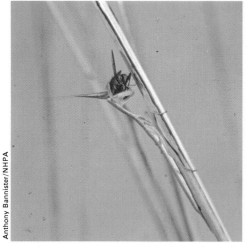

Anthony Bannister/NHPA

Below and right: It is often almost impossible to see stick insects in their natural habitats, so well do they blend in with their backgrounds. The stick insect in the photograph on the right even has spines resembling the prickles of the bramble on which it lives. Stick and leaf insects are sluggish animals, often remaining stationary for long periods. They are herbivorous, usually feeding on leaves. The longest living insect is a tropical stick insect which can grow to more than 30cm (1 ft). Because female stick insects can produce fertile eggs without mating, males are very rare and possibly do not exist in some species.

Natural Science Photos

roaches, mantids and stick insects. Cockroaches and mantids however are now generally placed in a separate group, the *Dictyoptera*, and the stick insects in the *Phasmida*. Typically, they have two pairs of wings although they may be reduced or absent as in some crickets and the common British cockroach. The male of this cockroach has reduced wings, the female is almost wingless, and both sexes are incapable of flight. The fore wings of orthopterans are leathery and when folded cover and protect the delicate membranous hindwings which are the flight wings. The large head has well developed compound eyes and strong chewing mouth parts.

There are about 3,500 species of cockroaches living mostly in the tropics but some have been accidentally transported throughout the world and are now cosmopolitan. In Britain there are six such imported species; the most common are the brown-black common cockroach, *Blatta orientalis*, the yellow brown German cockroach, *Blatta germanica*, and the reddish brown American cockroach, *Periplaneta americana*.

Cockroaches are nocturnal scavengers feeding on a very wide range of dead animal and plant material. In houses they will devour any kind of human food and although the amount eaten is relatively small the remainder is fouled. Females lay 16 eggs enclosed in a hard dark brown purse-like capsule, the *ootheca*, which is deposited in crevices. The eggs hatch after about two to three months, the ootheca splitting to let out the white wingless nymphs. As they grow, they become brown in colour and reach maturity in 6 to 12 months. In the German cockroach the ootheca contains up to 45 eggs and is carried by the female until about a day before hatching.

Grasshoppers are the most numerous of the *Orthoptera*. They prefer a grassy habitat and have greatly enlarged hindlegs which enable them to jump considerable distances when disturbed. The male attracts the female to mate by rubbing a row of very small projections on a hindleg joint against the veins of the forewing to produce the familiar chirping song, or *stridulation*, of grasshoppers. The song varies from species to species. Eggs are laid in pods in the soil, each pod containing up to 14 eggs. Grasshoppers are herbivorous, and when they occur in very large numbers can cause damage to crops.

Crickets and bush crickets, sometimes known as 'long-horned grasshoppers' or in America 'katydids', are cosmopolitan and resemble grasshoppers in possessing long, though less powerful hind legs for jumping. Their antennae, however, are long, they stridulate by rubbing the wing edges together and are nocturnal. Specialized organs, the *tympani*, are developed to receive soundwaves. Grasshoppers have a pair on the first abdomenal segment but in crickets they are on the forelegs. Crickets are herbivorous but bush crickets can be carnivorous. Eggs are laid singly in slits made in plant stems by a well developed blade-like or tubular organ called an *ovipositer*. Like grasshoppers there is one generation a year. Of particular interest is the mole cricket which is now rare in Britain. It does not have jumping legs, but the forelegs are powerful and armed with cutting edges which enable it to tunnel through the soil in a mole-like fashion.

A common grasshopper.
This is an example of
the variety which
appears most widely
in meadows and fields.

Butterflies and Moths

Of all the insects the butterflies and moths have been the most admired and popular. Butterflies are large and very beautiful but although we can understand the functioning of their colours it is difficult to explain why they should be so bright and exuberant. While the butterflies belong to a single well defined group, the popular name 'moth' covers a diversity of insects both large and small. Most moths are sombre-coloured and nocturnal although there are some that resemble butterflies inasmuch as they are brightly coloured and are active during the day. Butterflies and moths belong to the insect order *Lepidoptera*, a name which refers to their scaly wings, and there are about 100,000 different species.

The scales which are characteristic of butterflies and moths are hollow, flattened hairs covered with minute grooves and ridges. They usually contain pigment or give colour by reflecting and scattering

S. Bisserot

light. Sometimes the scales are shed, leaving the wings transparent as in the clearwing moths, which look like wasps or other members of the insect order *Hymenoptera*.

The colours of lepidopterans serve a number of purposes, for example to help members of the same species recognize each other and to camouflage them against predators. Butterflies carry their wings vertically when they are at rest, and the undersides of the wings are often coloured in such a way as to conceal the insect. For instance, the underside of the wing of the Indian leaf butterfly, *Kallima*, looks remarkably like a dead leaf and the grayling butterfly, *Eumenis semele*, even leans to one side when it is on the ground so that its shadow is minimized.

Unlike butterflies, most moths hold their wings flat over their backs when at rest, but these are also often cryptically patterned so that the moth blends into its background. Such moths as the yellow underwings, *Triphaena comes*, for example, have brightly coloured hind wings which provide flashes of colour as the insect flies along. When the moth settles the flashing suddenly stops and this can be confusing to predators as well as entomologists. Another method of defence

 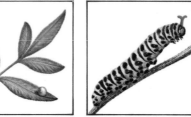 

Above: Three pictures showing the egg, larva (caterpillar) and pupa (chrysalis) of a swallowtail butterfly.

Left: The caterpillar of a swallowtail butterfly. It has a curious forked organ behind its head which it shoots rapidly in and out to disperse an unpleasant smell when disturbed.

Above: A swallowtail butterfly, *Papilio machaon*, newly emerged from its chrysalis. This is the only member of the *Papilionidae* family which is a permanent resident in Britain.

Above right: A swallowtail with its wings spread out. More usually they are held vertically.

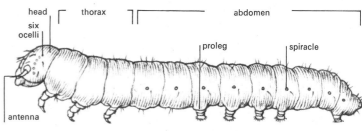

Above: A diagram to show the main features of a caterpillar of the cabbage white butterfly. Each of the thoracic segments carries a pair of legs, and five of the abdominal segments have pairs of fleshy extensions called prolegs. The outermost layer of the body, the cuticle, is quite soft but is able to act as an exoskeleton because the caterpillar's blood pressure is sufficiently high to keep it taut. The head does not have antennae or compound eyes. There are six simple eyes (ocelli) on each side. The animal has strong biting mandibles for chewing cabbage leaves.

Left: Diagrams to show how two different types of caterpillar crawl along. The most important organs are the prolegs which are alternately retracted and extended by contracting and relaxing 'locomotor' muscles. The lower diagrams show how caterpillars of the family *Geometridae* (the name means 'earth measuring') proceed by looping movements.

Right: The eggs of a privet hawk moth.

Heather Angel

against predators is shown by the peacock butterfly, *Nymphalis io*, and the eyed hawk moth, *Smerinthus ocellatus*. These insects have markings on their wings called 'eye spots' which look rather like the eyes of mammals. The eye spots are suddenly displayed when the insect is disturbed and may confuse or frighten off a predator.

Some of these insects, like the burnet moths, have bright colours to advertise the fact that they are unpalatable or poisonous and in many cases other, palatable species very closely resemble them, so gaining protection. It was from such observations a century ago that the British naturalist H. W. Bates first put forward his theories on the phenomenon of mimicry, now known to be widespread among insects. The milkweed butterflies, which belong to the family *Danaidae*, are distasteful and are very widely mimicked by other palatable butterflies. For the mimic to gain protection it has to be less common than the model, otherwise birds will learn that the common pattern means palatable rather than unpalatable prey. In the swallowtail butterfly *Papilio dardanus* there are five different-looking varieties of female, and four of these mimic four different species of distasteful butterfly. By this means the species maintains a larger population than if it mimicked only a single species.

Some butterflies show colour variations according to the season. The comma butterfly, *Polygonia c-album*, in Britain shows different colours in spring and summer broods, the spring generation being much paler and brighter than the summer one. The African butterfly *Precis octavia* is also well known for its marked seasonal forms. Some moths, particularly those species which rest during the day on rocks or soil, show variation in colour with geographical area. The peppered moth *Biston betularia*, for example, has a normal pale speckled form in rural areas, while a black, or *melanic*, form has become common in industrial areas where the lichens on trees have been killed and soot deposited. Experiments have shown that birds will mainly feed on the more conspicuous form: in cities the speckled form and in the country the black form. This phenomenon of industrial melanism has been much studied in the last 20 years or so and has given valuable information about how evolution takes place in nature and the rate at which it can become effective.

Migration

Butterflies and moths are usually strong fliers, although they may not always travel very far. Marking experiments in the Scilly Isles demonstrated that meadow brown butterflies remained in their own area of bramble and bracken and did not even fly the short distance across a grassy area to another bracken and bramble area inhabited by other meadow browns. In a few species such as the early moth, *Theria rupicapraria*, and the winter moth, *Operophtera brumata*, the male is normally winged but the female has very small wings or, in some species, none at all. After emerging from the pupa the female has to climb up the trunk of a tree to lay her eggs. In spite of these flightless varieties, however, the *Lepidoptera* contains some of the most powerfully flying insects and a number are known to be migratory.

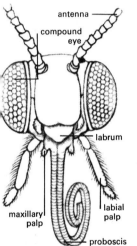

Right: A map to show the migrations of the bath white butterfly, *Pontia daplidice*, and the silver Y moth, *Plusia gamma*, in Europe.

Left and bottom left: Drawings of the heads of a butterfly and a moth. These insects feed on nectar and their mouth parts are specially adapted for this. The two maxillae are much longer than in other insects and they are joined together by a series of hooks and spines to form a tube called the proboscis through which the nectar is drawn. Feeding on fluids, butterflies and moths have no need for the cutting mandibles of insects like locusts, and these organs are very small or absent.

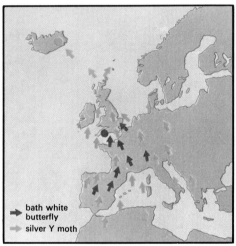

bath white butterfly
silver Y moth

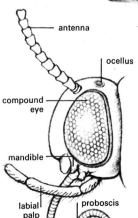

Above and right: A privet hawk-moth, *Sphinx ligustri*, and its caterpillar. The bodies and wings of butterflies and moths are covered with scales which not only give rise to the characteristic iridescent colouring of the wings, but also serve to conserve body heat by enclosing an insulating layer of air.

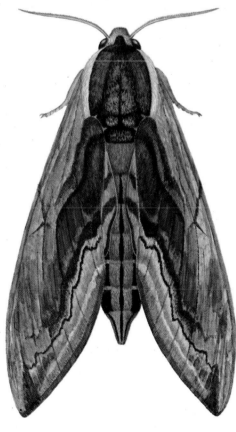

Heather Angel

Anthony Bannister/NHPA

Left: A pearl-bordered fritillary butterfly, *Argynnis euphrosyne*. In order to show the wing markings, the picture was taken with the insect's wings in the uncharacteristic spread position. This butterfly, like most others, has antennae which are enlarged, or 'clubbed', at their tips. Both butterflies and moths have a well developed sense of vision and can distinguish one colour from another. This is important in feeding and mating for both flowers and potential mates are recognized by sight.

Right: An African butterfly, *Charaxes saturnis.*

Below: The beautiful golden emperor moth of India.

In recent years it has been shown that the other two great migratory groups of insects, the locusts and the aphids, are both passively carried along with the prevailing wind, even though some of their short term flights appear oriented. The situation with butterflies and moths is far from clear. Pioneer work on butterfly migration was carried out by C. B. Williams who showed that many of the butterfly species that migrate to the British Isles in the summer return in the autumn, although it is the offspring of the original migrants that make the return. The red admiral, *Vanessa atalanta*, was the first species that was shown to make this return, but since then it has been demonstrated that other species do the same. It is characteristic of most butterflies when migrating to fly in a constant, clearly oriented direction. They do not seem to fix their direction by reference to wind, temperature or magnetic factors, and it has recently been argued that the Sun is the reference point. This is by no means impossible since other insects navigate by reference to the Sun.

The best known migratory species is the milkweed butterfly *Danaus plexippus*. It breeds in the northern USA and Canada during the summer and then migrates south in swarms in the late summer to California, Florida or New Mexico. Marked individuals have been recovered that have flown nearly 3,200 km (2,000 miles). The butterflies spend the winter in trees, using the same ones year after year, forming something of a tourist attraction. In the spring a northerly journey begins. As with other butterfly migrations the return flight is more scattered, with individuals flying singly rather than in a swarm. On the way back the insects lay their eggs and the species becomes spread throughout the northern part of its range. A number of moths also migrate, notable visitors to Britain being the humming-bird hawk moth, *Macroglossum stellatarum*, and the silver Y moth, *Plusia gamma*. The latter seems to show oriented flight early in its adult life when it flies by day, but later, nocturnal flights are downwind. It seems likely that prevailing winds bring it all the way from North Africa. The humming-bird hawk moth is an immigrant to Britain from southern Europe, and arrives from June onwards.

Flight

Moths and butterflies have their fore and hind wings coupled together, though the method of coupling varies from species to

Stephen Dalton/NHPA

species as does the rate of wing beat and speed of flight. The wings of moths are typically linked by a bristle which projects from the hind wing and engages a hook from a vein of the fore wing. Wing speed and flight may be quite rapid: a hawk moth may beat its wings 70 times a second and reach a speed of 55 kph (35 mph). In butterflies the wings merely overlap at the base. They flap about 12 times every second, giving the insect a top speed of about ten kph (six mph). Large butterflies can glide quite effectively, especially in the sheltered conditions of woodland.

A remarkable feature of some nocturnally flying moths is their ability to avoid bats. Bats detect their prey by an 'echo sounding' system of ultrasonic squeaks that reflect from any object such as a flying moth. Some moths have a pair of hearing organs called *tympanal organs* set at the sides of the base of the abdomen which can detect these ultrasonic signals. Thus the moth can tell when a hunting bat is nearby and even determine its angle of approach. Different moth species respond in different ways—some swing violently off course, some zig-zag and others drop to the ground. This manoeuvring brings to mind the technological warfare of our own species.

A very few moths can make audible sounds—the death's head hawk moth, *Acherontia atropos*, for example, squeaks when disturbed—but this is rare. Sight is important to most butterflies and moths, and the compound eyes are well developed. Antennae act as smell receptors and in some species the front legs are used for tasting. Many butterflies have small forelegs which are no use for walking but are important organs of taste.

Heather Angel

Above: The caterpillar of a puss moth, *Cerura vinula*, in its defence posture. Normally the caterpillar is well camouflaged against its background, and irregular purple markings on its green back break up the body outline. When attacked, however, the animal rears up to expose the vivid 'face' markings seen in the picture and lashes out with the threads attached to its tail. If this fearsome display is not enough to deter the predator, the caterpillar will squirt strong formic acid from a gland in its thorax.

Above right: A convolvulus hawk moth, *Herse convolvuli*, feeding on tobacco flowers. The long, uncoiled proboscis can be seen probing one of the flowers for nectar. There is a slight bend in the proboscis about one third of the way along its length, and this 'knee joint' allows the insect to feed whatever the angle of the flower. A moth picks out flowers by sight rather than smell, and the accuracy with which it can 'aim' its tongue shows just how good its sight must be.

46

Left: A scarlet windowed moth which lives in the Himalayan region of India is well disguised as a leaf. There is even a dark line running from one wing tip to the other to represent the mid-rib of the leaf.

Right: The broken irregular pattern and colour of this hawk moth, *Deilephila merii*, camouflage it against a background of foliage. The outline of the insect is broken by the pale band which extends across both wings and the front of the abdomen.

Below: The head of a buff-tip moth, *Phalera bucephala*. When at rest with its wings folded back, this insect looks exactly like a freshly broken twig covered with lichen.

Stephen Dalton/HNPA

W. Harstrick/Bavaria

Anthony Bannister/NHPA

Left: Three methods of avoiding predators. A moth from Trinidad, *Syssphinx molina*, (top, left and right) exposes eye spots on its hind wings when it is attacked. Superficially these resemble the eyes of mammals and when suddenly displayed they startle predators such as birds. The bee hawk moth, *Hemaris tityus*, and the lunar hornet moth, *Sphecia bembeciformis*, (centre, left and right) mimic stinging insects to escape the attention of predators. The peppered moth, *Biston betularia*, is normally a pale colour (bottom left) to camouflage it against lichen covered trees. In smoke-blackened industrial areas, however, a black variety (bottom right) has become common.

Right: The small yucca moth, *Pronubia yuccasella*, is vital for the survival of the yucca plant (and itself depends on the plant) in the southern parts of North America. The moth pollinates the plant, and in return the plant produces enough seeds both to feed the moth's larvae and ensure its own survival.

Life history

The life history of lepidopterans is well-known: the egg, a plant-eating caterpillar (the larva), an immobile chrysalis (the pupa) and finally the adult insect. In some species the virgin female produces a scent which attracts males from a considerable distance. The French entomologist J. H. Fabre described this phenomenon, and Victorian collectors used it to collect large numbers of lepidopterans like male emperor moths. Today a similar method is used to control populations of the gypsy moth, a forest pest; a synthetic female scent attracts males to a death by insecticide.

Caterpillars are soft-bodied and mostly found on plants; they are an important source of food for birds. Caterpillars protect themselves against their predators in a number of ways. Some are camouflaged by their green body colour while others resemble twigs. Several caterpillars are distasteful to birds and they generally have bright and characteristic markings to advertise the fact. The cinnabar moth, *Hypocrita jacobaeae*, for example, is marked with vivid black and yellow bands along its entire length, and birds soon learn to avoid the hairy caterpillars (often called 'woolly bears') of the tiger moth, *Arctia caja*. Many caterpillars suffer from parasites like ichneumon flies or other parasitic members of the insect group *Hymenoptera*.

W. Harstrick/ZEFA

Some moths are of considerable economic value to man. The silk from the pupal cocoon of certain species has been used to produce the fabric of that name from ancient times. Indeed, the silk moth, *Bombyx mori*, is a highly bred flightless species not found in the wild. However, wild silk is produced from such species as the giant atlas moth, *Attacus atlas*. Some species are also economically valuable because they pollinate night scented flowers like tobacco, a crop of immense commercial importance.

Conversely, caterpillars can cause enormous agricultural losses by feeding on crops. For example, the caterpillar of the codling moth, *Cydia pomonella*, damages apple orchards, the pink bollworm, *Platyedra gossypiella*, can reduce the yield of a cotton crop by as much as 25 per cent, and the maize stem borer, *Busseola fusca*, can completely destroy African maize crops. In marked contrast, the well named *Cactoblastis cactorum* was instrumental in the destruction of the great cactus plague in Australia. The *Lepidoptera* are an order that touches man in many ways.

Social Insects

Some species of insects associate together in hundreds, thousands or even millions to form colonies whose members all contribute in some way to the overall success of the community. Such insects, known as social insects, are found in the insect orders *Hymenoptera* (bees, wasps and ants) and *Isoptera* (termites).

It is the sharing of labour for the common good that distinguishes a true insect society like a colony of bees or an ants' nest from a collection of insects living in close proximity, such as a swarm of locusts. In some insect societies the individuals responsible for a particular task are structurally different from other members of the colony: worker ants, for example, can easily be distinguished from soldier ants.

In other insect societies most 'citizens' are virtually indistinguishable from one another and the division of labour is according to age. The worker honey bee acts as a nursemaid to the developing larvae for the first two weeks of its life. During the third week it is occupied in building and repairing the nest and converting collected nectar into the honey which is stored in special honey cells. Finally, after a spell of duty guarding the nest, it leaves the colony to forage for nectar and pollen.

Social insects plainly benefit by living together in a large community: the whole is stronger than its individual parts. For such a system to be successful, however,

Below: The nests of African termites, *Macrotermes bellicosus,* can reach skyscraper proportions. A nest six metres (20 ft) high is not uncommon. The nests have rock hard, water-tight walls of earth and plant material bound together with saliva and excreta. The walls help to insulate the nest from extremes of temperature.

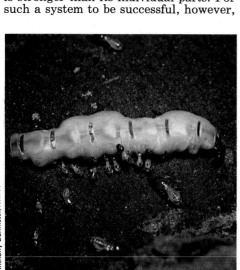

Anthony Bannister/NHPA

Above: A termite queen, *Macrotermes bellicosus,* her abdomen grossly distended with eggs, being tended by worker termites. Soldier termites, with enlarged heads and jaws stand guard. The queen lives in a 'royal chamber' deep within the termitaria. She may lay as many as 36,000 eggs in a single day.

J. L. Mason/Ardea

male

worker

soldier

queen

Above: The four castes of the North American termite, *Termes flavipes.* Winged termites develop only at certain times of the year. They soon leave to found new colonies.

Above: A column of foraging termites, *Macrotermes,* from Malaysia. Termites feed on wood and other vegetable matter. They can severely damage wooden constructions such as buildings, but can also serve a useful purpose in increasing the aeration and drainage of soil. These are worker termites.

Dr. F. Sauer/Bavaria

Below: a thick-walled nest belonging to a species of South African termite. Air circulates constantly through the living area of the nest and this keeps the temperature, humidity and oxygen concentration at the correct levels. The atmosphere in some termites nests contains enough carbon dioxide to make a man unconscious.

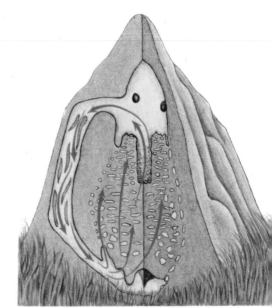

carpenter

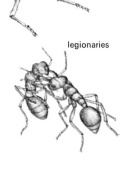

legionaries

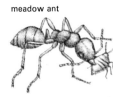

meadow ant

Left: Weaver ants build their nests in trees and shrubs by joining leaves together with silk secreted by their larvae. The worker ants grasp the larvae in their jaws and pass them back and forth between the leaves to bind them together.

Above and right: The way of life of ants varies from species to species. Carpenter ants will bore long galleries in rotting wood. Legionary ants are nomadic; they move in single file and hunt other insects. The meadow ant farms aphids for the sweet fluid called 'honeydew' which they secrete. Leaf cutter ants chew leaves to a spongy mass which acts as compost for a fungus, the ants' staple diet. Thief ants scavenge from other ants.

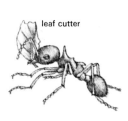

leaf cutter

Left: Worker garden black ants, *Lasius niger*, tending the larva of a queen ant. These common ants are often a pest in kitchens and larders. They live under stones or logs or in the walls of buildings.

Right: Leaf cutter ants, *Atta*, from Trinidad. The queen is being tended by the much smaller workers. These insects are sometimes called parasol ants because they carry cut pieces of leaves above their heads like banners or parasols back to the nest. Compared with a bee's or wasp's nest, an ant's nest is fairly simple consisting of a series of excavated galleries and chambers. Ants do not build cells for their larvae or pupae, so these can easily be moved.

Bruce Coleman

thief ant

there must be a complex communication and control network so that members of the community can respond quickly to tackle problems which are bound to arise from time to time.

One such control mechanism involves chemicals called *pheromones* which act rather like hormones to influence the behaviour of the colony members. A good example of this control is the rapid reaction to the loss of a queen in a colony of bees. The queen bee secretes a material known as 'queen substance' which contains the pheromone *oxodecanoic acid*, which becomes spread all over her body during grooming. The workers who constantly attend the queen pick up the material from her body and pass it to other bees. In this way traces of the pheromone are passed throughout the hive so that every bee 'knows' that the queen is present.

If the queen is removed, the behaviour of the workers changes: within 24 hours 'queen cells' are being built to make good the loss of the queen, and the ovaries of worker bees have developed so that egg-laying can resume as soon as possible (normally egg-laying is the sole responsibility of the queen). This dramatic change in behaviour is at least partly the result

of the sudden interruption to the supply of queen substance. This and other control mechanisms are constantly in operation in social insect colonies to ensure that the tasks necessary for the continued well-being of the community are carried out.

Termites

Termites are pale-coloured, soft-bodied insects living mainly in the tropics with a few inhabiting southern Europe and the USA. They are not found in northern Europe. Termites are sometimes referred to as 'white ants', but this is a misnomer since they are more closely related to cockroaches than ants. Like cockroaches, they are exopterygote insects.

The more primitive termites build nests called *termitaria* in decaying wood, often underground, but more advanced species can build huge mound-like nests.

A new nest is started at certain times of the year when winged males and females develop, leave the nest and mate. They break their wings off and both male and female start to excavate a new nest. The 'royal pair' as they are known constitute a king and queen whose only function is to produce young, so all members of the colony are derived from them. The queen's

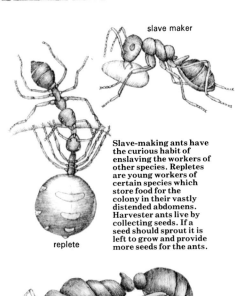

slave maker

replete

Slave-making ants have the curious habit of enslaving the workers of other species. Repletes are young workers of certain species which store food for the colony in their vastly distended abdomens. Harvester ants live by collecting seeds. If a seed should sprout it is left to grow and provide more seeds for the ants.

harvester

49

Above: Pupae of the wasp *Vespa germanica* in their cells. The cells are made of a papery material. The first larvae of the year are tended by the queen who feeds them on the juices of captured insects. As soon as the first workers appear, however, her function is limited to egg-laying. The workers tend the nest.

Below: A series of diagrams showing the operation of a wasp's sting. The sting is a modified ovipositor (egg-laying organ) and once it has penetrated the skin of the enemy, poison is injected as in a hypodermic syringe. The poison contains the chemical histamine and can be countered by antihistamine tablets.

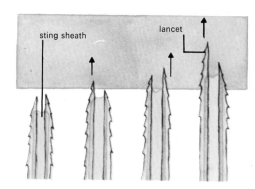

sting sheath

lancet

excavated stones

main pillar

root support

worker cells

entrance tunnel

queen cells

nest entrance

Dr. F. Sauer/ZEFA

abdomen becomes very large, particularly in mound-building termites, for the continuous production of eggs. A queen *Macrotermes* increases in length from 3.5 to 14 cm (1.4 to 5.5 in) and can produce 36,000 eggs a day; an average of one every two seconds. The royal pair are groomed and fed by worker termites and have a very long reproductive life, probably at least 15 years in *Amitermes*. Their eggs hatch into nymphs of four different types, known as *castes*.

The wingless soldier caste have large heads and jaws. They defend the nest against intruders, particularly ants. The worker caste are also wingless and serve to maintain the colony, foraging at night for food, cleaning the nest and feeding the soldiers and reproductives. Flightless but fertile secondary reproductives are also produced, which can take over from the royal pair if they die or their egg production decreases with age. They are stimulated to egg laying activity through special feeding by the workers and in this way a nest might last for up to 40 years or more. The fourth caste is produced at certain times of the year and consists of winged fertile males and females which disperse and form new colonies.

50

W. Kratz/ZEFA

Ardea

Left: A section through the nest of a common wasp, *Vespula vulgaris*. By the end of the summer the nest may measure 23 cm (9 in) in diameter, contain ten stories of nest cells and house 5,000 wasps. In the autumn fertile males and females are produced. After mating the males die and the females hibernate to start new colonies the following year.

Below: A female solitary wasp, *Ammophila campestris*, captures a caterpillar, paralyzes it by stinging, and places it in a prepared nest. She then lays an egg on the caterpillar and closes up the nest entrance with stones. When the larva hatches it will feed on the paralyzed caterpillar.

Left: An ichneumon wasp, *Psilimastrix*, on the chrysalis of a swallowtail butterfly, *Papilio asterias*. Ichneumons are parasitic insects. They lay their eggs in the larvae or pupae of other insects, particularly butterflies and moths. When the parasite's larva hatches it feeds on the body tissue of the host.

Below: A queen wasp, *Vespa media*, feeding the first larvae of the year. Like bees, wasps lay their eggs in hexagonal cells. The eggs hatch after three to four weeks into sterile female worker wasps which forage for food and extend the nest. Hornets are considerably larger than wasps, but they have a similar life history.

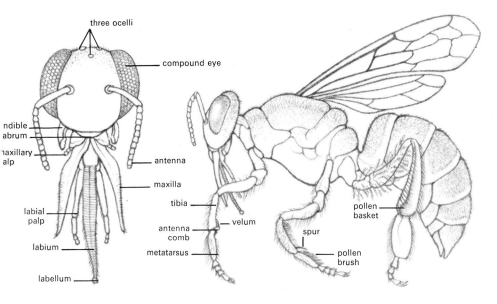

three ocelli

compound eye

ndible
abrum

aaxillary
alp

mandible

antenna

maxilla

tibia

labial
palp

antenna
comb

velum

labium

metatarsus

spur

labellum

pollen
basket

pollen
brush

Frank Lane

Above: The sting of a
bee. It consists of two
barbed darts guided by a
sheath. After initial
penetration by the two
darts, the sheath is
inserted into the wound
and poison is injected.
The barbs hold the sting
in position. After
stinging, the sting and
part of the intestine
are usually pulled away
and the bee dies.

Above: Diagrams
showing the head and
legs of a honeybee. The
legs are specially
modified for collecting
pollen. The hind leg is
equipped with long hairs
forming a 'pollen basket'
which carries most of the
pollen load. The joint
between the tibia and the
metatarsus of the front
leg is modified to act as
an antenna cleaner.

Below: A honeybee, *Apis
mellifera*, with the
'pollen baskets' on its
hind legs full of pollen.
Pollen and nectar are
stored in special cells
in the nest. A worker
draws nectar into its
crop where the action of
saliva converts it into
honey. The honey may
then be regurgitated to
provide the community
with a food store.

Below: A swarm of
honeybees clinging to a
bush. Normally a colony
of bees will contain
only one queen, but in
exceptional circum-
stances a new queen may
appear. The old queen
will leave the nest with an
entourage of workers. A
queen cannot found a
colony on her own since
she cannot forage for
food or build a nest.

Frank Lane

Ants

Ants can easily be distinguished from
termites by the presence of a narrow waist
between the thorax and abdomen, an
abdominal sting, a thick, dark cuticle and
larval and pupal stages in the life cycle.
Ants, like all *Hymenoptera*, are endopterygote insects. There are over 6,000
different species of ant and although
cosmopolitan they are largely restricted
to the tropics.

Ants usually inhabit a more or less
permanent subterranean nest, but the
tropical army ants of South America and
driver ants of Africa are nomadic; a
temporary nest is made each day by masses
of ants coming together and hooking on
to each other with their legs, leaving
spaces for the queen and juvenile stages.
Such 'nests' may be formed in a hollow
tree hanging from a branch or simply in a
depression in the ground. The common
European wood ant, *Formica rufa*, builds
huge mounds of twigs and pine needles
which may be 150cm (five feet) high and
300cm (ten feet) in diameter, over its
underground nest. This thatching to the
nest helps to waterproof and insulate it.

Each nest, depending on species, may
contain anything from 10 to several
million adults. The nest is founded by a
single reproductive queen, the male dying
after mating. Normally there is no more
than one queen ant in a nest, but wood
ant nests may contain two or three
queens. In all hymenopteran colonies,
including those of ants, there are two
main castes besides the queen.

The worker caste are flightless, infertile
females which develop from fertilized
eggs and are specialized for food foraging,
care of larvae and nest building. Some
workers of species such as army and
harvester ants develop into large soldier
ants with big heads and jaws. They
function to guard the nest or, in army
ants, the marching columns.

The second caste are the winged males
that develop at intervals from unfertilized
eggs and serve to fertilize the queen on
her nuptial flight. In wood ants, however,
although both sexes are winged, mating
takes place on the ground near the nest,
and the queen may re-enter the nest where
she lived as a larva or found a new nest.

Army ants have a definite cycle of
reproductive behaviour. Every 30 to 40
days the column stops marching and
forms a more permanent nest where the
queen produces up to 35,000 eggs over a
period of 2 days. The eggs hatch into
larvae at the same time as the pupae of
the previous generation of larvae 'hatch'
into adult ants.

Wood ants and army ants are fierce
predators. The marching columns of army
ants contain millions of ants and at night
constantly scour large areas, attacking
and eating every living thing in their
path; a tethered horse is soon reduced to
a skeleton. Soldier scouts march ahead
and lay scent trails for the main columns
to follow.

Wasps

Ants together with bees and wasps belong
to a subdivision of the *Hymenoptera*, the
Apocrita, whose members are character-
ized by the presence of a narrow waist
between thorax and abdomen and the
absence of legs on the maggot-like larvae.
Generally the *Apocrita* are beneficial to
agriculture. Bees, for example, pollinate
flowers, and many insect pests are

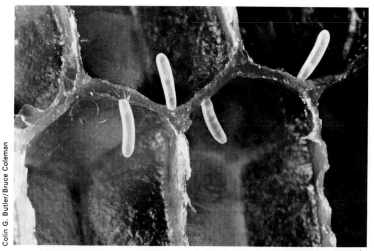

Left: Newly laid eggs of the honeybee, *Apis mellifera*, in their hexagonal cells. When they hatch, the larvae will be tended by young worker bees who feed them on regurgitated food and a jelly-like secretion called 'royal jelly'. If large amounts of royal jelly are fed to a larva, it will develop into a queen rather than a worker. This will be done if, for example, the queen of the colony should die. The cells in which the eggs are laid and the larvae develop are made of wax produced by a special abdominal gland. All the egg-laying in a colony of bees is done by the queen. She has a useful life span of three or four years after which time she is ruthlessly killed.

preyed on by wasps and parasitized by ichneumon and chalcid 'flies' which, in spite of their names, are types of wasp. The other subdivision of the *Hymenoptera*, the *Symphyta*, which is considered to be the more primitive, contains woodwasps such as sawflies whose thorax and abdomen are broadly joined and whose caterpillar-like larvae have legs.

Sawflies have an extremely long egg-laying organ called the ovipositor and are sometimes mistaken for common wasps, particularly since their bodies are also coloured yellow and black. Their adult life is very short, for the male dies after mating and the female soon after laying her eggs (in slits made in wood or leaves) with her saw-like ovipositor.

The chalcid 'flies' are minute insects and one of their close relations, the fairy 'fly' *Alpatus magnanimus*, is the smallest known insect, being only 0.12 mm (0.0047 in) long. Many chalcids are parasitic on moths and butterflies, laying minute eggs in their eggs and pupae.

The ichneumon 'flies' are also parasitic on insect larvae. The largest British ichneumon, *Rhyssa persuasoria*, lays its eggs in the larva of the sawfly, *Sirex*, which burrows in pine trees, ruining the timber. The female ichneumon has an extremely long ovipositor, which is capable of boring through a few inches of solid wood to reach the sawfly larva.

Many wasps such as the hunting wasps are solitary in their nesting habits, laying a single egg in a nest and leaving it to develop. Hunting wasps hunt other insects, paralyze them with their sting and place them in their nest to serve as a fresh but immobile food store for the

Above: The brood cells in a colony of honeybees. At the bottom of the picture is the queen. The remaining insects are workers and drones. There are normally only a few drones in a nest. They are males whose only function is to fertilize the queen on her mating flight. Like the queen and the larvae, they are fed by the workers.

Below: A carpenter bee, *Xylocopa*, from Malaysia. This is a solitary bee which bores into wood to build its nest and so can damage wooden structures. Solitary bees do not have castes such as queen, worker and drone. Eggs are laid in cells which are separately provisioned with pollen and honey for the larvae.

developing larva. Numerous separate nests are constructed, some no more than burrows in sandy soil.

Some species of wasp, however, such as the European hornet, *Vespa crabro*, the common wasp, *Vespula vulgaris*, and the paper wasp, *Polistes*, are social insects living in a nest of papery material. Hornets will build their nests above the ground in trees or buildings but wasps nests are often found below ground. The paper wasp builds a small nest above ground which is unusual since the egg cells are not covered with a papery cap as in other wasps but are left open. Wasp colonies last for only a single year. The only wasps to survive the winter are young fertilized queens.

Bees

The bees, like wasps, are cosmopolitan and only some bees such as the bumble or humble bee and the European honey bee are social insects. The bumble bee, *Bombus*, closely resembles the honey bee except that it has a larger body covered in stiff yellow, orange and red hairs, also its sting is not barbed so it can be used again and again, unlike the honey bee that can sting only once. In general the social life of bumble bees resembles that of the common wasp. The nest may be below ground or on the surface and is usually constructed from very fine grass and other vegetation. Eggs are laid in hexagonal egg cells constructed from wax produced by a special abdominal gland. On hatching the larvae are fed on a mixture of pollen and nectar, collected by worker bees from flowers.

The nectar is sucked up through a special extendible tube leading from the mouth and stored in the crop. Pollen, deposited on the bee's hairy body when it forces its way into a flower for nectar, is scraped off by the second pair of legs into pollen baskets attached to the outer face of each hind leg. On returning to the nest, pollen is removed from the baskets by the forelegs and placed in an egg cell as a food store for the developing larvae. Surplus nectar is placed in a large 'honeypot' cell near the nest entrance to serve as a food store for workers when the weather is too bad for foraging. It is during food collection that the cross pollination of flowers occurs.

When food is located by a foraging bee, its position is indicated to other workers in the nest by a complicated dance accompanied by wagging of the abdomen and a vibration of the wings. In this way information is given relating the food source to the position of the sun. On cloudy days the pattern of polarized light in the sky is used as a reference source.

There are four species of honey bee, one of which *Apis mellifera*, is the western European domestic bee. Unlike other social insects in temperate climates, honey bee colonies can survive the winter because of extensive food reserves in the form of honey that are built up during the summer months. The value of this reserve honey as a human food has made the honey bee economically important.

In midsummer a colony of bees may contain about 60,000 workers, a few hundred males known as *drones*, whose only function is to mate with the queen, and one queen. In winter the bees enter into a semidormant condition huddled together in the centre of the nest for warmth.

Honey bees removing pollen from their storage baskets into the pollen store. The brood cells provide food for the developing larvae.

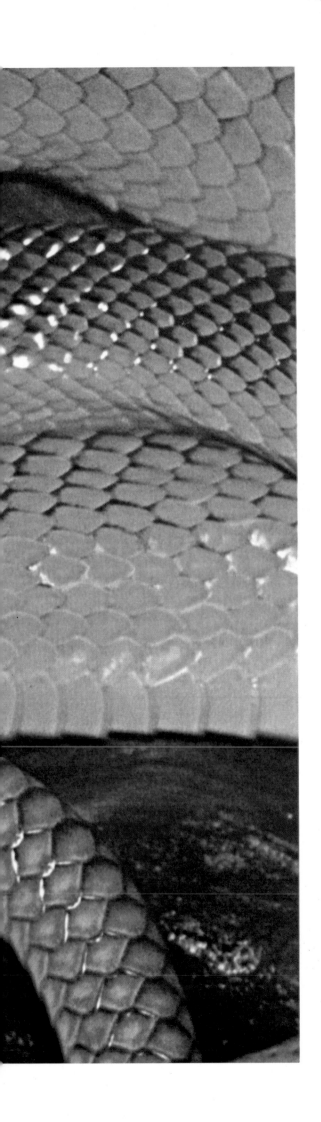

The Vertebrates

Snakes are an excellent example of
adaptation in nature – elongation of
the body has led to an increase in the
number of vertebrae, and articular
surfaces between them ensure that
the vertebral column is flexible and
strong.

The Bird Kingdom

Before studying any group of animals, particularly a group as large and diverse as the birds, it is helpful to put the various members into subgroups which reflect evolutionary trends and affinities. Unfortunately, the fossil record is frequently far from complete so that the reconstruction of the various branches of the evolutionary tree must to some extent be a matter of guesswork. Although this is certainly true of the bird kingdom, it is nevertheless possible to classify birds in a reasonably satisfactory manner.

Where the classification of animals or plants is concerned, much is owed to the great Swedish naturalist, Carl von Linné (1707-1778), often known as Linnaeus, who introduced what is known as the binomial system of scientific or Latin names. His system involves the use of two Latin names—one for the genus and one for the species. The genus is a purely artificial concept whereby species which are assumed to be close relatives are grouped together under a single name. Most surface-feeding ducks, for example, are put together into the genus *Anas*. The species, on the other hand, is a fundamental unit because it refers to a particular animal that exists in nature, for example *Anas platyrhynchos*, commonly known as the mallard.

Families and orders

Higher classification involves the grouping of genera into families and families into orders. For completeness the name of the first person to describe the animal scientifically may be placed after the name of the species. Thus in the case of the mallard (which was described by von Linné) its classification would be given as follows: order *Anseriformes*, family *Anatidae* (which is simply the Latin name for the duck family), genus *Anas* and species *Anas platyrhynchos* Linné. If the describer's name is shown in brackets the species has been transferred from the genus in which it was originally placed. For example the rock thrush, was first named by von Linné as *Turdus saxatilis* Linné, but further study showed that it resembled birds in the genus *Monticola* rather than those in the genus *Turdus*. The same bird is now known as *Monticola saxatilis* (Linné).

Both internal and external features of a species are taken into account when classifying it into a particular genus, family or order. Often, though by no means always, members of the same order are so very alike, for example the owls (order *Strigiformes*), that classification presents few difficulties.

Just as no two humans are exactly alike no two specimens of a species are ever exactly alike, although no one would doubt that they are of the same kind and should be classified together. How then is a species to be defined when individual characteristics vary? A suitable definition might be that it is a group of similar animals occupying a well defined geographical area and breeding with each other but not with those that differ from them either physically or in behaviour.

Left and above: A purple heron, *Ardea purpurea*, with its young, and a bluethroat, *Luscinia svecica*. The herons constitute one of six families belonging to the order *Ciconiiformes*, the others being the shoebills, the storks, the hammerheads, the ibises and the flamingos. All these birds have long legs and live close to water. They move about in the shallows with slow, deliberate steps. The bluethroat is a typical member of the order *Passeriformes*, the perching birds.

Below: A blue-footed booby, *Sula nebouxii*, with its young. These birds belong to the order *Pelecaniformes*. One of the features which characterize members of this order is the curious structure of their feet which, in addition to being webbed, have a forward pointing hind toe. This is a clear distinction from ducks and geese. Most *Pelecaniformes* are large or medium-sized birds which obtain their food from the sea, often by diving. Gannets may dive from heights of 15 m (50 ft) or more.

Right: A peregrine falcon, *Falco peregrinus*, with its young. Birds of prey belong to the order *Falconiformes* and they are easily distinguished from other birds by their short, hooked beaks and powerful talons. They have very keen eyesight. These characteristics are adaptations for seizing and feeding on living prey. Peregrine falcons are perhaps the most effective of all birds of prey. They can reach speeds of nearly 320 kph (200 mph) when swooping on their prey.

Emperor Penguins, the largest of the sphenisciformes, stand waist high to a man. They gather in April and May to begin courting, displaying their orange ear patches.

The ostrich is the largest living bird, often growing to 8 feet, of which nearly half is neck. Only one species now survives of the nine in existence during the Pliocene era.

Left: A bird of paradise, *Diphyllodes magnificus*, from New Guinea. These are perching birds belonging to the order *Passeriformes*. In the classification of birds, genera with very similar features are placed in the same family, and families which broadly resemble each other will belong to the same order. Sometimes members of the same order may look so very different from each other that it is difficult to see how they can be related. They will, however, have at least one characteristic in common, perhaps the structure of part of the skeleton, which to a scientist definitely relates them. Passeriformes have feet designed for perching. Four toes project from the same point of the leg—three forwards and one backwards. The design of the bony palate is characteristic of the order, and is only rarely seen in other birds. More than a fifth of all living bird species are *Passeriformes*.

Right: The brown pelican, *Pelecanus occidentalis*. Pelicans belong to the order *Pelecaniformes* as do a number of other sea birds, such as gannets and cormorants, which nest in colonies.

Marc Lelo/Jacana

Okapia

Right: The razor-billed auk, *Alca torda*, is a sea bird which inhabits the shores and islands of the North Atlantic. It belongs to the order *Charadriiformes* along with a wide variety of wading birds, gulls and terns. Although members of this order come in many different forms and sizes, they are related by internal similarities and by the composition of their blood albumin. The auk family, which also includes the guillemots and puffins, feeds mainly on small fish and invertebrates.

Bavaria

Below: The golden eagle, *Aquila chryseatos*, is the most powerful of all birds of prey. Its victims include other birds, young deer, foxes (as in this picture) and even wolves. It is a typical member of the order *Falconiformes*. Eagles of the genus *Aquila* (there are nine different species) are found in all parts of the world except South America. The largest of these, the golden eagle, has a wingspan of about 2.1 m (7 ft), the females being slightly larger than the males.

This is by no means a perfect definition, but it is perhaps the closest to the facts as they are observed in nature.

Sub-species

Within any individual species, particularly one with a wide distribution, a further problem may be the existence of separate, distinctive populations. These are called sub-species or geographical races. They are distinguished by the addition of a third scientific name added to the name of the species. Thus it has been shown that the mallard of Greenland is slightly different from that found in Europe. The form occurring in Europe is therefore named *Anas platyrhynchos platyrhynchos* Linné while the Greenland variant is called *Anas platyrhynchos conboschas* Brehm. The naturalist C. L. Brehm was the first to distinguish the Greenland mallard from the common European variety.

In most cases sub-species of birds differ from each other only in slight variations in their colour and size. It is often necessary to examine a specimen very closely before it can be distinguished from allied races with any degree of certainty. Indeed, there are some ornithologists who do not consider that these minor differences should be recognized by name, in the belief that it is quite enough to note the localities where the variants live.

Excluding the various sub-species, there are something like 8,600 species of birds living in the world today. Ornithologists hold diverse opinions as to the number of orders and families that these represent, but the system of classification most widely adopted today is that of the American ornithologist J. L. Peters, based on the system of his fellow American Alexander Westmore. This system recognizes 27 orders and about 150 families. In the chart that follows the English equivalent of the family name is used.

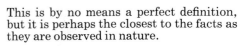

Visage/Jacana

THE ORDERS AND FAMILIES OF BIRDS

Struthioniformes
Ostrich

Rheiformes
Rhea

Casuariiformes
1. Cassowary
2. Emu

Apterygiformes
Kiwi

Tinamiformes
Tinamou

Sphenisciformes
Penguin

Gaviiformes
Diver

Podicipediformes
Grebe

Procellariiformes
1. Albatross
2. Shearwater
3. Storm petrel
4. Diving petrel

Pelecaniformes
1. Tropicbird
2. Pelican
3. Gannet
4. Cormorant
5. Darter
6. Frigate bird

Ciconiiformes
1. Heron and bittern
2. Shoebill
3. Hammerhead
4. Stork
5. Ibis and spoonbill
6. Flamingo

Anseriformes
1. Screamer
2. Swan, goose and duck

Falconiformes
1. Condor and king vulture
2. Osprey
3. Hawk, buzzard, kite, eagle and Old World vulture
4. Falcon and caracara
5. Secretary bird

Galliformes
1. Mound bird
2. Curassow
3. Grouse, ptarmigan, capercaillie and prairie chicken
4. Pheasant, quail and partridge
5. Guineafowl
6. Turkey
7. Hoatzin

Gruiformes
1. Mesite
2. Buttonquail
3. Plainswanderer
4. Crane
5. Limpkin
6. Trumpeter
7. Rail
8. Sungrebe
9. Kagu
10. Sunbittern
11. Seriema
12. Bustard

Charadriiformes
1. Jacana
2. Painted snipe
3. Oystercatcher
4. Plover
5. Sandpiper
6. Avocet
7. Phalarope
8. Crab plover
9. Thick-knee
10. Courser
11. Seed snipe
12. Sheathbill
13. Skua
14. Gull and tern
15. Skimmer
60 16. Auk

Ostrich
Struthioniformes

Rhea
Rheiformes

Cassowary
Casuariiformes

Albatross
Procellariiformes

Pelican
Pelecaniformes

Flamingo
Ciconiiformes

Parrot
Psittaciformes

Crane
Gruiformes

Gull
Charadriiformes

Pigeon
Columbiformes

Mousebird
Coliiformes

Humming bird
Apodiformes

THE 27 ORDERS OF LIVING BIRDS

Kiwi
Apterygiformes

Tinamou
Tinamiformes

Penguin
Sphenisciformes

Diver
Gaviiformes

Goose
Anseriformes

Grebe
Podicipediformes

Secretary bird
Falconiformes

Turaco
Cuculiformes

Owl
Strigiformes

Curassow
Galliformes

Frogmouth
Caprimulgiformes

Roller
Coraciiformes

Toucan
Piciformes

Crow
Passeriformes

ogon
ogoniformes

Columbiformes
1. Sandgrouse
2. Pigeon

Psittaciformes
Parrot

Cuculiformes
1. Turaco
2. Cuckoo

Strigiformes
1. Barn owl
2. Typical owl

Caprimulgiformes
1. Oil bird
2. Frogmouth
3. Potoo
4. Owlet frogmouth
5. Nightjar

Apodiformes
1. Swift
2. Crested swift
3. Humming bird

Coliiformes
Mousebird

Trogoniformes
Trogon

Coraciiformes
1. Kingfisher
2. Tody
3. Motmot
4. Bee-eater
5. Cuckoo roller
6. Roller
7. Hoopoe
8. Wood hoopoe
9. Hornbill

Piciformes
1. Jacamar
2. Puffbird
3. Barbet
4. Honeyguide
5. Toucan
6. Woodpecker

Passeriformes
1. Broadbill
2. Woodhewer
3. Ovenbird
4. Antbird
5. Antpipit
6. Tapaculo
7. Pitta
8. Asity
9. New Zealand wren
10. Tyrant flycatcher
11. Manakin
12. Cotinga
13. Plantcutter
14. Lyrebird
15. Scrub bird
16. Lark
17. Swallow
18. Wagtail
19. Cuckoo shrike
20. Bulbul
21. Leafbird
22. Shrike
23. Vanga
24. Waxwing
25. Palmchat
26. Dipper
27. Wren
28. Mockingbird
29. Accentor
30. Thrush, gnatcatcher, warbler and babbler
31. Tit
32. Nuthatch
33. Treecreeper
34. Flowerpecker
35. Sunbird
36. White eye
37. Honeyeater
38. Bunting
39. American warbler
40. Honeycreeper
41. Vireo
42. Oriole
43. Finch
44. Weaver finch
45. Weaver and sparrow
46. Starling
47. Drongo
48. Wattlebird
49. Magpie lark
50. Wood swallow
51. Magpie
52. Bowerbird
53. Bird of paradise
54. Crow

61

Bird Migration

Migration is fairly common in the animal kingdom—some species of fish, whales, turtles, insects, bats and land mammals (including man) all migrate. But birds are unique among the migratory animals; their powers of flight give them exceptional mobility and they have a remarkable ability to navigate over immense distances.

Bird migration is a seasonal shift in the centre of gravity of a population; a regular move both in season and direction involving a 'round trip'. In many cases the entire population of the species moves from a winter to a summer range separated by hundreds or even thousands of kilometres: these are called total migrants. Sometimes, however, the summer and winter ranges overlap or only part of the population migrates. Birds which follow this pattern of migration are known as partial migrants.

Some groups that regularly disperse at a particular season are not, strictly speaking, migrants at all because there is no mass movement in any particular direction; the population simply becomes more scattered. Some British seabirds arrive with great regularity each spring at their coastal colonies and depart again when breeding is over, but during the winter they wander widely. Kittiwakes, *Rissa tridactyla*, for example, range extensively over the Atlantic, reaching as far south as 40°N (the latitude of Madrid), westwards to the Grand Bank of Newfoundland and north to Greenland, while others may remain in home waters.

The reasons for migration
Apart from the enormous physical demands they make, these journeys can only be hazardous—they lead birds across hostile environments and, especially in the case of young birds, to unfamiliar habitats. For those species which do migrate, however, the risks involved in doing so are clearly less than those involved in staying put; were it not so, natural selection would have eliminated the migrating habit.

Migration is therefore concerned with survival and with food supply, and in the case of those species such as swallows, *Hirundinidae*, swifts, *Apodidae*, and flycatchers, *Muscicapidae*, which feed on flying insects, to remain in colder climates in winter would be impossible. Because the long cold winter night of the Arctic is an impossibly harsh environment for all but a very few highly specialized birds, many residents migrate southwards after feeding on the myriads of insects which flourish in the short summer.

The reasons for some migratory patterns, however, are less obvious. Many European swallows winter north of the equator, where there is evidently an adequate supply of insect food. Yet British breeding swallows fly on for thousands of kilometres to winter in the extreme south of Africa. What benefit they derive from this further journey is a mystery.

Equally perplexing is the case of the lapwing, *Vanellus vanellus*. This familiar bird is a partial migrant which suggests that the balance of advantage between staying put and migrating is a delicate one and not yet firmly resolved one way or the other. Each year countless lapwings from northern and central Europe come to winter in Britain and Ireland, escaping the snow-covered landscape which deprives them of access to food. In Britain, and especially in Ireland, the snow cover is usually brief, so the advantage to the immigrant lapwings is obvious. The odd thing is that perhaps half of all British lapwings migrate to spend the winter in the south of France and Spain, their places being taken by the immigrant lapwings from the North.

The evolution of migration
The wheatear, *Oenanthe oenanthe*, is one of the clearest examples of the evolution of migration. Primarily a bird of rocky uplands, the population breeding in western Europe has a relatively simple journey southward into Africa, where it winters in semi-desert country to the south of the Sahara. At some time after the last ice age, however, the species colonised first Iceland, then Greenland, and finally northeast Canada. Remarkably, these pioneering populations retained the same winter home in Africa, their migratory journeys getting longer and longer with each stage. In the process of evolution these northern birds have grown bigger and longer winged than their southern relatives, so becoming better equipped to face the long overseas flights.

It seems probable that a number of species originally made rather short simple migratory journeys which subsequently became much longer as they extended their range. The pied flycatcher, *Ficedula hypoleuca*, appears to have evolved in the west of Europe; it migrates from there southwards to Spain and Africa each autumn. A successful species, it has spread eastwards in the course of history and now breeds well to the east of Moscow. One might suppose that these eastern birds would follow a simple southward route into Africa, yet ringing has shown that they travel in a south westerly direction and first fly to the

Right: One of the most remarkable migrants is the wheatear, *Oenanthe oenanthe*. Colonies are found in Alaska and Greenland, and both groups spend the winter in Africa. Curiously they migrate to their winter home by quite different routes. The Alaskan birds travel westwards across Asia while the Greenland group travel eastwards by way of Iceland and western Europe.

Below: It is not only large species like the pintail duck, *Anas acuta*, that are capable of migration. The tiny ruby-throated humming bird, *Archilochus colubris*, migrates each year across the Gulf of Mexico from the eastern United States to central America.

D. N. Dalton/NHPA

Pintail duck

Ruby-throated humming bird

Below: Golden plovers, *Pluvialis apricaria*, on migration. The golden plover nests in northern Europe and Canada, migrating to southwest Europe, North Africa and South America for the winter. It is a wading bird but prefers drier land than its cousins the curlews, sandpipers and snipe.

Frank Lane

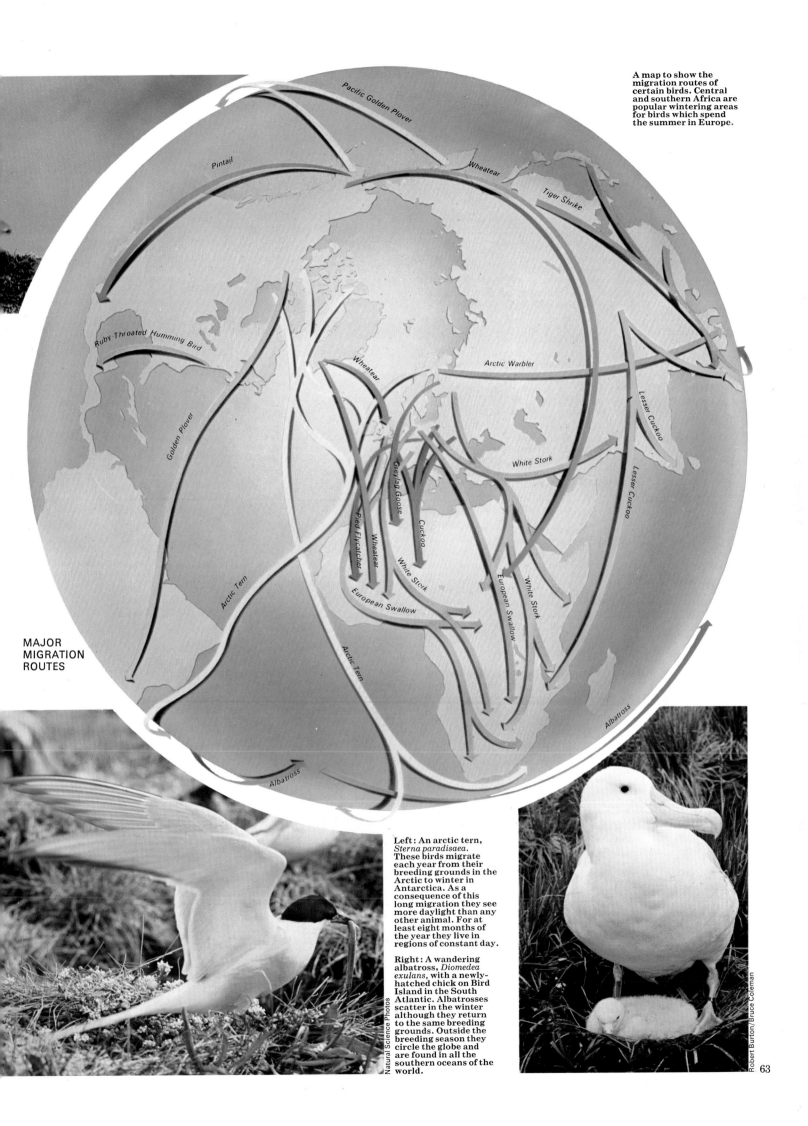

A map to show the
migration routes of
certain birds. Central
and southern Africa are
popular wintering areas
for birds which spend
the summer in Europe.

Pacific Golden Plover

Pintail

Wheatear

Tiger Shrike

Ruby Throated Humming Bird

Wheatear

Arctic Warbler

Lesser Cuckoo

Golden Plover

White Stork

Lesser Cuckoo

Greylag Goose

Pied Flycatcher

Wheatear

Cuckoo

White Stork

Arctic Tern

European Swallow

European Swallow

White Stork

MAJOR
MIGRATION
ROUTES

Arctic Tern

Albatross

Albatross

Albatross

Left: An arctic tern,
Sterna paradisaea.
These birds migrate
each year from their
breeding grounds in the
Arctic to winter in
Antarctica. As a
consequence of this
long migration they see
more daylight than any
other animal. For at
least eight months of
the year they live in
regions of constant day.

Right: A wandering
albatross, *Diomedea
exulans*, with a newly-
hatched chick on Bird
Island in the South
Atlantic. Albatrosses
scatter in the winter
although they return
to the same breeding
grounds. Outside the
breeding season they
circle the globe and
are found in all the
southern oceans of the
world.

Natural Science Photos

Robert Burton/Bruce Coleman

63

coast of Portugal before heading south.

Migration is, of course, part of an annual cycle. Into each twelve month period every bird must fit a breeding season, rarely lasting less than six to eight weeks and sometimes many months. There is also a period of moult, during which the bird replaces all its worn plumage with a new set of feathers. Then, for the migrants, there has to be time for two travel seasons.

The timing of migration

Most birds moult immediately after breeding is completed but some migratory species postpone the process until they have reached their winter quarters. In just a few species which breed in the extreme north, where the summer season is very short, the moult starts on the breeding grounds, is suspended for migration and is then resumed and completed further south. One species, the tiny willow warbler, *Phylloscopus trochilus*, actually undertakes two complete moults in the year, one immediately after breeding in the autumn and one in Africa before the start of the spring migration. A moult may last for six weeks or even longer in some species and, since birds normally do not moult and migrate at the same time, migration has to be fitted into those parts of the year not affected by breeding and moulting.

A migrating bird covers its long journey in a series of stages, and the time spent feeding at each 'staging post', and therefore the amount of fat deposited seems to depend on the length of the stage ahead. Thus a small insect-eating bird might leave southern Britain (most departures occur at dusk) with sufficient reserves for a flight of several hundred kilometres. There may be two or more such stages, but then for migrants travelling to tropical Africa comes the critical phase of the journey across the Sahara—a flight stage of not less than 1,600 km (1,000 miles). Remarkable though such a flight may seem, there is strong circumstantial evidence that many species take off from Spain or even from France, flying over both the Mediterranean and the Sahara in a single stage. Since their flying speed in still air is generally between 30 and 40 kph (20 to 24 mph) it is evident that many of them must fly uninterruptedly for 60 hours or more—a prodigious feat of endurance.

Navigation

One fascinating aspect of migrating birds is their ability to navigate with great precision. Using identification rings, it has been established that adult swallows and swifts, which winter south of the Sahara, tend to return to the same nest each year throughout their lives, while young ones normally return at least to the district of their birth. By taking the eggs of migratory species from the wild, hatching them in incubators and hand rearing them in isolation from others of their kind, it has been proved that young birds inherit not only a knowledge of the direction in which they must fly in autumn, but also the ability to determine that direction. Young cuckoos, *Cuculus canorus*, also travel alone to southern West Africa, departing a month or two after the adults.

Navigators require some means of holding a steady course across the featureless ocean and, before the invention of the

Frank Lane

Above and right: The greylag goose, *Anser anser*, lives in central and northern Europe, migrating to southern and western Europe and Africa for the winter. As in other birds, the yearly cycle of migration is controlled by a biological 'programme' in each bird. This releases into the bloodstream at the correct times of year the hormones responsible for migration, breeding and moulting. The V-shaped flight formation is typical of many wild geese. The leading birds will probably have been on several previous migrations, so they will have learnt to recognize landmarks on the route. Younger birds will lie at the back of the group.

Ken Fink/Ardea

Left: A North American screech owl, *Otis asio*. A European owl belonging to the same genus, the scops owl, *Otis scops*, is a night migrant. Each year it makes its way under cover of darkness to winter in equatorial Africa.

Below: A curlew sandpiper, *Calidris ferruginea*. Many birds interrupt their long migratory journeys to build up strength for the next stage. Curlew sandpipers can be seen feeding around the coasts of Britain in the spring and autumn as they break their northerly and southerly journeys. Staging posts of this sort are vital to migrants which have to fly long distances over sea or desert. Many species seem to use traditional 'fattening areas' in southern Europe in the autumn and central Africa in the spring. These areas are vital for their survival.

Ardea

Above: Starlings, *Sturnus vulgaris*, depend at least partly on the sun for their navigational skill. When the sun is shining they are able to orient themselves without difficulty, but on an overcast day their movements are much more random. Pigeons also need to see the sun for accurate navigation.

cuckoo

white stork

swallow

Three species which spend the winter in Africa: the European white stork, *Ciconia ciconia*, the swallow, *Hirundo rustica*, and the cuckoo, *Cuculus canorus*. The swallow is common in Britain during the summer but in the winter months it may be found as far south as the southern tip of Africa.

Right: In order to study the movements of birds it is necessary to mark individuals and this is usually done by means of light aluminium rings fixed around the right leg. The bird being ringed in this picture is a whinchat, *Saxicola rubetra*, which migrates from Europe to Africa for the winter.

Below: Adelie penguins, *Pygoscelis adeliae*, move each spring from the pack ice to the Antarctic mainland for breeding. They not only return to the same colony each year but individual birds even occupy the same nest site year after year. Among other penguin migrants are the crested penguins, *Eudyptes*.

Frank Lane

Eric Hosking

Ardea

compass, primitive man made use of both the sun and the stars. Many years ago it was noted that migrating birds tend to become disoriented when the sky is totally overcast, and this observation prompted experiments which proved that birds, too, make use of the sun to set their course. However, many migrants set off at dusk and must be able to steer in darkness. At first it was thought that they might somehow 'remember' the position of the setting sun, but the true explanation proved more remarkable. It was discovered that birds kept in a windowless room could, when taken outdoors, nevertheless 'read' the night sky. This observation led to a series of studies involving placing living birds in planetaria, from which it was deduced that while they may recognize certain constellations, they make use of the north-south axis about which the night sky appears to rotate.

Thus it seems that in determining direction birds primarily use celestial clues. Recently, however, it has been discovered that some species are apparently able to use the earth's magnetic field to guide them. Even more surprising is an Italian discovery that some birds' ability to orientate is impaired if their olfactory nerves are severed. This new evidence presents two difficulties. Firstly, because the olfactory lobes in the brains of birds are very poorly developed it has always been thought that they have very little sense of smell; secondly, even if they do have a sense of smell, it is very difficult to see how it could help them navigate.

One feature which is undoubtedly important in helping birds to navigate is their 'built-in clock'. (Human navigators need chronometers to determine the exact longitude of any position.) This clock is so accurate that even if a bird is confined for several weeks in a cellar, whose lighting bears no relation to that outside, they still follow a normal 24-hour rhythm.

Although birds do inherit a sense of direction, their navigational ability also depends to some extent on learning details of the migratory route. It is significant that most young birds fly in the company of adults; this ensures that they will arrive safely at their destination in spite of their inexperience. On the way they learn to recognize landmarks, feeding grounds and the position of their winter home. In this way some essential aspects of navigation and the geographical positions of their summer and winter homes are passed on from one generation to the next.

Marsupials

Rat opossum

The largest and best known members of the order *Marsupialia*, or pouched mammals, are the kangaroos of Australia. They were first discovered by a Dutch explorer, Francisco Pelsaert, in 1629 but his report of strange new animals did not arouse much interest in Europe. It was not until more than 140 years later, in 1770, when kangaroos were rediscovered by Captain James Cook, that naturalists first took notice of the new family of animals. Several years later the first live specimens to reach Europe caused a considerable stir when they were put on show in London. Although their upright gait and powerful hind legs immediately distinguish kangaroos from other animals, it is their unusual method of reproduction —the young develop in a pouch on the mother's abdomen—that makes them fundamentally different from non-marsupial animals.

The offspring of most mammals (placental mammals) reach a fairly advanced stage of development while still inside the mother's womb. The growing embryo receives oxygen and nourishment from its mother's bloodstream by means of a connecting organ called the *placenta* and the umbilical cord. Kangaroos, however, like most other marsupials, have no placenta and the embryo feeds on the yolk-sac of the egg. Although the marsupial egg is much larger than that of placental mammals, the food supply provided by the yolk-sac does not last for very long, and so marsupials are born at a very early stage in their development. The embryonic kangaroo when born is extremely small and hardly resembles its parent at all, but it is nevertheless able to crawl to its mother's pouch and there to find one of the nipples.

This is a remarkable feat for an animal which weighs only 0.9 gm (0.03 oz) at birth as compared with 25 kg (55 lb) for an adult kangaroo, and not surprisingly the newly born animal is specially adapted for the climb. Its fore limbs and shoulder region are relatively well developed and the digits are equipped with sharp curved claws for clinging to its mother's fur.

Once in the pouch the young animal finds the nipple by trial and error; as soon as the teat is touched it stops moving and takes hold. If it fails to find a nipple to supply it with milk, as may happen if there are already other young in the pouch, the young kangaroo is doomed to starvation. Once on the nipple the young does not release its grip and, because it is unable to suckle by itself, the muscles of the mother's mammary gland regulate the flow of milk. The epiglottis, which in placental mammals covers the trachea (the tube leading to the lungs), is extended upwards to form a tube leading into the nasal chamber. Thus a continuous passage is formed from the nostrils to the trachea so that air passes down to the windpipe as milk flows to the gullet.

All marsupials share the kangaroo's basic method of reproduction, with only minor variations from species to species. The group includes the wombats and marsupial moles, which are tunnellers, the gliding possums which are the only aerial representatives, the tree-dwelling

Above: A South American marsupial, the Ecuador rat opossum, *Caenolestes fuliginosus.*

Right: A view inside the pouch of an Australian brush-tailed possum, *Trichosurus vulpecula*, shows a young possum clinging to its mother's teat. The picture clearly shows how undeveloped newly born marsupials are. As soon as it is born the tiny and virtually helpless animal crawls into its mother's pouch to suckle. At this stage it is unable to feed for itself and muscles in the mother's milk gland control the flow of milk to her offspring. The young possum will remain in its mother's pouch for about five months.

Left: The common opossum, *Didelphis marsupialis*, lives in both North and South America. It was the first marsupial to be discovered by Europeans (in 1520) and in the years after its discovery its then unique method of reproduction aroused considerable interest.

Below: A ringtail possum, *Pseudocheirus*, from Australia. The animal usually curls the end of its tail into a ring, and this accounts for its name. Ringtail possums are nocturnal animals and they feed on fruit and leaves as well as small vertebrates such as lizards. They are solitary animals and, as this picture suggests, they live in trees.

koala bears and a variety of surface land animals ranging in size from the marsupial mice to the kangaroos.

The ancestors of the marsupials separated from the main evolutionary line of mammals about 100 million years ago. Since then both marsupials and placental mammals have evolved a wide variety of adaptations to different ways of life, and it is surprising how similar these adaptations are. The kangaroo, for example, is the marsupial equivalent of the antelope. There are also marsupial versions of the mouse, the wolf, the mole, the cat and the anteater, and these animals look remarkably like their placental mammal counterparts. Although today most marsupials are quite small, this was not always the case: one extinct marsupial, *Diprotodon*, was as big as a rhinoceros.

Right: The koala bear, *Phascolarctos cinereus*, is one of the most familiar marsupials. It feeds exclusively on eucalyptus leaves and this makes it a difficult animal to keep in captivity outside Australia. A curious feature of this diet is that young eucalyptus leaves and shoots often contain lethal amounts of hydrogen cyanide, especially in winter, and this accounted for many deaths among the first zoo animals in Australia. In the wild, koalas avoid the young shoots, feeding almost exclusively on the more mature leaves. Only a century ago there were many millions of koalas in Australia, but today the total population must be measured in thousands. They have completely disappeared from southern and western Australia, exterminated by hunting and by natural epidemics. In 1927 alone more than half a million koala furs were exported from the state of Queensland. Fortunately the animals are now protected and the population is on the increase. Koalas have been reintroduced in some areas.

The geographical distribution of the marsupials is unusual—they are found only in Australia and South America (except for a few opossums which have spread to North America relatively recently). The reason for this odd distribution is obscure—possibly Antarctica once formed a bridge between the two continents so that their animal populations merged. At any event it seems likely that competition from placental mammals drove them out of all other regions of the world (fossils of marsupials have been found in both North America and Europe). Marsupials were most successful in Australia where such competition was least.

Australian marsupials

Of the nine marsupial families, seven are exclusively Australian: the kangaroos, *Macropodidae*, the carnivorous marsupials, *Dasyuridae*, the phalangers, *Phalangeridae*, the wombats, *Vombatidae*, the bandicoots, *Peramelidae*, the marsupial anteaters, *Myrmecobiidae*, and the marsupial moles, *Notoryctidae*.

The word 'kangaroo' is often restricted to the three members of the genus *Macropus* (the word means great foot): the red kangaroo, *Macropus rufus*, of the plains, the great grey kangaroo, *Macropus giganteus*, of the open forests, and the stocky, powerful wallaroo, *Macropus robustus*, of the rocky mountain ranges. The many smaller species of the kangaroo family are usually called 'wallabies'.

Kangaroos and wallabies occupy the same ecological niche as the grazing animals such as deer and antelopes of other lands. Like ruminants (animals which chew the cud) they have specialized bacteria in their stomach to break down the cellulose in the sparse vegetation which forms their diet. Some species have even developed the ability to regurgitate food and chew the cud like cattle. Because they can digest plant material efficiently kangaroos and wallabies can survive in the most inhospitable environments.

The long tapering tail is used as a balance and rudder for leaps and turns. At high speed the tail does not hit the ground with every bound, but is used more to help turning. The tail is so powerful that the animal may actually stand upon it and take its hind legs off the ground. Large kangaroos can achieve speeds of about 50 kph (30 mph) for short bursts and can sustain a speed of 40 kph (25 mph) for some time. An adult grey kangaroo may stand over two metres (seven feet) tall and weigh 90 kg (200 lb) or more.

The family *Phalangeridae* contains a wide variety of marsupials, including the koala, *Phascolarctos cinereus*, the slow moving cuscuses, *Phalanger*, with prehensible (grasping) tails and big eyes, the flying possums, *Petaurus*, which glide from tree to tree like flying squirrels, and the doormouse possums, *Cercartetus*. The solitary koala 'bear' is one of the most interesting and attractive of all marsupials. It is rarely seen in zoos outside Australia because it thrives only on a diet of leaves from the native eucalyptus tree, which have a high oil content. Koalas seldom drink water, apparently deriving sufficient moisture from the eucalyptus leaf diet and dew. The reproductive rate of koalas is low. The female produces a single young every two years

Left: A female rabbit bandicoot, *Macrotis leucura*, with her young. These animals get their name from their long rabbit-like ears and their habit of building long burrows to a depth of 1.5 m (4.8 ft) or more. They are beneficial to man because they have a large appetite for pests such as insect larvae and mice.

Below: A young long-nosed bandicoot, *Perameles nasuta*, climbs into its mother's pouch. Most burrowing marsupials, like the bandicoots, have pouches which open to the rear. Bandicoots are found in most parts of Australia and some species ,such as the spiny bandicoots, live in New Guinea.

Long-nosed bandicoot

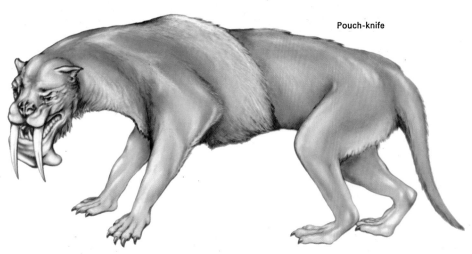

Pouch-knife

after a pregnancy of about a month. At birth the young koala weighs only about five grams (0.2 oz) and, after reaching its mother's pouch, it remains there for six months being suckled. As in many other marsupials such as the Tasmanian wolf and the wombats the koala's pouch opens to the rear. After weaning, the young koala clings to its mother's back until it is able to fend for itself.

Bandicoots are shy nocturnal animals which inhabit New Guinea as well as Australia. They range in size from that of a rat to that of a badger and have pointed noses. They feed on insects and roots which they scratch from the ground. Wombats are stocky rodent-like animals which live in burrows; they are solitary and feed mainly on roots.

Marsupial moles have adapted to a burrowing existence in just the same way as the placental mammals of the same name, and this has resulted in a striking resemblance between the two groups. Although they are quite unrelated the marsupial mole, *Notoryctes*, is outwardly very like the African golden mole, *Chrysochloris*; it has fine silky fur varying in colour from white to a rich golden red.

Carnivorous marsupials

The largest and rarest of the flesh-eating marsupials is the marsupial wolf, *Thylacinus cynocephalus*, which lives in caverns among the rocks in the most mountainous part of Tasmania. Very few of these creatures survive today and unless drastic steps are taken to protect them they will shortly become extinct. The animal looks like a dog with chocolate coloured stripes across its lower back. Most of the day is spent in a lair from which it emerges at dusk in search of prey, hunting either singly or in pairs. Its natural food consists of wallabies and smaller marsupials, rats and birds.

Another carnivorous marsupial is the Tasmanian devil, *Sarcophilus harrisi*, which is still quite common in Tasmania. It received its unfortunate name after early reports of its aggressive temperament. In fact it is no more aggressive than many other animals, but it will use its powerful jaws to defend itself if attacked. The Australian native cats, *Dasyurus*, are slender carnivores which look rather like martens and feed on birds, small mammals and lizards.

The rare marsupial anteater or numbat, *Myrmecobius fasciatus*, is sometimes placed with the marsupial carnivores in the family *Dasyuridae* rather than in a separate family of its own. It has a pointed

Above: *Thylacosmilus,* a large carnivorous marsupial which once roamed the forests of South America. Its similarity to the sabre-toothed tiger is remarkable because the two animals were quite unrelated. Evidently both animals evolved in the same way to meet similar environmental conditions.

Right: An albino brush wallaby, *Wallabia.* Members of the kangaroo family normally produce only a single young at a time, and twins, as seen here, are rare. Albinism, the absence of body pigmentation, is a genetically produced condition and, although not common, it occurs in many mammals, including man.

Douglas Baglin/NHPA

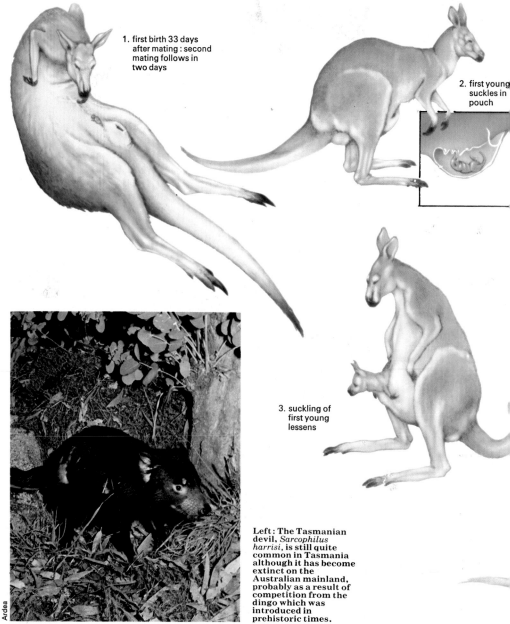

1. first birth 33 days after mating : second mating follows in two days

2. first young suckles in pouch

3. suckling of first young lessens

Left: The Tasmanian devil, *Sarcophilus harrisi*, is still quite common in Tasmania although it has become extinct on the Australian mainland, probably as a result of competition from the dingo which was introduced in prehistoric times.

Ardea

Left: Illustrations to show the characteristic hopping movement of kangaroos. The very powerful hind legs and long slender feet enable the animals to move extremely rapidly by a series of jumps which may measure nine metres (30 ft) or more.

Above: Matschie's tree kangaroo, *Dendrolagus matschiei*. This strange animal lives in the forests of northern Australia and New Guinea feeding on fruit and leaves. It is not at all well adapted to its tree-dwelling existence, but this does not seem to matter because it has no natural enemies and food is plentiful.

Right: An Australian 'tiger cat', *Dasyurus maculatus*, devouring a crimson rosella parrot. These carnivorous marsupials are excellent climbers and they prey on lizards, fish and small mammals as well as birds. They were once slaughtered in large numbers for raiding chicken coops and are now quite rare.

4. second birth after first young has left pouch: about seven months after second mating

5. second young suckles in pouch and first young returns to suckle occasionally

Left: A typical breeding sequence for the red kangaroo, *Macropus rufus*. After the first young is born (the mother leans back as the tiny embryo crawls up into her pouch) mating takes place for the second time. The fertilized egg, however, only begins to develop when the suckling of the first young has lessened. By the time the second animal is born, the first will have left the pouch, although it may still return to suckle occasionally.

snout, long hair and a long bushy tail. Its diet consists mainly of termites which it extracts from crevices and rotten wood with its long tongue. It lives only in a few small regions of central and southern Australia.

American marsupials

The two American marsupial families are the rat opossums, *Caenolestidae*, and the opossums, *Didelphidae*. There are only three species of rat opossums. They are small animals found in the forests of the Andes from Venezuela to southern Chile. Fossil evidence suggests that they are the survivors of a much larger marsupial group which flourished in the Tertiary period.

The most widely distributed member of the opossum family is the common opossum, *Didelphis marsupialis*, which is found from Argentina to Canada. It inhabits forests at all altitudes, feeding on insects and small mammals, but avoids grasslands and the high plains of the Andes. Opossums are solitary, nocturnal animals; they spend the hours of daylight in dens or nests taken over from other species. Despite their fairly large size— about 75 cm (2.5 ft) from head to tail— opossums do not live long. The average lifespan from weaning has been estimated to be only 1.3 years and the longest four years, so few opossums live beyond the summer following their birth. Even though females become mature at six months, they rarely breed more than once in a lifetime.

The water opossum, *Chironectes minimus*, of South America has the distinction of being the only marsupial adapted to an aquatic existence although its cousin the thick-tailed opossum, *Lutreolina crassicaudata*, is also a good swimmer. It lives on the banks of ponds and rivers feeding on shellfish, spawn and crayfish. The pouch of the water opossum, which opens to the rear, is equipped with a muscle so that it can be closed off when the animal dives, ensuring that the young remain dry while their mother searches for food.

Hedgehogs, Moles and Shrews

Hedgehogs, moles, shrews and a number of other small insect-eating mammals all belong to the order *Insectivora*. The grouping is largely one of convenience because its various members do not have many structural features in common: they are linked more by their way of life than anything else. Insectivores are small animals—none is larger than a rabbit and most are considerably smaller—which lead secret, often nocturnal, lives hidden in the undergrowth and the earth. It is not therefore surprising that although they are quite common they are only rarely seen.

The insectivores are placental mammals: they differ from both monotremes (such as the duck-billed platypus) and marsupials (such as kangaroos) in a number of important ways. The main distinction is that the young are retained within the mother's womb until an advanced stage of development and are nourished through a connecting organ called the placenta, a complex system of blood vessels and tissue. This arrangement provides maximum protection and a controlled environment for the growing embryo. Another important feature seen in placental mammals but not monotremes or marsupials is the *corpus callosum*, a bundle of nerve fibres which connects the left and right cerebral hemispheres of the brain providing improved co-ordination.

Hedgehogs and moles

Altogether there are more than 350 known species of insectivores and these are normally divided into eight families. The family *Erinaceidae* contains the hedgehogs and the moon rats. Hedgehogs are found throughout Europe, Africa and Asia, north to the latitude of Oslo and east as far as Borneo. They will inhabit any region where they can find food and dry shelter: hollow trees, the bases of hedges and cavities underneath farm buildings make popular living quarters. They line their nests with moss, leaves and grass but only rarely dig burrows of their own.

The most familiar feature of the hedge-

Hans Reinhard/Bruce Coleman

Above: A group of young European hedgehogs, *Erinaceus europaeus*, at the base of a tree. Hedgehogs are most active in the evening and early in the morning, probing among leaves and moss and under stones with their sensitive noses. They feed on insects, snails and even mice. In the autumn when the outside air temperature drops to around 10°C (50°F) hedgehogs begin their hibernation. First they burrow into their nest material and roll themselves into a ball to minimize heat loss. Then the body processes slow down: the breathing rate falls to about seven per minute and the heart rate to 20 per minute. The blood temperature falls dramatically although it is never allowed to drop below about 2°C (36°F). With the onset of warmer weather in the spring, the animal 'wakes' and immediately begins feeding.

Right: A common mole, *Talpa europaea*, feeding on an earthworm.

Below: The bizarre star-nosed mole, *Condylura cristata*, from North America.

Heather Angel

P. Morris

Left: The pen-tailed tree shrew, *Ptilocercus lowii*, belongs to the family *Tupaiidae*. Members of this group were once regarded as insectivores—there are some affinities with the elephant shrews—but are now normally classified with the primates, the order which includes lemurs, monkeys and man.

Right: When alarmed a hedgehog rolls itself up into a ball, presenting a mass of sharp spines to its attacker.

Left: The bones in the hand of a mole are specially adapted to equip the animal for its burrowing way of life.

Below right: The lesser tenrec, *Echinops telfairi*, from Madagascar is a typical insectivore. It lives in gardens, the drier forests and sandy areas where it forages for snails, worms, insects and lizards. The sense of smell is well developed and the animal uses its long snout as well as its claws to uncover food.

Below: An elephant shrew, *Elephantulus brachyrhynchus*, eating an insect. Most elephant shrews, which inhabit central and southern Africa, have longer trunk-like snouts than this species. Their long hind legs enable them to jump and hop rapidly for considerable distances, and this, together with their long snouts, distinguishes them from other insectivores.

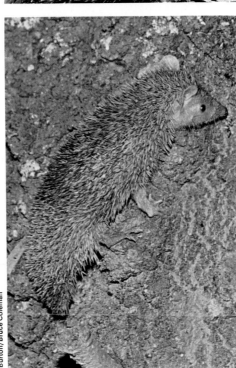

Left: The bicoloured white-toothed shrew, *Crocidura leucodon*, is common in central and southern Europe. It inhabits the undergrowth of hedges, fields and gardens, and like most insectivores it feeds mainly on invertebrate animals such as insects and earthworms. The smallest of all mammals is a shrew—Savis' pygmy shrew, *Suncus etruscus*—which measures only about 7 cm (2.7 in) from nose to tail.

Right: A Cape golden mole, *Chrysochloris asiatica*. It belongs to a different family from the European moles but has a similar way of life, constructing long burrows just below the surface and feeding on insects and earthworms.

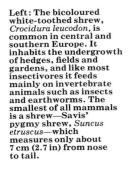

hog is its covering of spines—as many as 16,000 extend over the animal's back and sides from its forehead to its rump. On the face and underside of the body is a covering of soft hair. The spines provide an almost impregnable defence against possible predators such as foxes, for when a hedgehog is alarmed it curls up into a tight ball by contracting its well developed skin muscles so that the soft parts of the body are protected and the spines point outwards. Hedgehogs are fairly agile and will eat almost anything, from insects, slugs and snails (their preferred diet) to fruit and berries, the young of nesting birds and amphibians and reptiles.

Some of the stranger habits of hedgehogs are not fully understood, including the peculiar habit of anointing the spines with saliva when chewing strong-smelling food, be it a toad or carrion. This behaviour may be to do with grooming or it may simply be a way of disguising the animal's own scent. Not surprisingly the many spines make grooming a difficult operation, and as a result hedgehogs are frequently plagued with parasites. Almost all wild hedgehogs are infested with fleas, *Archaeopsylla erinacei*, and many also carry ticks, mites and nematode worms.

Hedgehogs are remarkably resistant to poisons that would prove deadly to other mammals. It is well known that the European hedgehog will tackle a large adder; the snake has little chance of biting because of the hedgehog's spines and defence tactics. Hedgehogs eat blister beetles, which contain the powerful poison cantharidin, with no harmful effect and reputedly can tolerate 7,000 times as much tetanus toxin as a human. In the same family as the hedgehogs are the moon rats which are large opossum-like insectivores with striking black and white markings. They are nocturnal creatures and live in the lowland and mangrove forests of Malaysia.

The moles are classified in the family *Talpidae*. Among the several sub-families are the shrew moles of South East Asia, the desmans of east and southwest Europe, the Old World moles of Europe and Asia and the star-nosed moles of North America. The diversity of animals within one family is typical of the insectivores.

Moles, especially those of the genus *Talpa*, are well adapted to an underground life. The forelimbs and the hands are specialized; in the most extreme types, like the European mole, *Talpa europaea*, the shoulder girdle is shifted close to the neck and the front joint of the breast plate is prolonged forward and broadened to

give a large area for the attachment of digging muscles. The size of the hand is increased by a special sickle-shaped bone and there is an equivalent bone in the feet which probably helps the animal to get a grip on the sides of its burrow. Most species of mole throw out the excavated earth from their burrows as 'molehills', pushing it up from below with the palms of the hands. The nest, made of dry leaves and grasses, is usually below ground and covered with a particularly large mound of earth known as a 'fortress'.

Most moles eat earthworms, and stocks of immobilized worms with their heads cut off are often kept as a food store. This diet is supplemented with insects while some of the North American moles eat large quantities of vegetable matter. Although moles have a poor sense of smell and poor eyesight, they make up for this by having extremely sensitive tactile organs located on the snout, as well as sensitive hairs on the nose and wrist. The extraordinary star-nosed mole of North America has a ring of 22 fleshy tentacles surrounding its nostrils. No doubt these help the animal to feel its way through the earth and locate its prey.

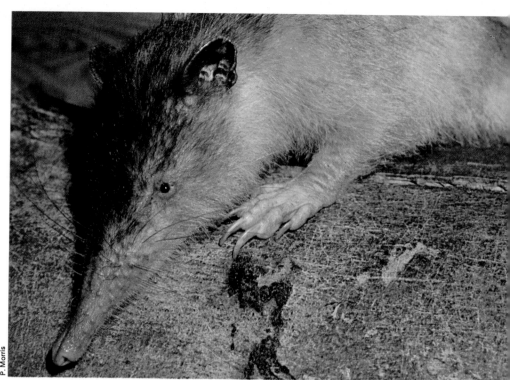

P. Morris

Shrews

The shrews form the largest family of insectivores (*Soricidae*) with over 300 species. They are found in most parts of the world, being absent only from Australasia and the southern part of South America. Shrews forage in and under the leaf litter and undergrowth of woods where they construct runs and shallow burrows. They are forever on the move and are extremely aggressive little animals, communicating with each other by high-pitched squeaks and twitterings. Like bats, they probably use echo location to help detect each other and their prey. Although they eat all kinds of insects, shrews will also tackle any other prey that they can overpower. The European common and pygmy shrews appear to favour woodlice, while the diet of some North American shrews includes a high proportion of vegetable matter.

To maintain their high metabolic rate, shrews have to eat a great deal of food, indeed their life is one continuous meal. The food consumed each day often exceeds the animal's body weight and digestion is very rapid, the gut being emptied in three hours. Common shrews are often found lying dead during the autumn; the cause of death most probably being cold and starvation. The reason why so many are found is that their skin contains strong-smelling glands which make them unpalatable to most carnivorous mammals which would otherwise eat them. The main predators of shrews are birds of prey, particularly owls.

It is easy to think of shrews as typical of European woodlands but they have an immense range and the 300 forms are spread throughout most of the world, with many species confined to the remote mountain streams of Tibet and eastern Asia. The strangest of all are the armoured shrews of tropical Africa. These medium-sized shrews show no outward appearance of anything unusual but their internal anatomy is quite extraordinary; the details of the vertebral column are like nothing found in any other mammal. The dorsal and many of the lumbar vertebrae are large and have a complex system of extensions, so that most of the backbone

MOLE'S NEST COMPLEX

Tony Bemish/Ardea

forms a strong braced girder. The purpose of this strange fortified backbone remains a mystery but illustrates the unusual make-up of many insectivores.

The elephant shrews belong to a separate insectivore family, the *Macroscelididae*. They look like long-nosed rodents, and have large eyes, long legs and a stance and way of moving that is unlike other insectivores. Most elephant shrews (they get their name from their long, mobile snout) are about the size of a mouse and they live in the rocky scrub areas of northern Algeria and Morocco as well as in central and southern Africa. Some members of the group, like the giant elephant shrews, *Petrodromus* and *Rhynchocyon*, are forest dwellers and differ from the others in having only four toes on the hind feet. Elephant shrews feed almost exclusively on ants which they prise out of rotting wood and other crevices with their long snouts.

Other insectivore families

The smallest insectivore family, the *Solenodontidae*, contains only two rare species which are found on the islands of Cuba and Hispaniola (Haiti and the Dominican Republic) in the West Indies. Solenodons are odd-looking mammals about the size of a guinea pig, with long pointed snouts bristling with sensitive hairs. They have large naked ears and an equally naked rat-like tail. Solenodons live in rocky, wooded country where they hunt smaller mammals, reptiles and ground-nesting birds as well as the more usual insect diet.

Another group of island insectivores is the family *Tenrecidae* found only in Madagascar and the nearby Comoro Islands in the Indian Ocean. Most of the twenty or so species are nocturnal and dig their own burrows and nests. The tenrec, *Tenrec ecaudatus*, is the largest living insectivore and the most widely distributed and commonest member of the family. It has a long snout and a coat of mixed hairs and spines. The spines, mostly on the nape of the neck, are raised when the animal is alarmed giving this small mammal a ferocious appearance.

Closely related to the large family of tenrecs are the otter shrews of the family *Potamogalidae* which live on the mainland of Africa. As their name suggests, these aquatic insectivores look and behave like miniature otters. There are only three species of which the giant African otter shrew, *Potamogale velox*, is the largest. It inhabits lowland equatorial West Africa whereas the other two species (of the genus *Micropotamogale*) live only in the mountain streams of West Africa. All have a broad, flat head, small eyes and short soft fur, and they feed on a variety of prey such as fish, amphibians and crustaceans.

The golden moles make up the final family of insectivores, the *Chrysochloridae*. Although looking superficially like the true moles, these animals are more exotic in appearance: their fur is thick with a dense soft underfur and has an iridescent bronzy sheen of green, violet, yellow or red. The forelimbs are very powerful and have four digits, the outer ones small but the central two very large and armed with huge pointed claws. There is a hard leathery pad on top of the snout. They live in Africa south of the equator where they feed on insects, earthworms and lizards. The prey is held by the long fore-claws while being eaten.

Left: A solenodon, *Solenodon paradoxus*, from Haiti. Solenodons are not as defenceless as they look for they have very large incisors and also poisonous salivary glands (an unusual feature for a mammal) which they use to subdue large prey such as rodents. They are now quite rare and face extinction.

Above: A colugo, *Cynocephalus volans*, from the Philippines. Unlike other mammals which have developed the ability to glide, these animals have a web of skin stretching between the hind legs and the tail. Often misleadingly called 'flying lemurs', they are classified in an order of their own, the *Dermoptera*.

Below: All insectivores have much the same way of life. They live under the ground or on the surface sheltered by the undergrowth, feeding mainly on small invertebrates such as insects and earthworms. In this illustration of a typical insectivore habitat can be seen a European hedgehog, *Erinaceus europaeus*, a common mole, *Talpa europaea*, and its young, and a common European white-toothed shrew, *Crocidura russula*. Many beetle grubs lie buried in the ground—they will probably fall prey to moles. The inset shows how a mole's nest is surrounded by a network of tunnels. It often lies under a large mound of earth.

Bats

Bats inhabit almost every corner of the globe. Only in Antarctica, the Arctic tundra and a few remote islands are they unknown. The total number of individuals runs into tens of billions and there are more than 1,200 known species and sub-species. They belong to the order *Chiroptera* and, second only to the rodents (order *Rodentia*), constitute the largest population of mammals on earth.

Their small furry bodies and large membranous wings make bats instantly recognizable. They are the only mammals that can fly, although a number of creatures, such as the flying squirrels of West Africa, are able to glide from tree to tree. In most respects bats are typical placental mammals: their young are born alive and feed on their mother's milk. The group is divided into two sub-orders: the *Megachiroptera*, fruit-eating bats with large eyes, a clawed thumb and second finger and a small or non-existent tail, and the *Microchiroptera*, mainly insect-eating bats with claws only on the thumbs, a tail forming part of the wing and the ability to find their prey by echo location, or 'sonar'.

Bats are nocturnal, and this way of life suits them in several respects. Firstly, most species are tropical so daytime activity would expose the thin skin of their wings to the harmful effects of the ultra-violet radiation in sunlight. Also, the heat would increase the rate of water loss from these large surfaces, and so would restrict bats to feeding grounds close to water sources. For most bats, however, the most important advantage of a nocturnal lifestyle is that it makes available the enormous food supply of night-flying insects. During the day bats roost in caves or trees, hanging upside down from suitable perches.

Bats usually mate in the autumn before hibernating. The sperm from the male remains in the female's fallopian tubes

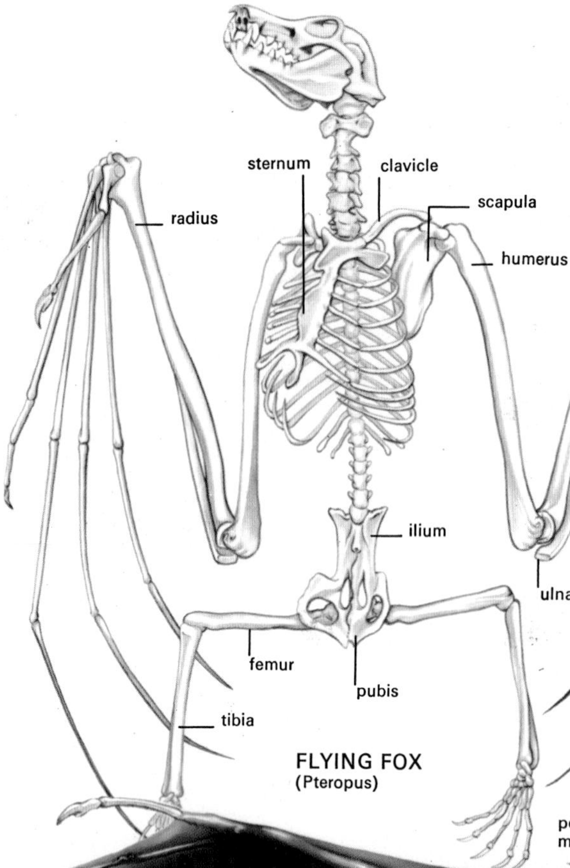

FLYING FOX
(Pteropus)

radius · sternum · clavicle · scapula · humerus · ilium · ulna · femur · pubis · tibia

pectoral muscles · thigh muscles · calcar · tail · foot

Left: The skeleton of a flying fox, *Pteropus*. It has long arms and particularly long fingers for supporting the wings. The breast bone (sternum) has a keel to which the powerful flight muscles are attached. Ignoring those features which are special adaptations for flight, bats resemble the insectivores, such as shrews and moles.

Right: A nectar bat, *Leptonycteris sanborni*, feeds on the pollen and nectar of an agave flower and pollinates the plant. These bats have long tongues for probing flowers, but they also feed on insects. During the day they cluster together in groups in the hollows of cliffs and trees.

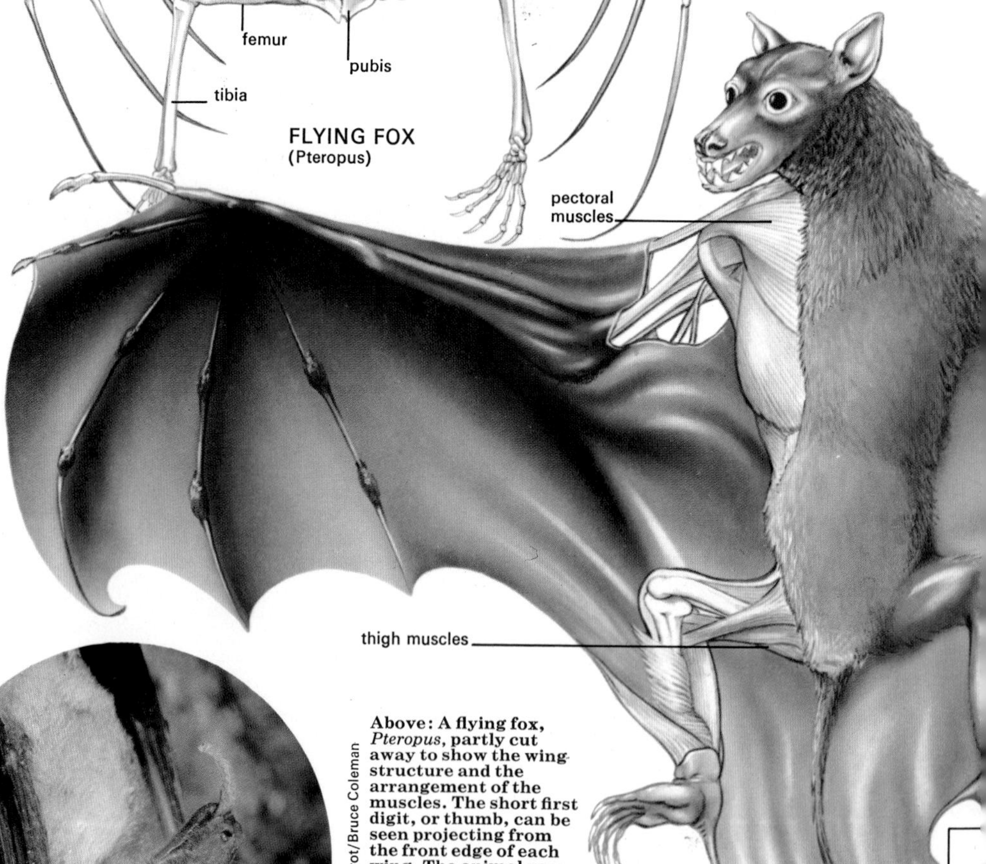

Above: A flying fox, *Pteropus*, partly cut away to show the wing structure and the arrangement of the muscles. The short first digit, or thumb, can be seen projecting from the front edge of each wing. The animal uses these for climbing. The wing membrane, or patagium, is joined to the fore and hind limbs.

S. C. Bisserot/Bruce Coleman

Above: A long-tongued fruit bat, *Macroglossus logichilus*, from South East Asia. This species is the smallest of all fruit bats, having a body length of only about 6 cm (2.4 in).

Left: A flying fox, *Pteropus*, from the Seychelles. During the day, fruit bats like the flying fox roost in trees, wrapping their wing membranes around their bodies.

Right: An Indian short-nosed fruit bat, *Cynopterus sphinx*, feeds on a banana.

ZEFA

Heather Angel

74

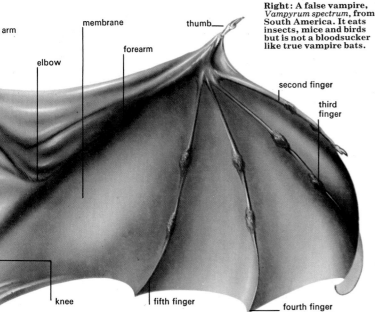

arm   membrane   thumb
elbow
forearm
second finger
third finger
knee   fifth finger   fourth finger

Right: A false vampire, *Vampyrum spectrum,* **from South America. It eats insects, mice and birds but is not a bloodsucker like true vampire bats.**

until the following spring, when the first egg is produced. A single foetus develops from the fertilized egg and the baby is born in the summer. At birth the young bat is naked and blind, and it clings to its mother's body to keep warm, travelling with her when she leaves the roost at night to feed. As the bat grows older it becomes less dependent on its mother, flying behind her at night and hanging next to her during the daytime rest period. Insect-eating bats develop quickly and are able to fly at an early age; they are fully grown in no more than eight weeks. Unlike birds, young bats seem to inherit their skill at flying, for they fly well from the beginning without any practice flights.

Flight

The wings of a bat are formed of skin and in this respect they resemble prehistoric flying reptiles like the pterodactyl more than birds. The design of the wings is essentially the same in all bats: there is a short, stout upper arm, a long, slender forearm and extremely long fingers which support the skin of the wing. The second finger extends along the leading edge of the wing; immediately behind it is the third and longest finger; and behind that are the fourth and fifth fingers, which are

well spaced out and serve as 'struts' to support and control the shape of about half of the wing membrane. The wing extends between the fingers and continues beyond the fifth finger to the side of the body and leg. It consists of upper and lower layers of skin enclosing a network of fine blood vessels. The animal's thumb, or first finger, projects from the front edge of the wing and carries a claw; it plays no part in supporting the wing.

Bats usually roost upside down. As they approach a landing they flip over in full flight, throw their hind claws against the roost, grasp it and hang. To take off they simply release their grip, fall for a short distance and begin to fly. A few heavier bats, such as the flying foxes, flap their wings to raise the body to a horizontal position before releasing their hold. Many bats do not fly more than two kilometres or so from their roost, although some species may cover 100 km (60 miles) or more on a round trip. A few species are known to migrate; the nectar bat, *Leptonycteris,* for example, travels from Mexico to Arizona for the summer. Bats fly at altitudes of anything up to about 300 m (1,000 ft); insect-eaters will naturally tend to fly at the same height as their insect prey.

Senses

The expression 'as blind as a bat' is very much misplaced. Many bats can see very well, and their eyes have become adapted to operating in extremely dim light. Bats that feed on fruit or flowers no doubt also use their sense of smell to detect their food. One of the most remarkable features of bats, however, is their sonar system which enables them to catch their prey and avoid obstructions such as trees and buildings when it is almost completely dark. Only one genus, *Rousettus,* of the sub-order *Megachiroptera* possesses it, but all members of the other sub-order *Microchiroptera* have this ability.

The bat sends out a series of high-pitched squeaks as it flies along, and the pattern of sounds in the echo tells it what objects are ahead, how far away they are and whether or not they are moving. The squeaks are short and intense, but their pitch (wave frequency) is too high to be heard by the human ear. However, bats also emit audible sounds as they fly about at dusk catching their prey. These sounds lie at the high frequency end of the human hearing ability and are more easily heard by children than adults. The sounds are emitted through the animal's mouth or nostrils, depending on the species. Those

Bavaria

Eric Hosking

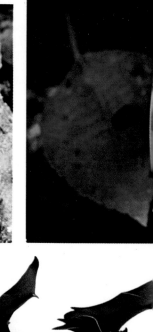

Above: Common pipistrelle bats, *Pipistrellus*, **clinging to a wall. Insect-eaters are smaller than fruit-bats, and they have the advantage of a 'sonar system'.**

Left: A long-eared bat, *Plecotus auritus*. **These creatures belong to the largest of the bat families, the** *Vespertilionidae*, **and they are common throughout Europe. The enormous ears help give the animal the keen sense of hearing needed for its sonar system.**

Right: A tomb bat, *Taphozous melanopogon*, **from Malaya. The genus was first discovered in ancient Egyptian tombs by French naturalists in the late 18th century.**

S. C. Bisserot

bats that emit sound nasally usually have a large nose 'leaf' which probably acts rather like a reflector to 'aim' the sound in a particular direction. Bats which emit sound orally, on the other hand, usually form their mouth and lips into a megaphone shape to project the sound. The squeak of a bat is not a continuous sound but rather a series of individual sound pulses and the pitch of each pulse varies depending on whether the animal is cruising or closing in on a target.

Flying foxes

The largest of all bats are the flying foxes, *Pteropus*, from India, South-East Asia and Australia, which can weigh up to 1.5 kg (3.3 lb) and have a wingspan of up to 1.5 m (5 ft). They have a fox-like face and long sharp canine teeth, but despite their forbidding appearance they are strictly vegetarian. They use their teeth for tearing husks or even cracking coconuts. Flying foxes belong to the sub-order *Megachiroptera* and they have prominent well-developed eyes but no sonar system. Flying foxes live in colonies of many thousands of individuals. They roost in high trees during the day, moving to food trees, which they detect mainly by smell, in the evening. After returning to their roost the following morning they fly noisily around for several hours before settling down for the day. The roost is not a permanent site, for the bats will always rest close to a suitable source of food.

Insectivorous bats

Insect-eating bats are smaller than fruit bats. One of the smallest, *Pipistrellus nanulus*, from West Africa, has a body length of only four centimetres (1.6 in) when fully grown. Among the larger families of insect-eating bats are the horseshoe bats, *Rhinolophidae*, which are found from Western Europe across Asia to Australia; the Old World leaf-nosed bats, *Hipposideridae*, of Africa, southern Asia and Australia; and the New World leaf-nosed bats, *Phyllostomatidae*, of the southern United States and northern South America. The largest family of all

A BAT IN FLIGHT

S. C. Bisserot

Above: A series of illustrations of a bat in flight.

Left: A Bechstein's bat, *Myotis bechsteini*, **is frozen by the camera in mid-flight. This is one of about 60 species of mouse-eared bats (genus** *Myotis*) **which are found in most parts of Europe. This particular species has larger ears than most other members of the genus. Mouse-eared bats roost together in large colonies, and their summer and winter quarters may be separated by as much as 200 km (120 miles). They hibernate in natural or artificial chambers such as caves and buildings.**

Right: A diadem round-leaf bat, *Hipposideros diadema*. **The strange shape of the nose has to do with the transmission of the ultrasonic 'squeaks' of the animal's echo location system. As with other leaf-nosed bats, the squeaks are emitted from the nostrils and not the mouth. Closely related to the leaf-nosed bats are the horseshoe bats which also have nostrils surrounded by skin growths.**

Below: A bat emits 'squeaks' at frequencies of up to 100,000 Hz (the limit of human hearing is 20,000 Hz) and the character of the echoes reflected back provides information about what lies in its path— how far away it is, its size and so on.

A BAT'S 'SONAR SYSTEM'

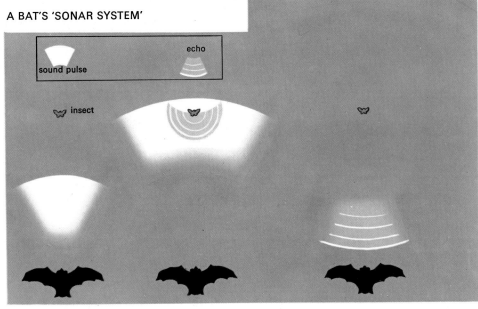

S. C. Bisserot

Left: A dog-faced fruit bat, *Cynopterus brachyotis*, roosting in a tree. As its name suggests, this bat's diet consists mainly of fruit: figs, bananas, guavos and mangos are popular food items. It inhabits the forests of India and South-East Asia. Very few predators feed on bats to any great extent; one that does is the bat hawk, *Machaeramphus alcinus*, from the tropics. Occasionally a bat will be taken by an owl, a mammal predator or a snake, but this is rare. Bats do, however, suffer from the attentions of parasites, particularly fleas, lice, ticks and mites. One family of wingless insects is found only on bats.

S. C. Bisserot

is the *Vespertilionidae* which is worldwide in its distribution.

Many insect-eating bats have adapted themselves to other food sources in order to supplement their diet. One of the most remarkable examples of this is the fishing bulldog bat, *Noctilio leporinus*, of Mexico and Central America. It uses its echo location system to detect fish under the water and then flies down to the surface and rakes the water with its long claws. In this way it usually succeeds in impaling a fish which it transfers to its mouth while in flight. If it is a long way from its roost the bat may chop up the fish with its teeth and store the pieces in its cheeks until it can eat them at leisure.

Another curious group of bats are the false vampires of the family *Megadermatidae*, which are strongly built animals with long, razor-sharp teeth. In addition to their normal diet of insects they prey on birds, smaller bats (though never their own species) and other small mammals. The African species *Lavia frons* is a dove-grey colour with pink wings and nose while the ghost bat of Australia, *Macroderma gigas*, has white wings, large white ears and a very pale body. These creatures are far removed from the popular conception of bats as dark, sinister animals.

Vampire bats

The notorious vampire bats belong to the family *Desmodontidae* and are related to the leaf-nosed bats. They are found only in the tropics and sub-tropics of the Americas and feed exclusively on the blood of vertebrate animals such as cattle, horses, dogs, poultry and even humans. Their prey is almost always warm-blooded. They are not particularly large bats, but have a broad skull and enormous incisor and canine teeth. The two upper incisors are curved and extremely sharp, the upper canines are large and pointed and the back molar and lower teeth are small.

The common vampire, *Desmodus rotundus*, lives in darkened caves which shelter many other kinds of bats. It feeds at night on the blood of cattle, landing very lightly on its victim. First of all it licks the spot it intends to bite, and this may serve as an anaesthetic since animals rarely stir when they are bitten. If the animal does wake the bat will immediately fly off. The wound is made by the front incisors and the tongue is extended and curled over at the edges. In conjunction with a deep groove in the lower lip, this forms a sort of 'straw' through which the blood is channelled. An anticoagulant in the bat's saliva prevents the blood from clotting while it is feeding.

The usual nightly consumption is about 30 g (1 oz). This may be taken from a single animal such as a cow, which may be bitten on the neck, ears or anal region, or from several smaller animals. Small birds are known to have been drained of blood by a vampire bat and so killed. Although the amount of blood taken by a single bat is relatively little, even quite a small colony may consume a considerable amount: 1,000 bats will need about 70 litres (15 gallons) of blood every night. Humans are attacked only rarely and when they are, the fingers, toes, ears, forehead or lips are usually the areas singled out. The loss of 30 g of blood is very unlikely to be serious, but vampire bats are carriers of the deadly disease of rabies and so a bite can be dangerous.

Elephants and Hyraxes

Man's association with the elephant dates from the earliest times. Many thousands of years ago the elephant and its relatives were a prized source of food: if a band of Paleolithic hunters could kill an elephant or a mammoth they would not need to hunt again for many days. More recently elephants have been hunted for their tusks, and countless animals were slaughtered in the 18th century and the first half of this century. Fortunately the ivory trade is now strictly controlled in most countries, so the pressure on the elephant population has been eased.

The Carthaginians were probably the first people to train elephants—they were used in the Punic Wars against the Romans. The Carthaginian general Hannibal took 38 elephants with him when he crossed the Alps with his army in 218 BC. Trained elephants are still used today in the forests of India and Burma for handling timber.

The elephant's closest living relatives are much less familiar creatures. They are the hyraxes, which belong to the order *Hyracoidea*, and the sea cows, which belong to the order *Sirenia*. The hyraxes are small furry animals looking rather like large guinea pigs, while the sea cows are aquatic mammals which resemble seals. From its outward appearance the hyrax would seem an unlikely relative of

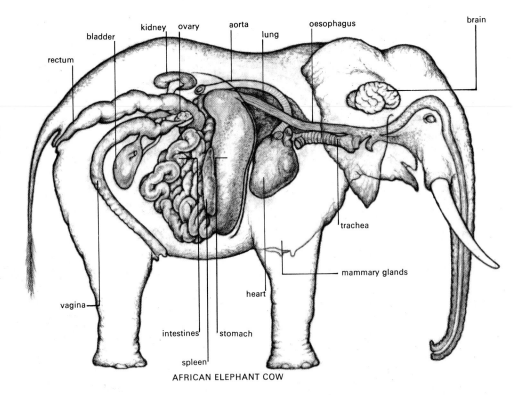

AFRICAN ELEPHANT COW

Above: A body plan of a female African elephant, *Loxodonta africana,* **showing most of the main body organs. The brain is larger than that of any other land mammal, and research has shown that elephants have a well developed learning ability. There may therefore be some truth in the saying 'elephants never forget'.**

Below: Only rarely will elephants charge in earnest; usually they halt or veer off before reaching their target, but wounded animals can be very dangerous. The African elephant was once found throughout Africa, but the ivory trade drastically reduced the population and now they are rarely found outside reserves.

Above: An Indian elephant feeding on bamboo in the Chitwan National Park of Nepal. An elephant's digestive system is inefficient; about half of what it eats is excreted undigested. To allow for this, elephants must eat even more food than the already enormous amount their bodies actually need.

Below: The great weight of an African elephant enables it to fell sizeable trees without much difficulty. It does this to get at the leaves near the top of the tree, which would otherwise be out of reach. A herd of elephants can quite quickly demolish whole stands of trees in this manner.

Left: An Indian elephant, *Elephas maximus*, at work lifting rocks. Although the species is in decline, wild Indian elephants are still hunted and put to work in such countries as Burma. The hunt, called a *khedda*, may involve as many as 2,000 drivers and 50 tame work elephants. A herd of wild elephants is slowly surrounded by this army of hunters and driven into a strong wooden enclosure. Once caught, the elephants are easily trained, and each animals will have just one keeper and driver, the *mahout*, throughout its working life.

Below: A herd of African elephants on the march. These animals can migrate hundreds of kilometres to escape from regions of drought, often negotiating formidable obstacles in their path. They have been known to swim across more than one kilometre of open ocean to get from one island to another—they swim with their trunks held above their heads like a snorkel. Steep slopes present few problems for elephants; even large bulls are surefooted.

Sylva/Tierbilder Okapia

Des Bartlett/Bruce Coleman

mature cow

immature cow

immature bull

young

mature bull

Left: A herd of elephants has a well defined structure. The main part of the herd is led by a large cow elephant and is composed only of females, immature animals and calves. Mature bulls live apart from the herd, and the oldest bulls, which are often very bad tempered, are completely solitary.

the elephant, but scientists have shown that the two animals must have had a common ancestor in comparatively recent times. Skeletal features such as the crossing of the bones of the forelimb and the flattening of the bones below the wrist are shared by animals in both groups.

Evolution

Elephants are descended from a small animal, *Moeritherium*, which lived in what is now Egypt about 45 million years ago. This creature was only about 60 cm (2 ft) high and had no trunk. In the course of time its descendants grew larger and developed long trunks and tusks. They colonised all the continents of the world except Australia, Antarctica and much of South America.

The closest and most recent of the elephant's ancestors were the mammoths, *Mammuthus*, and the mastodons, *Mammut*. Mammoths flourished only in cold climates: during periods of glaciation they inhabited central and southern Europe, but during interglacial periods they would retreat northwards with the ice. The largest of these creatures was the mammoth *Mammuthus imperator*, an enormous animal with a shoulder height of around 4.5 m (15 ft), which roamed the southern half of North America.

We know a considerable amount about the woolly mammoth, *Mammuthus primigenius*, which inhabited Europe and Asia and probably died out less than 10,000 years ago in Siberia. Paintings of the animal, made in French caves by its Paleolithic hunters, show a creature outwardly like an elephant but with very long hair, long curved tusks and a huge hump at the back of the neck. These drawings are now known to be remarkably accurate, for the remains of complete animals 'deep frozen' in the Siberian ice have the same features. The excellent state of preservation of many of these frozen mammoths has allowed a detailed study of them—even the contents of their stomachs have been found intact.

The evolution of the hyraxes has been much less varied than that of the elephants. The group probably branched from the same evolutionary line as the elephants in the late Paleocene epoch about 55 million years ago. Fossils found in Africa show that hyraxes have existed in more or less their modern form at least since the Oligocene epoch 35 million years ago.

Hyraxes

Hyraxes are alert, energetic animals, rather fat with pointed muzzles and small rounded ears. They are about the same size as a rabbit and have brown fur with a patch of yellow, white or black fur surrounding a scent gland in the middle of the back. Like elephants they are herbivores and feed on leaves, climbing trees to reach them, and grass. There are eleven species divided between three genera. The members of two genera (*Heterohyrax* and *Procavia*) are called rock hyraxes while the members of the third (*Dendrohyrax*) are known as tree hyraxes. Hyraxes are found only in Africa, Arabia and Syria.

Rock hyraxes live in colonies of from 30 to 60 individuals. They are found in the dry, semi-arid areas bordering deserts and also high up mountains, such as Mount Kenya, in the rain and mist. They are unable to burrow for themselves and make their homes in existing holes beneath the

ZEFA

Left: A group of African elephants (cows and young) leaving a water hole. A young elephant is protected not only by its own mother but also by other cows in the herd. Sometimes 'kindergarten' groups composed of several young animals and one or two adult cows will split off from the main body of the herd.

Right: An Indian elephant bathing in a river. Elephants usually bathe several times each day; it helps them to cool off as well as providing an opportunity to drink. They can drink about 50 litres on each occasion, sucking the water up into the trunk and then squirting it into the mouth.

Below: A newly born African elephant is helped to its feet for the first time by its mother. It weighs about 100 kg (220 lb) and is about 1 m (3 ft) tall.

Tierbilder Okapia

rocks. Normally they are careful to choose holes with small entrances so that they can escape from their chief predator, the leopard. As its name implies the tree hyrax is arboreal—it inhabits the great rain forests of West Africa. It is a solitary animal, an extremely agile climber and lives in hollow trees.

Elephants

Only two species of elephant (order *Proboscidea*) survive today: the Asiatic elephant, *Elephas maximus*, and the African elephant, *Loxodonta africana*. The African elephant is the larger of the two, a mature bull standing 3.4 m (11 ft) or more at the shoulder and carrying tusks between 1.8 and 2.4 m long (6-8 ft). The largest elephant ever recorded was shot in Angola in 1955: it measured 4 m (13 ft) at the shoulder and weighed nearly 11 tonnes.

The Asiatic elephant seldom stands more than three metres (10 ft) at the shoulder and its tusks are usually between 1.2 and 1.5 m long (4-5 ft). While female African elephants have long, if slender tusks, females of the Asiatic species are either tuskless or have very small tusks, known as 'tushes', which do not project beyond the jaw. The females of both species weigh between one and two tonnes less than the males.

In side view the two species look very different. The ears are the most obvious distinguishing feature, being so large in the African species that they cover the whole of the neck and shoulders and reach as low as the breast; the ears of the Asiatic species are relatively small. The back of the African elephant has a marked dip between the fore and hind quarters,

B. Leidmann/Bavaria

Left: The woolly mammoth, *Mammuthus primigenius*, was one of the more recent relatives of the modern elephant. It flourished in the late Ice Age and had a thick coat of long hair to resist the cold. It was hunted by prehistoric man for its flesh and hide, and died out less than 10,000 years ago.

Above: An African elephant dusting itself. This behaviour may help to keep down the number of insects, such as elephant lice, which live in the many folds of the animal's skin. An elephant's skin is quite sensitive and the animal quickly feels uncomfortable if it is carrying too many parasites.

whereas the back of the Asiatic elephant tends to be slightly humped. The trunks of the two species are also slightly different: in the African elephant it is marked by horizontal ridges and ends in two fleshy outgrowths or 'fingers', but in the Asiatic species it is relatively smooth and has only a single outgrowth.

Next to its size the elephant's most distinctive feature is its trunk. This is an extremely sensitive organ both of touch and smell, and is ideally suited to searching for food. It has evolved from the animal's upper lip rather than its nose, although it does enclose the nostrils which open at its tip. An elephant uses its trunk not only to search for food but also to transfer the food to its mouth. It grasps leaves and grass by coiling its trunk around them or by holding them between the fingerlike outgrowths at the tip of the trunk. When drinking, water is sucked into the trunk and then squirted into the mouth. The trunk also acts as an amplifier for a variety of different sounds expressing pleasure, dislike, apprehension and so on. Elephants produce a distinctive trumpeting sound when they are excited and this is actually created in the trunk itself rather than the larynx.

Elephants have to learn how to use their trunks; it is not an instinctive skill. Baby elephants evidently find their trunk a considerable inconvenience—not only do they have no use for it at first (they drink and feed with their mouths) but also it gets in their way and they tend to trip over it. They solve the problem by curling it up or holding it to one side.

Feeding

Elephants are herbivorous animals, feeding mainly on grass and leaves. As with other plant-eating mammals their molar teeth are particularly suited to grinding vegetable material. During its life an elephant develops 24 of these molars, although only one or two on each side of each jaw are ever in use at the same time. While the first group of four are being worn down, four new teeth are growing behind them; these gradually move forward to replace the old teeth, which are eventually shed. Each successive tooth is larger than the last, and when the sixth and largest tooth, which may be 30 cm (one foot) long and weigh 4 kg (9 lb), has passed through each half of each jaw no further teeth can be grown. It is the rate of deterioration of these final teeth that determines an elephant's maximum lifespan, for it cannot survive without them. Normally

they will be very worn by the time the animal is 60 and elephants rarely live beyond this age.

Not surprisingly, elephants eat an enormous quantity of food. A fully grown elephant in a zoo will eat about 45 kg (100 lb) of hay every day. Zoo animals are usually females, however, and a large bull might be expected to eat twice as much. An elephant's thirst matches its appetite; the daily water intake for an adult animal is between 130 and 230 litres (30 to 50 gallons).

Social behaviour

Elephants are gregarious animals and live in herds. The herd is composed of a number of distinct family groups, each consisting of a matriarch, her daughters and her grandchildren. Males, except for the younger ones, are not normally tolerated within these groups and they spend much of their time alone or in small groups some way off from the rest of the herd. For communal activities such as bathing or drinking, however, the herd becomes more integrated, while females will temporarily leave the family group for mating. Bull elephants become bad tempered and unpredictable in their old age and they then live entirely alone.

Pregnancy in elephants lasts for between 19 and 22 months, and at birth the calf weighs about 100 kg (220 lb) and is about 85cm (34 in) high. Sometimes other females in the family group assist the birth by removing the foetal membrane and then helping the calf to its feet. After about 20 minutes the baby elephant can stand on its own. The mother will help her clumsy offspring while it is very young by moving obstacles such as fallen trees out of its way or even lifting it over them. All the cows in the family group are attentive to the young; they fondle them, wash them and protect them from danger. The bulls rarely come into contact with the calves and have nothing to do with their upbringing.

When the herd is on the move the elephants travel in single file. The cows usually go first, their calves trotting behind, while the young males form separate contingents. Normal marching speed is about 10 kph (6 mph) but this can be raised in an emergency to a fast shuffle of 25 kph (15 mph) or more. An elephant walks on its toes—its 'knee' joint is really the equivalent of our wrist—and its legs are ideally adapted to support its vast bulk. Elephants can neither trot nor gallop, but they can move through the jungle very quietly.

Left: A group of Cape hyraxes, *Procavia capensis*, resting on a rock. They live in small colonies and one or two animals act as guards while the remainder of the group feed or rest. The main predators are eagles and leopards. Cape hyraxes feed on grass and shrubs during the day, spending the night in holes and crevices among the rocks.

Right: A common tree hyrax, *Dendrohyrax arboreus*, from East Africa. Unlike rock hyraxes, tree hyraxes are nocturnal and solitary animals. They proclaim their territory at night by loud and penetrating calls each consisting of a succession of screams.

Tierbilder Okapia

Jane Burton/Bruce Coleman

Rhinos and Tapirs

The largest living land mammal after the elephant is the rare square-lipped rhinoceros of Africa: adult males may stand over 1.8 m (6 ft) at the shoulders and weigh more than three tonnes. Their huge size and strange 'armoured' appearance have long fascinated Europeans: Dürer's well known woodcut of an Indian rhino, executed in 1515, aroused a great deal of interest. The large pointed horn on the rhino's snout has earned the animal an undeserved reputation for fierceness—in fact this timid creature will charge an intruder only if suddenly alarmed.

The rhino's nearest relatives are the tapirs. They have much the same body shape as rhinos, but are considerably smaller, lack the rhino's horn and have a generous coat of hair. Rhinos and tapirs, together with their more fleet-footed cousins the horses and zebras, belong to the order *Perissodactyla*. Members of this group have a number of important features in common: they are all plant-eaters and have noticeably elongated skulls to accommodate the continuous row of broad cheek teeth needed to cope with their diet of grass and leaves. Their feet have an odd number of toes, the weight of the body being carried mainly or entirely by the third toe of each limb, which terminates in a hoof.

Tapirs

The tapirs living today are the survivors of a much larger group, which in its heyday populated much of the globe. Fossil remains from that time (the Miocene epoch, which began about 26 million years ago) show that tapirs have remained almost unchanged for many millions of years: the modern species look very much the same as their ancestors must have done. But they are now found only in Central and South America and Malaya.

Tapirs are solitary jungle animals with short legs, rounded ears, small eyes and a short proboscis or trunk formed by an extension of the upper lip and the nose. They are animals of habit, keeping to well-used paths through the thick undergrowth where they browse on leaves and shoots. Like many forest dwellers they have poor eyesight, but make up for this by good hearing and an acute sense of smell.

Tapirs are particularly fond of water and frequently wallow in river shallows. Bathing probably helps them to get rid of irritating parasites such as ticks and other biting insects. In the wild tapirs often defecate in or near their favourite water hole; possibly this serves as a recognition signal to others of the species. Rhinos behave in the same way. There is only one genus of tapirs, *Tapirus*, with four species of which one is Asiatic and three South American.

The Malayan tapir inhabits the Malay peninsula and the island of Sumatra and is the largest of the four species, having a nose to tail length of around 2.5 m (8 ft). The body markings of the adult animal are unusual: the head, shoulders, limbs

Left: Albrecht Dürer's famous woodcut of an Indian rhinoceros, executed in 1515. Dürer clearly shows the heavy 'armour' of this huge beast which, unlike the African rhinos, normally has one horn only. Dürer cannot have drawn from life, for he also shows a small extra horn on this rhino's back.

Right: A young black rhino, *Diceros bicornis*. The two large horns characteristic of this species are only partly formed. Black rhinos are found only in Africa, where they were once widely distributed. Today their numbers are seriously depleted—a 1967 estimate gave a total of about 12,000, of which almost one-third were in Tanzania.

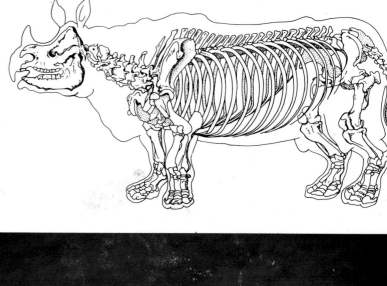

Right: The skeleton of an Indian rhinoceros. The anatomical structure has changed very little in the last million years. The vertebral column acts like a girder balanced on the front legs, and the weight of the body is carried almost entirely by the third toe of each foot, which ends in a kind of hoof.

Below: Black rhinos rarely travel in groups of more than five; when two are found together they will usually be a bull and a female, or a mother and her young. It was once thought that the birds which follow rhinos picked the ticks from their skin, but it now appears they are interested only in the insects stirred up by the animals walking.

Mansell

Giuseppe Mazza

Tierbilder Okapia

and belly are black, while the back and flanks are white. The young, like those of all tapirs, are strikingly marked with a series of horizontal stripes and dots. Both the adult's body pattern and that of the young has a camouflaging effect, breaking up the animal's outline and making it difficult to detect in the changing light and shade of the jungle.

The three South American tapirs all have a uniform brownish coat with slight differences in shade, thickness and texture between the species. The Central American tapir is the largest mammal of the American tropics and also has the distinction of being one of the rarest. The second species, the lowland tapir, is the most common, and inhabits the forests of the northern part of South America. The mountain tapir is the rarest of all and lives in the northern Andes at altitudes between 1,800 and 3,600 m (6,000 to 12,000 ft). It has a thicker coat than its lowland relatives to protect it from exposure and extremes of temperature.

Being solitary and rather shy animals, tapirs avoid areas which are inhabited by man, retreating further into the forest whenever a part of their territory is cleared for cultivation. Consequently, the populations of all tapir species are declining as their jungle habits are eroded, and this trend will only be halted if areas of tropical forest are set aside as sanctuaries, free from development by man.

Left: Black rhinos mating. During their courtship, the animals sniff at each others' mouths, frequently uttering gurgling noises. The female will often charge the male, butting hard into his flanks. Black rhinos can conceive at any time of year; the gestation period is about 15 months.

Below: Black rhinos are mainly nocturnal, and spend most of the day sleeping in sand or dust-filled hollows. Sometimes seen in mountain forests as high up as 2,100 m (7,000 ft), their normal habitat is the open plain, with mixed vegetation. Their pointed upper lip is used for stripping foliage from shrubs and bushes. They have no incisors or canine teeth.

Jacana

Rhinos

The rhinos are the only surviving large perissodactyls. Like tapirs they are mainly nocturnal and timid creatures, though they will charge when threatened, especially when protecting their young. The skin is characteristically thick and has little hair. The horns are composed entirely of hair-like growths set above thickenings of the nasal bone and (in two-horned species) the frontal bones. They are not attached to the skull, and may even be torn off in fighting; when this happens they quickly grow again.

The largest rhinoceros is the square-lipped rhino, *Ceratotherium simum*, from Africa. The upper lip is very broad, having evolved to equip the animal for grazing. This rhino is a gregarious creature, living in small herds on the open savannah, and at one time it occupied most of the open grassland south of the Sahara. In the Pleistocene epoch, about one million years ago, it could be found as far north as Algeria and Morocco.

There are two surviving races of square-lipped rhino, separated by more than 1,200 miles (2,000 km). The northern race lives in southwest Sudan, Uganda and Zaire, and it is seriously threatened with extinction—only about 300 individuals still survive in the wild. Early white settlers pursued the animal for its tasty flesh and for its hide, and nowadays it is poached for its horn, which the Chinese value for its undeserved reputation as a powerful aphrodisiac. The southern race, which lives in Natal, South Africa, is more fortunate. Although it is found only in a relatively small region, it has been protected there since 1897 and its future seems assured.

The black rhino, *Diceros bicornis*, is smaller than the 'square lip', standing less than 1.5 m (5 ft) at the shoulder. It is a browser rather than a grazer and has a prehensile upper lip which it uses for reaching and stripping off foliage from

Frank Lake

Above: *Dicerorhinus sumatrensis*, the Sumatran rhino, is the smallest and hairiest species. It is now extremely rare and expected to become extinct, for its natural habitat is being destroyed by the timber and rubber industries. Moreover, the Chinese believe powdered rhino horn to be aphrodisiac, and poaching has proved impossible to reduce significantly.

Left: The great Indian rhino, *Rhinoceros unicornis*, is found today only in protected areas. Large folds divide the skin into sections marked by flat bumps which look like rivets. Despite its appearance, the skin is not very thick, and many bulls carry large scars caused by fighting.

Above: Four related species of perissodactyls. Remains of the wholly rhino (1), now extinct, have been found as far apart as China, Russia and Spain. The Javan rhino, (2) *Rhinocerus sondaicus*, is practically extinct. (3) *Tapirus bairdi*, the Central American tapir. (4) The mountain tapir, *Tapirus pinchaque*.

Left: *Ceratotherium simum*, the square-lipped rhinoceros, is better known as the 'white' rhino—a mistranslation of the Afrikaans work *wijde*, meaning 'wide'. The largest of all rhinos, they reach a height of some 2 m, and weigh up to 3 tonnes. Their horns are attached rather loosely to the skin and are easily torn off, but quickly grow again.

Right: *Tapirus terrestris*, the most common of the tapir species. All young tapirs have horizontal stripes and dots on their coats; these usually take about a year to disappear. The projecting upper lip is adapted for tearing off leaves and shoots from trees and bushes.

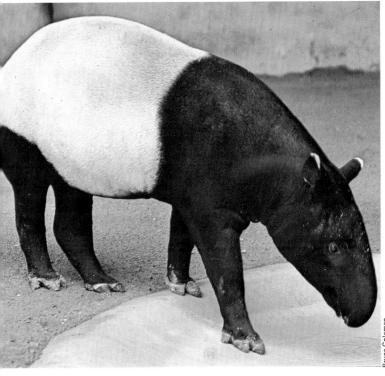

Left: The Malayan tapir, *tapirus indicus*, is easily identified by its distinctive markings. These are ideal for camouflage in the changing patterns of light and shade of its natural forest habitat. They break up the outlines of the body so that, lying down in the daytime, the tapir looks just like a pile of stones.

Below: Past and present distribution of tapirs and rhinos. The South American lowland tapir and the African black rhino are the only species with a good chance of survival, although both their populations have been seriously reduced in recent years. Rhinos are hunted for their meat and their horns, which are prized for their supposed medicinal properties. The animal is rarely found today outside protected areas. Tapirs live mainly in forested regions and their habitats are being progressively destroyed by timber companies and rubber plantations. They are hunted for meat and for their skins, which can be tanned and cut into long straps for reins and whips. They are often killed as pests.

Bruce Coleman

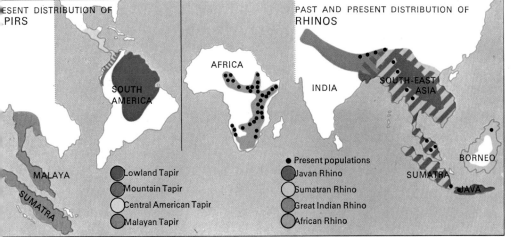

ESENT DISTRIBUTION OF PIRS

PAST AND PRESENT DISTRIBUTION OF RHINOS

SOUTH AMERICA

AFRICA

INDIA

SOUTH-EAST ASIA

BORNEO

SUMATRA

JAVA

MALAYA

SUMATRA

- Lowland Tapir
- Mountain Tapir
- Central American Tapir
- Malayan Tapir

● Present populations
- Javan Rhino
- Sumatran Rhino
- Great Indian Rhino
- African Rhino

Bruce Coleman

shrubs and bushes. It was once widely distributed in Africa, from Cape Province to eastern Africa and as far north as the Sudan, but only scattered populations remain today. Although not classed as endangered its status is vulnerable.

The black rhino spends much of its life within a well defined home range which may vary from 8 to 50 sq km (3 to 20 sq miles) in area and changes according to the seasons and consequent food supply. When they meet their neighbours in overlapping parts of their ranges black rhinos are not usually aggressive, but determined trespassing is not tolerated and a large intruder may be suddenly charged.

The largest of the Asiatic rhinos is the great Indian rhino, *Rhinoceros unicornis*, which can approach the size of a square-lipped rhino. Unlike its African relatives it has only a single horn. The upper lip is prehensile and the lower jaw contains a large pair of incisor teeth which have developed into tusks and are used with great effect for self-defence.

The Indian rhino once inhabited a wide tract of country in northern India and Nepal, from the foothills of the Hindu Kush to the Burmese border, but today less than 1,000 individuals remain in eight reserves in India and Nepal. This impressive animal lives a slow and quiet existence in secluded swampy areas where there is an abundance of tall grass and reeds. Its diet includes a large number of food plants, including many agricultural crops.

The Javan rhinoceros, *Rhinoceros sondaicus*, is the rarest of all rhinos. It looks like a smaller version of the Indian rhino, but the skin folds are slightly different and the male's horn is shorter—it is absent altogether in females. The Javan rhino's favourite food has been reported to be the peculiar 'tepus' plant, one of the ginger family which throws up 5.5 m (18 ft) broad-leaved spikes but carries its red flowers at or below ground level. The horn trade has wiped out all but a few of these creatures and it seems likely that the population of Javan rhinos is now too small for the species to survive, and it will probably soon be extinct.

The smallest and hairiest rhino is the Sumatran rhino, *Dicerorhinus sumatrensis*. Small isolated populations occur in widely separated areas of Asia from Burma southeast through Thailand to Sumatra and Borneo. It has two horns—the front one reaches a length of up to a foot (30 cm) while the back one is usually no more than a slight hump.

Sumatran rhinos favour forested hill country and are extremely agile: they can climb up steep mountain slopes with no apparent difficulty. They browse on twigs and leaves, invariably feeding in virgin forest or very old regenerated jungle. Like the Javan rhino they are very rare and the principal cause of their decline has been over-hunting. In 1972 a single rhino carcass was worth more than 2,000 US dollars, many times the annual earnings of most local farmers, so it is hardly surprising that the animals are so ruthlessly hunted.

Responsibility for the survival of both rhinos and tapirs rests with man. Conservation areas, such as the famous Chitwan National Park in Nepal (where there is now a good stable population of Indian rhinos), are likely to play an increasingly important role as the animals' natural habitats are destroyed.

Hippos, Pigs and Peccaries

The most prolific large mammals living today are the members of the order *Artiodactyla*. These are hoofed animals with an even number of toes on each foot and they rely on speedy running or sheer bulk as a defence against predators. The group includes the camels, deer, antelopes, cattle, goats and sheep, as well as pigs, peccaries and hippopotamuses. One of the key factors in their success is the ability to make efficient use of the most readily available of all food sources—plants.

All artiodactyls have highly developed digestive systems which can break down cellulose, the main structural material of plants, and most have evolved the habit of ruminating, or chewing the cud, which further improves the digestion process. Pigs, peccaries and hippopotamuses, however, are non-ruminants and they have changed relatively little since the first artiodactyls appeared about 45 million years ago.

Pigs

The artiodactyls' remote ancestors were not plant-eaters, but were related to the ancestors of the modern carnivorous mammals. With this ancestry it is not surprising that the surviving members of the pig family are by no means purely herbivorous. Their molar and premolar teeth have low, rounded cusps not unlike those of other omnivorous mammals, such as man, and certainly pigs have omnivorous tendencies, feeding on such things as small animals, roots and fruit. Most omnivorous mammals, such as brown rats or bears, are basically either herbivores or carnivores but are simply not very fussy about what they eat. Pigs, however, like our own order, the primates, seem to have been omnivorous throughout their history.

For hoofed animals, pigs have relatively short legs. They have four toes on each foot, the thumb and big toe being absent as is always the case in artiodactyls. The two middle toes are the largest and usually carry all the weight, the hoofs on the outside toes coming into use only on marshy ground or very uneven surfaces. Pigs are not very fleet-footed: the wart hog, for example, has a maximum speed of about 18 kph (11 mph). Because they are not very tall, however, pigs are able to run beneath branches, and their heavy bodies are ideal for crashing through thick undergrowth. This is more important to them than sheer speed, for pigs are typically inhabitants of forests and bush. They are also good swimmers.

One rather unusual feature of the pig family is the way in which they keep their bodies warm. Almost all land mammals are kept warm by their hair, the skin being only loosely joined to the body, rather than bound to it by layers of fatty tissue. But examination of a rasher of bacon reveals that immediately beneath a pig's skin there is a great deal of fat, an excellent insulator but more commonly found in aquatic mammals such as seals and whales. Apart from pigs the only other land mammals primarily insulated

Bruce Coleman

Above: A female wart hog, *Phacochoerus aethiopicus*, with her young. The wart hog inhabits the savannahs and bush country of Africa south of the Sahara. Unlike most members of the pig family, wart hogs are only active during the day; at night they sleep in dens which are usually the abandoned homes of other animals such as aardvarks. The long curved canine teeth are formidable weapons and can inflict very severe injuries on predators such as lions and leopards.

ZEFA

Right: A wild boar, *Sus scrofa*, in a West German forest. In cultivated areas the wild boar can cause considerable damage to crops by its continual rooting in the ground, but in forests it assists growth by feeding on tree parasites such as sawfly larvae and by loosening the soil.

Below: Two African bush pigs, *Potamochoerus porcus*. Like most pigs, these creatures eat a wide variety of both animal and plant food. In South Africa they sometimes damage peanut and fruit crops.

Keith Dowson/Natural Science Photos

by subcutaneous fat are human beings. In each case the reason is obscure.

Wild pigs usually feed by rooting in the ground and they have a keen sense of smell. The domestic pigs in France which are trained to smell out truffles (rare fungi considered a delicacy since classical times), which grow beneath the ground, behave in a very natural way for members of the pig family. The only thing that they have to be taught to do is to indicate the presence of truffles to their human trainers, rather than digging them up and eating them on their own account.

Wild pigs root in the ground for fungi, roots, bulbs, tubers and earthworms, and also eat leaves, fruits and nuts, and sometimes small vertebrates and carrion. They are gregarious animals, living in herds of up to 50, although male wart hogs are often observed on their own. When not feeding or resting, they often wallow in mud to keep their skins in good condition. Contrary to popular belief, wild pigs (and properly kept domestic ones) are clean in their habits, and not notably greedy.

Wild boars

There are eight living species in the pig family, and by far the most widely distributed of these is the wild boar, *Sus*

Above: The breeding capacity of the pig was undoubtedly one of the factors which led to its domestication. A Danish sow is on record as having given birth to as many as 34 young in a single litter, the largest number for any mammal. In the wild, where infant mortality is high, large litters are a great advantage.

Above: In France the keen sense of smell of a trained domestic pig enables it to sniff out truffles. All domestic pigs are descended from wild boars.

Below: The babirusa, *Babyrousa babyrussa*, is a strange-looking pig from the Celebes Islands of South-East Asia. In males the canine teeth of both the upper

and lower jaws are particularly long and curved. The survival of the species is threatened by the clearing of forested areas for cultivation.

Above: Although these collared peccaries, *Tayassu tajacu*, from Texas look like the wild pigs of Europe, Asia and Africa, they are only distant relations.

scrofa. Before man reduced its range the wild boar was found in most parts of Europe; it only became extinct in Britain in the early 17th century. It still inhabits parts of central Europe as well as North Africa and Asia, from its western border to Java, Sumatra, Formosa and Japan. A male wild boar may weigh as much as 200 kg (440 lb) and, although flight is its normal defence, it can be a fierce adversary. Hunting wild boar with lances, as was once the custom in India, was by no means a one-sided sport. A wounded or cornered wild boar uses its teeth in self-defence, and they are formidable weapons. The constantly growing tusks, which are canine teeth, are razor sharp, and the molar and premolar teeth have great biting power. A bite from a wild boar is said to be worse than a bite from a lion.

Wild boars are prolific breeders, and the female may have up to 12 young in a litter. They are born after a pregnancy of about 115 days and, in contrast to the brindled brown appearance of the adults, have boldly striped markings which provide good camouflage in dappled shade. No doubt it was the wild boar's breeding capacity combined with its ability to thrive on almost anything edible that caused man to domesticate it.

The domestic pig is so similar to the wild boar from which it was derived that it is regarded as belonging to the same

Heather Angel

hippopotamus

Left: A hippopotamus, *Hippopotamus amphibius*, wallowing in mud. These creatures spend much of their time lying on the muddy shores of lakes and rivers or standing almost entirely submerged in the water. In this way the animal's legs are spared the effort of supporting the enormous body weight (it is not uncommon for a hippo to weigh as much as three tonnes).

Right: A pygmy hippopotamus, *Choeropsis liberiensis*. As its name suggests, it is a much smaller animal than its more abundant relative. Being very shy, the pygmy hippo is difficult to study in its swampy forest homeland and little is known about its way of life in the wild.

Below: A herd of hippos in the Virunga National Park, Zaire. Within the herd mother and child groups live slightly apart from the other animals, and young hippos usually stick very close to their mothers. Old aggressive males live very much on their own.

Bruce Coleman

Bruce Coleman

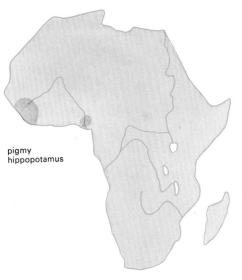

pigmy
hippopotamus

Geoffrey Kinnis/Natural Science Photos

species, *Sus scrofa*. However, selective breeding by man has resulted in greater efficiency in producing meat. The heaviest domestic pig can weigh twice as much as a wild boar, a large part of this increase being in the form of fat, and domestic sows have even larger litters than their wild cousins.

Closely related to the wild boar and very similar in appearance, are three Asian species which are much less widely distributed. These are the rare pygmy hog, *Sus salvanius*, of southern Asia, the Javan pig, *Sus verrucosus*, of Java, Celebes, and the Philippines, and the Bornean pig, *Sus barbatus*, of Borneo and the Philippines.

Another species from the same part of the world, the babirusa, *Babyrousa babyrussa*, of Celebes and neighbouring small islands is remarkable for the development of the canine tusks of the males. In addition to the lower tusks which emerge from the side of the mouth and curve upwards, the upper tusks protrude from the top of the snout and curve upwards and backwards. These tusks are too long to be kept sharp by wear and have no apparent function except as distinguishing characteristics of males. The native legend that babirusas sleep hanging from branches hooked on by means of their tusks is certainly untrue.

The remaining species of wild pigs live in Africa. The most common is the wart hog, *Phacochoerus aethiopicus*, which owes its popular name to thickenings of the skin in front of the eyes of males. Unlike most other pigs, wart hogs are mainly active by day, and they live in grasslands as well as the open forests of Africa south of the Sahara. The giant forest hog, *Hylochoerus meinertzhageni*, inhabits only thick equatorial forests. This is the only kind of pig with glands on the face, immediately in front of the eye. These glands are probably scent glands, used in signalling. The bush pig, or water hog, *Potamochoerus porcus*, usually lives in long grass of southern Africa and Madagascar. It is the hairiest of the pigs, has extremely sharp canine teeth and long ear tufts.

Peccaries

Wild pigs have never existed in America. Here their place is taken by the peccaries, which have evolved from the same ancestors as the pigs but have a long history of their own; they have evolved their pig-like characteristics quite separately as an adaptation to much the same way of life. They are therefore placed in a different family. They look very much like small, rather densely-haired pigs but have shorter tusks, those of the upper jaw growing downwards rather than upwards or outwards.

There are two species. The collared peccary, *Tayassu tajacu*, is distinguished by a band of lighter hair round the neck, and inhabits semi-deserts and dry woodlands from Texas to Patagonia, while the white-lipped peccary, *Tayassu pecari*, lives in rain forests from southern Mexico to Paraguay. Peccaries have scent-glands producing a strong musky odour on their backs. They breed less prolifically than pigs, usually only having two young at a time, and rarely more than four.

Hippopotamuses

Although fossil hippopotamuses occur in Europe, parts of Asia including Sri Lanka (Ceylon) and Madagascar, the surviving members of the family are found only in Africa. In many ways they are like large pigs, but in order to support their weight on soft ground they have four large toes on each foot and, because of the difference in their feeding habits their muzzles are not at all like pigs' snouts. Both their incisor and canine teeth grow continuously throughout life, the incisors pointing forwards and being rounded in section, while the canines, especially the lower canines, form formidable, sharp tusks. They have three-chambered stomachs, but do not chew the cud.

The common hippopotamus, *Hippopotamus amphibius*, can weigh over four tonnes, and is therefore one of the heaviest of all land animals. However, common hippos are amphibious, spending much of their time in the water where they are almost weightless, and perhaps should be judged among such aquatic mammals as the whales: in this company they are but small fry.

The position of the eyes, ears and slit-like, closeable nostrils on the upper surface of a hippo's head is typical of the way these organs are placed in amphibious animals, permitting breathing, seeing and hearing when the animal is almost completely submerged. Hippos spend much of the day in rivers and lakes, diving for as long as ten minutes at a time in search of the water plants on which they feed. When they surface they expel the air from their lungs with a snort that can be heard many hundreds of metres away. They have huge appetites and in order to satisfy them they also feed for part of the night, coming ashore to graze. Although hippos are normally placid animals, they will sometimes attack humans; old hippos are notoriously bad tempered and aggressive. Attacks usually occur when the animals are grazing on land and suddenly find their retreat to the water cut off.

Hippos live in herds of up to 40 animals. Large male hippos defend territories, scent-marking by means of their faeces, which are scattered by vigorous wagging of the short brush-like tail, in order to warn rivals to keep clear. When necessary they fight, using their bulk and their tusks. Females have only one young at a time, giving birth in the water after a pregnancy of up to 240 days. Young hippos weigh about 40 kg (90 lb) at birth, and can swim before they can walk. They are mature at about 3 years, and may live to be 40 or 50.

The pygmy hippopotamus, *Choeropsis liberiensis*, is less aquatic in its habits, and is found only in the dense forests and swamps of Ivory Coast, Liberia and Sierra Leone in West Africa. Apart from having a rounder head and circular nostrils, it looks very much like a smaller version of the common hippo, but is no bigger than a large pig, weighing up to 240 kg (540 lb). Pygmy hippos seem to live singly or in pairs, but they are shy and partly nocturnal in their habits and difficult to study in the wild.

Giraffe
and Okapi

Gawky and ungainly though it may appear, the giraffe has survived where many members of its family have not. It has only a single living relation, the okapi, an inhabitant of the impenetrable equatorial forests of Africa so secretive that it was unknown until early this century. Both animals belong to the family *Giraffidae*, which is part of the great mammalian order *Artiodactyla*. They are cud-chewing, hoofed animals found only in the continent of Africa, although they once lived in eastern Europe and many parts of Asia.

Fossil remains of the giraffe have been found in Greece, southern Russia, Asia Minor, India and China, and it is thought that the ancestors of the modern species entered Africa about one million years ago. In more recent times giraffes were brought to Europe in about 46 BC by Julius Caesar to feature as an attraction in the Roman arenas. The giraffe is by far the tallest mammal, reaching a height of almost six metres (20 ft).

Like other ruminants (animals that chew the cud), giraffes and okapis feed exclusively on plants, which they are able to digest very efficiently. They have large back teeth for grinding up their plant diet, but no teeth in the front of the upper jaw. A giraffe's tongue is prehensile and very long (often 45 cm, 18 in); it is used to draw leaves and twigs into the mouth where they are cut off by sharply twisting them over the lower front teeth (incisors).

Giraffes

The most obvious distinguishing feature of the giraffe is its enormously long neck and limbs, clearly an advantage to an animal which browses on the foliage of trees. This arrangement does, however, present some physiological problems. In particular, a high blood pressure is needed to maintain the flow of blood to the head, and the creature has to have a special system of blood channels to prevent a brain haemorrhage when it lowers its head the six metres (20 ft) or so down to the ground to graze or drink. These channels are controlled by reflex muscles and they automatically 'short circuit' the blood flow to stop any rush of blood to the head.

Surprisingly, the neck contains no more bones than that of most other mammals: the same seven cervical vertebrae (bones of the spine) are present in both man and the giraffe, but in the latter they are enormously long. Similarly, the leg bones are basically the same as in man but again they are very long. The forelegs are longer than the hind legs and the shoulder is deep, so accounting for the downward slope of the giraffe's back. All four limbs end in two hoofed toes, each forefoot being about 30cm (one foot) across.

The giraffe's back legs are its chief defence against predators. Few carnivores will take on anything so large as a giraffe, but lions do occasionally attack them if other game is scarce. A single blow from the hind leg of a giraffe is powerful enough to kill a lion and encounters between the

ZEFA

Left: This short-necked giraffe, *Sivatherium*, became extinct in the Pleistocene epoch. It was a large, sturdy animal and its flattened horns were much larger than those of its modern relatives. Although they now live only in Africa, giraffes originated in Asia and Europe. This creature inhabited southern Asia.

Above: Giraffes feed on the leaves and twigs of trees such as acacia and mimosa. They have long, prehensile tongues to tear the foliage from the branches.

Jacana

Left and above: The giraffe's enormous height is a distinct disadvantage when it comes to drinking. It must either splay its front legs wide apart (left) or bend them in a rather ungainly way (above) to reach the water. Giraffes are very vulnerable to attacks from predators when drinking.

Frank Lane

Frank Lane

Above: A giraffe gallops away from danger in the Kenyan bush. Because it is such a large animal it cannot keep up this pace for long, but its chief predators, lions, usually give up the chase early if they do not succeed right away. Giraffes pursued for long distances have been known to collapse and die of heart failure.

Above and above right: Male giraffes, using their heads and necks as clubs, fight for the possession of females. Each animal tries to swing its head against the opponent's neck or shoulders. Although these contests are normally fairly harmless, they sometimes result in serious injuries and even death.

Giraffes may have anything between two and five 'horns'. The main horns are situated above the eyes and are crowned with tufts of hair. Any additional horns are simply bony protruberances. The animals shown here have three (above) and five (below) horns.

Hans Reinhard/Bruce Coleman

Left: The giraffe, *Giraffa camelopardalis*, has keen eyesight, unlike its relation the okapi. Also, because it is so tall it has an excellent field of view and these two factors make it a difficult animal for a lion to stalk successfully. Even by night giraffes are watchful, rarely lying down or sleeping.

two animals quite often end in the death of the hunter rather than the hunted. Although adult giraffes do not normally attack lions, they will do so if young animals in the herd are threatened.

Giraffes have at least two short 'horns' located above the eyes. These are bony protuberances covered with hairy skin and structurally they resemble deer's antlers more than the horns of antelopes or cattle. Unlike a deer's antlers, however, which are shed and replaced each year, a giraffe's horn is permanent. Moreover the bony part of the horn develops separately from the skull at first but becomes joined to it as the animal grows older. Some giraffes possess four horns and occasionally, in certain northern races, there is a central swelling between the eyes which is almost as long as the horns. In southern races this swelling is so small as to be hardly noticeable.

The giraffe's pale, buff coloured coat is covered to a greater or lesser extent with reddish brown spots that range from regular geometric designs to irregular, blotchy shapes. Various methods of classifying giraffes into species, subspecies and even sub-subspecies have been devised but none is very satisfactory because the animals vary so much; giraffes with different colours and patterns can sometimes be observed even within a single herd. Nowadays a single species is normally recognized, *Giraffa camelopardalis*, with many different forms. Broadly these fall into two types—the reticulated giraffes with clear geometric markings, and the blotched giraffes with irregular or leaf-shaped markings—but there are many intermediate forms.

In the equatorial regions of Africa, where most reticulated giraffes live, there are sharp contrasts between the bright sunlight and deep shadows, so the distinct light and dark markings of the animals' coat blend in well with its natural background. Blotched giraffes are normally larger than the reticulated variety and they have a wider range extending over most of Africa south of

91

the Sahara. Their markings are more suited to the softer light and less well defined shadows of non-equatorial regions.

The giraffe lives in open country; dry bush regions with scattered acacia and mimosa trees are favourite haunts. It never moves to the forest since its long legs and neck would make movement through the dense trees and creepers difficult, and wet forest swamps would be deadly traps for its long legs.

Because trees for forage are often scattered over a wide area, giraffes are nomadic. They travel in herds of 20 to 30 animals, the herds usually being composed of an old bull, females and calves. Younger bulls usually keep a small distance apart from the rest of the herd, but when sufficiently mature they may challenge for the leadership of the herd. Giraffes can trot, run or gallop and when in full flight the legs on each side of the body move together though not quite simultaneously. When galloping they can reach a speed of about 50 kph (30 mph).

Mating occurs at any time of the year, and there is considerable competition between the bulls for the females. The bulls fight each other by swinging their heads against the neck and shoulders of their opponent. Since a giraffe's head weighs something like 45 kg (100 lb) and the neck is about two metres (6 ft 6 in) long the blows are severe and can quite easily cause a broken or dislocated neck. Usually, however, these fights do not end in death, merely the exhaustion of one or both animals.

The young are born about 14 months after mating and they are on their feet within 20 minutes of birth. Normally only a single young is produced at one time but occasionally twins are born. The lifespan of the giraffe may be as much as 30 years in captivity, but is probably considerably less than this in the wild.

As with many other animal species, man is the most dangerous enemy of the giraffe. The natives of Africa and the early European settlers prized the giraffe for its palatable flesh and also for its hide which is as much as 2.5 cm (one inch) thick and was used to make the long reins needed for teams of six or eight horses. As a result of indiscriminate killing the numbers were severely reduced and the giraffe has disappeared from large areas of northern, western and southern Africa. It is still fairly numerous in East Africa where it is a protected species, but populations elsewhere are small.

Okapis

The only living relative of the giraffe is the okapi, *Okapia johnstoni*. It is a rare mammal, native to the dense tropical forests of central equatorial Africa, and it has changed little since, like the giraffe, it migrated to Africa from Europe and Asia in prehistoric times. The okapi rarely emerges from its forest home and has hardly ever been seen in the wild.

When European explorers like Henry Stanley penetrated central Africa at the end of the nineteenth century they found that the pygmies of the region were not surprised at the sight of their horses and claimed that similar animals were to be found in the local forests. At first little attention was paid to these reports but when Sir Harry Johnston, governor of Uganda, obtained a skin and several skulls in 1901 the existence of a new species was confirmed. Zoologists were

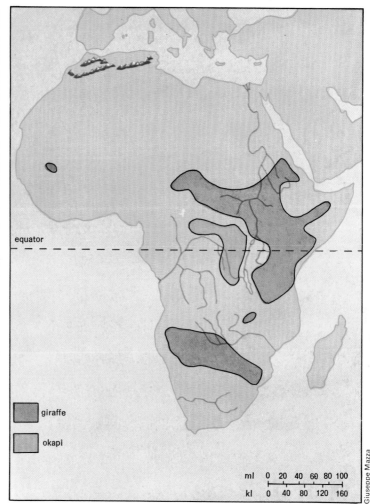

equator

giraffe

okapi

| ml | 0 | 20 | 40 | 60 | 80 | 100 |
| kl | 0 | 40 | 80 | 120 | 160 |

Giuseppe Mazza

Above: A map showing the distribution of giraffes and okapis in the wild. Giraffes were once much more wide-ranging than they are today, particularly in western Africa. Even within their present ranges there are large areas where the animals have disappeared. Little is known of the former range of the okapi.

Below: The Masai giraffe with its leaf-shaped body markings is a typical blotched giraffe. Young giraffes are about 2 m (7 ft) tall at birth and they are on their feet within 20 minutes. The young animal suckles for about six months and during this time it never strays far from its mother.

Right: A water hole in Africa attracts all sorts of animals from the surrounding area, both predators and their prey. Because giraffes are so vulnerable when drinking, one of the older members of the herd keeps watch while the remaining animals quench their thirst and feed on leaves.

Giuseppe Mazza

Left: A reticulated giraffe has sharply outlined geometrical markings so that it blends in with its background when seen from a distance.

Below: A white giraffe. Unusual colours and markings do sometimes occur, but albinos, with pure white coats and pink eyes, are rare.

Above: The okapi, *Okapia johnstoni*, which lives in the equatorial forests of central Africa has rarely been seen in the wild, but it is not uncommon in zoos. Although the first okapis to reach Europe were infested with worms and soon died, a healthy, breeding zoo population has now been established.

immediately struck by the resemblance between the new species and the extinct short-necked giraffe, *Helladotherium*, which inhabited Europe and Asia over ten million years ago.

It was surprising that such a large animal could have remained undiscovered for so long, and expeditions were soon mounted to capture an okapi alive. Although several animals were caught in the early 1900s they soon died and it was not until 1928 that one reached a European zoo (Antwerp) and survived there. Today okapis flourish in various zoos throughout the world, and something like half the zoo population has been bred in captivity.

The most obvious points of resemblance between the okapi and its relative the giraffe are the long front legs and the shape of the head. Like the giraffe, the okapi has bony 'horns' above the eyes. These grow independently of the skull but become joined to it as the animal matures. The horns, however, are present only in male animals. An adult okapi stands about 1.8 metres (6 ft) high. Its coat is a rich plum colour over most of the body but the hindquarters and the upper parts of all four limbs are horizontally striped with black and white. The lower parts of the legs, from hock to hoof, are white.

Whereas the giraffe lives in herds, the okapi lives in small family groups of one male and one or two females with their calves: life in the dense tropical forests would be difficult for larger groups of animals. Okapis have rather poor eyesight but they compensate for this by having keen senses of hearing and smell which in fact are much more useful in the jungle where vision is in any case limited. Because okapis are so shy and their habitat so inaccessible it is difficult to estimate their population with any accuracy, and until they have been studied more closely in the wild it will be impossible to say whether or not they are an endangered species. Certainly any attempt to clear their jungle homes for cultivation would threaten their survival.

Natural Science Photos

93

Snakes and Lizards

For about 150 million years reptiles were the dominant form of life on earth. The best known prehistoric reptiles are the often enormous dinosaurs of the Jurassic and Cretaceous periods. The plant-eating *Brontosaurus*, for example, was the largest land animal that ever lived, reaching a length of 18 m (60 ft) and a weight of 20 tonnes. Preying on the many plant-eating species were a variety of carnivorous dinosaurs, the most ferocious being *Tyrannosaurus rex* which walked on its two hind legs, reached a height of about 5 m (17 ft) and had almost 1,000 teeth.

About 65 million years ago, at the end of the Cretaceous period, a profound change both on land and in the sea drastically reduced the number of reptiles, and dinosaurs became extinct. Just what these sudden changes were is not known. Possibly some widespread climatic change affected the plant life on which all dinosaurs ultimately depended for their survival. Today, of the many groups of reptiles which flourished in prehistoric times only four remain: the turtles and tortoises, *Chelonia*, the crocodiles and alligators, *Crocodilia*, the beak-nosed reptiles, *Rhynchocephalia*, of which only one species survives, and the snakes and lizards, *Squamata*.

Snakes

The oldest fossil snakes date from about 65 million years ago. They resembled modern boas and pythons in being stout-bodied and large. Undoubtedly the loss of the limbs, elongation of the body and joined eyelids were originally adaptations to a burrowing lifestyle, though the increase in size probably represents a subsequent adaptation to life above the ground, feeding on the increasing numbers of rodents which developed during the Eocene period. The smaller predecessors of these snakes might not be expected to leave a significant fossil record.

Adapting to a life above ground must have raised enormous problems of locomotion for a legless animal, but it was a problem the snakes overcame well. There are three important methods of movement. The main method is by waves of muscular contraction which produce a side to side undulation from head to tail. In water, their movement is almost identical to that of a fish.

On land, snakes can also move by using ventral (underneath) plates which extend from the throat to the junction of the tail. These overlapping plates cover much of the body and are attached to pairs of ribs by muscles. Since the near edges are free, the muscles can move the plates forwards and backwards and to some extent up and down. Thus, a plate may be lifted, moved forward, lowered and moved backwards. Waves of movement of such plates pass along the body from front to rear, producing a slow crawl which enables snakes to climb steep gradients or squeeze through narrow apertures. For example, the corn snake, *Elaphe guttata*, which can climb vertically up the trunks of trees, uses this method.

Anthony Bannister/NHPA

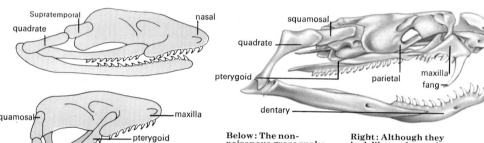

Supratemporal · quadrate · nasal

squamosal · quadrate · pterygoid · parietal · maxilla · fang · dentary

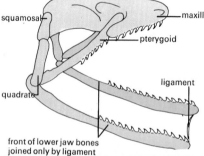

squamosal · maxilla · pterygoid · quadrate · ligament

front of lower jaw bones joined only by ligament

Right: South African sand snakes, *Psammophis sibilans*, hatching out. The leathery egg shell is cut open by a special 'egg tooth' which projects forwards from the upper jaw of the young snake.

Below right: The marine iguana, *Amblyrhynchus cristatus*, is one of the unique animals which live on the Galapagos Islands in the eastern Pacific. It is the only lizard which is truly marine, feeding on algae and seaweed. It has special glands in the nose cavities to excrete excess salt.

Below: The bearded lizard, *Amphibolurus barbatus*, from central Australia sunning itself in the open.

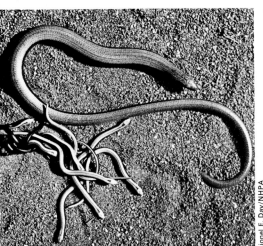

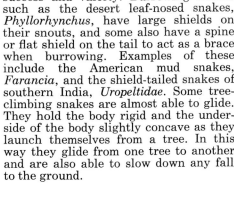

Left: An egg-eating snake, *Dasypeltis*, lives up to its name. The extreme flexibility of the neck and mouth allows the snake to swallow large eggs. The vertebrae which make up the backbone have downward pointing projections to help in swallowing and then breaking the egg. The shell is eventually regurgitated.

Below: A series of diagrams to show how a snake moves through a narrow space such as a burrow. The snake gets a grip by pressing against the sides of the burrow while waves of muscular contraction pass along the body. Snakes can hardly move at all on smooth surfaces such as glass which they cannot grip.

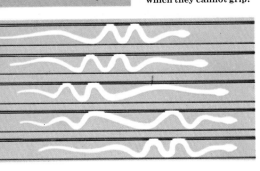

Another method of movement is known as 'side-winding'. This may be used for moving rapidly on very loose soil or in desert conditions. In sidewinding a grip is maintained with a sideways loop. The head is arched forwards so that the front part of the body does not touch the ground. It is then put down in a sideways loop and the back of the body is drawn up. Perhaps the most famous snake to move in this way is the American rattlesnake, or side-winder, *Crotalus cerastes*.

These varied methods of movement have allowed snakes to colonise a wide range of habitats and thus contributed to their success and variety. Burrowing snakes such as the desert leaf-nosed snakes, *Phyllorhynchus*, have large shields on their snouts, and some also have a spine or flat shield on the tail to act as a brace when burrowing. Examples of these include the American mud snakes, *Farancia*, and the shield-tailed snakes of southern India, *Uropeltidae*. Some tree-climbing snakes are almost able to glide. They hold the body rigid and the under-side of the body slightly concave as they launch themselves from a tree. In this way they glide from one tree to another and are also able to slow down any fall to the ground.

Feeding

In their original development from an underground way of life a problem also confronted the snakes in feeding. They were largely carnivorous, but catching prey without limbs posed a considerable problem, as did the chewing or tearing of food with teeth little adapted for the purpose. They developed a number of mechanisms to overcome these handicaps.

Because they have no limbs, snakes do not require a shoulder girdle or pelvis and this made it possible for them to develop a means of swallowing prey larger than their own body diameter. To allow the victim's body to pass through the mouth, a flexible joint was developed in the middle of each lower jaw, and the brain became completely encased in bone to protect it during swallowing. Snakes have well developed ribs which can enlarge to accommodate the swallowed prey.

To swallow, the teeth take a good grip on the prey. The outer rows of upper teeth are alternately moved forwards and outwards and pulled back again into position, in such a way that the curved teeth drag the prey back to the throat. The lower teeth are only used to hold the prey while the upper teeth are freed and refastened but otherwise play no part in the swallowing. As the bulk of the prey enters the throat, the jaws spread out and the neck muscles start to push the prey onwards to the stomach. Once past the head, spine movements help in further swallowing. The process can be slow: it often takes 30 minutes or more to swallow large prey.

Such a slow swallowing process requires the prey to be at least subdued, if not dead. The larger snakes such as boas,

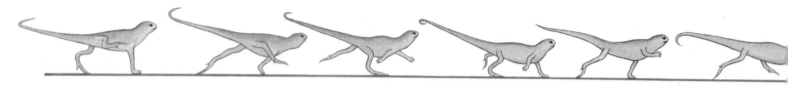

Boinae, or pythons, *Pythoninae*, strike at their prey, seizing it in their jaws and then throwing one or more coils around the prey killing it by constriction.

Smaller snakes developed an even more effective way of subduing prey—poison. The evolution of this means of killing prey occurred by modification of some salivary glands into venom glands and the development of fangs. The group with the most specialized fangs include the vipers and the pit vipers, where the fang is situated well forward in the upper jaw. It is not rigid as in other snakes but can be swivelled to lie flat in the mouth when not in use. The venom is forced through an enclosed duct running through the tooth rather than just trickling down a groove in the fang as in some other snakes. This arrangement, like a hypodermic needle, allows the prey to be killed quickly with a minimum amount of venom, thus reducing the risk to the snake.

Among the most venomous snakes in the world are the taipan, *Oxyuranus scutulatus*, of Australia and the banded krait, *Bungarus fasciatus*, from south-east Asia. The latter, however, is virtually harmless for much of the time because it very rarely, if ever, bites during the day, even if severely provoked.

Reproduction

In the breeding season many snakes go through a form of rivalry and courtship. They do not stake out territory, but some species such as vipers indulge in protracted combat in which their heads rear up and each snake tries to push over his rival. The male snake trails a female by picking up the scent left by secretions of her skin. He does this by using not only his nose but also a special organ, called Jacobson's organ, which opens into the mouth and is situated above it. The Jacobson's organ probably acts as a sensor for substances picked up by the snake's tongue as it flicks in and out. Certainly it is common during courtship for the male to rub his chin along the female's back while playing his tongue in and out.

For the act of coitus the two snakes lie extended side by side, and the process frequently lasts for several hours. Eggs are usually deposited in clutches, under stones or in rotting vegetation. Female pythons incubate their eggs in the coils of their bodies. Only a few snakes such as the sea snakes, *Hydrophiinae*, give birth to live young like mammals.

Many snakes hibernate in groups; there are, for example, numerous accounts of rattlesnake dens in the US. How long they live varies greatly from one species to another; large pythons probably live the longest and some have been recorded as living for more than 25 years.

Lizards

The lizards are closely related to the snakes, but there are obvious differences. Snakes have neither limbs nor eardrums, their eyes are covered by a transparent film and a single row of wide scales run along the belly. The 'typical' lizards on the other hand, have four limbs, moveable eyelids, a visible eardrum and many scales

Above and below: A European chameleon, *Chamaeleo chamaeleon*, and a brightly coloured South African species. Chameleons clamber about among the branches of trees, anchoring themselves with their long prehensile tails. They feed mainly on insects which they catch with their long sticky tongues.

Bottom: Diagrams to show how a lizard like a chameleon alters the colour of its skin. Impulses from the spinal cord are transmitted through nerve fibres to melanophore cells which then disperse a black pigment. Thus the colour observed through the outermost layer of the skin (epidermis) darkens.

Above: A giant monitor, *Varanus giganteus*, from Australia. These animals reach a maximum length of about 2.4 m (7 ft). Monitors prey on smaller animals such as birds, rats, snakes and frogs. Like snakes, but unlike other lizards, they can drop the lower part of the jaw when swallowing large prey.

Below: A flying lizard, *Draco volans*, from south-east Asia. These animals have ribs which extend outside the body wall and support a membrane of skin in much the same way as the ribs of an umbrella support its fabric. By spreading this apparatus on each side of its body, the lizard is able to glide from tree to tree in search of insects.

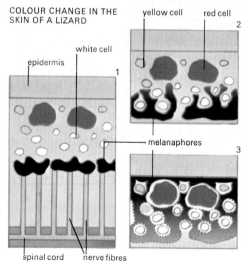

COLOUR CHANGE IN THE SKIN OF A LIZARD

yellow cell

red cell

white cell

epidermis

melanaphores

spinal cord   nerve fibres

96

Above, left to right: Most lizards run on all fours to escape their enemies, but for short rapid bursts some species such as the zebra-tailed lizard, *Callisaurus draconoides*, of North America run on their hind legs alone, using the tail as a balance. All reptiles are cold-blooded animals: they have no mechanism for regulating their blood temperature. Most therefore prefer hot climates where they can raise their body temperature in the sun. The warmer the blood the more active the animal can be. At night reptiles are normally very sluggish.

Below: A gecko from Madagascar, *Phelsuma madagascariensis*. Unlike other geckos these lizards are active during the day and are brightly coloured. They live in trees and have a call like the croak of a frog.

Heather Angel

Left: The tuatara, *Sphenodon punctatum*, is the only surviving species of the reptile group *Rhynchocephalia*. It lives only on a few small islands off the coast of New Zealand and is strictly protected. Curiously, tuataras prefer a much lower temperature than other reptiles, and they live longer.

Below: Lizards usually move about with their bellies sliding along the ground. Undulating movements of the body help to push the animal along. In moments of crisis when they have to move rapidly the body is lifted off the ground even though, because of the position of the legs, this needs considerable effort.

Anthony Bannister/NHPA

Right: The strange-looking moloch, *Moloch horridus*, of central Australia. Despite its forbidding appearance, the moloch is quite harmless. It feeds on black ants. A store of fat under its spiny skin helps it to survive in the desert. When water is available tiny canals in the skin lead it to the animal's mouth.

NHPA

on their undersurface. They differ from mammals in having legs which stick out on each side of the body rather than under it. The belly usually rests on the ground and the legs push the lizard along, helped by undulating or wriggling movements.

Lizards found in tropical climates are often spectacular. The geckos, *Gekkonidae*, are small lizards with flattened bodies and curious adhesive pads on their toes which enable them to run easily on vertical or overhanging surfaces. Most geckos are partly nocturnal, appearing in the evenings when they can be seen stalking insects on walls—they are often seen lying in wait close to electric lights where insects collect. There are also some geckos that live in the desert, and many of these have enlarged tails which probably act as a food reserve.

Perhaps the most spectacular, however, are the huge monitor lizards which look like incarnations of mythical dragons. Inhabiting a number of Indonesian islands, the largest of these creatures is appropriately named the Komodo dragon, *Varanus komodoensis*, and can reach a length of 3 m (10 ft). Monitor lizards are predatory; they feed on invertebrates and smaller vertebrates, including snakes, and sometimes raid poultry farms killing chickens and stealing eggs. They are fierce animals and defend themselves vigorously with teeth, claws and by using their powerful tails. Often confused with the monitor lizards are the iguanas, large lizards which live in the Americas.

Lizards are sexually mature when they are two years old and are fully grown at four or five years. The average lifespan is about 10 years although some, such as the slow worm, will live for up to 50 years.

Turtles and Crocodiles

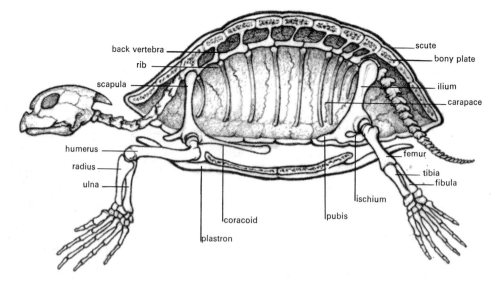

Many reptiles have found the key to survival in the evolution of body armour to protect them from their enemies. Perhaps no other reptiles, however, have armoured themselves so completely as those of the group *Chelonia*. This order includes the typical land tortoises, the amphibious terrapins and marine turtles. It is an ancient order, the members of which have undergone little change since the late Triassic 200 million years ago.

Turtles and tortoises

All turtles and tortoises have shells consisting of two main pieces, the *carapace* above and the *plastron* below. These are usually joined in the middle region of each side, leaving apertures in front and behind for the head, legs and tail. The shell is made up of two materials, an outer layer of horny *scutes*, and an inner layer of bony plates. The skeleton is enclosed in the shell and is partly joined to the carapace. To compensate for the resulting rigidity of the trunk, the neck is long and mobile, and in most species the head can be drawn back until it is almost hidden by the carapace.

The most numerous of the group are the sea turtles and of these the leatherback turtle, *Dermochelys coriacea*, is the largest, reaching a length of over two metres (6.5 ft), a width of about 3.6 m (12 ft) across the front paddles and a weight of over 675 kg (1,500 lb). Like all reptiles they evolved on land, but they have since reverted to an aquatic life. They are a small but fascinating group found in the world's tropical and sub-tropical seas. To equip them for this life, turtles have evolved special glands around the eyes to dispose of excess salt, their fingers are joined together to form paddles and, compared with those of tortoises, their shells are light and streamlined. The front paddles are considerably longer than the hind ones, allowing turtles to swim well despite their considerable bulk. When swimming, the paddles sweep gracefully up and down with a motion that has been compared to a bird's wings. On land, marine turtles are very clumsy and, like tortoises, have great difficulty in righting themselves when turned on their backs. This is not too much of a disadvantage because they rarely come out of the sea except to lay their eggs.

Turtles often make prodigiously long sea journeys to lay their eggs, returning to the same beaches on remote islands. Whereas there is an obvious advantage to laying their eggs in sparsely populated

Above: The skeleton of a turtle. The shell of a turtle or tortoise is made up of two main pieces, the carapace above and the plastron below. It is composed of two materials, an outer layer of horny scutes and an inner layer of bony plates. The skeleton is enclosed in the shell and is partly joined to the carapace.

Right: A brightly marked terrapin, *Pseudemys dorbicny.* Terrapins live in ponds and rivers, particularly in North and South America. They are often seen basking in the sun on logs or tree stumps. Terrapins are often kept as pets, but these usually die from malnutrition before reaching maturity.

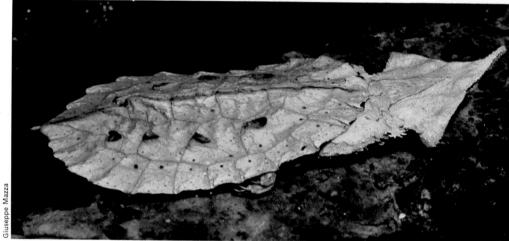

Below, left to right: A female turtle digs a nest hole in the sand before laying her eggs. The young turtles all hatch out together and begin to dig upwards. On reaching the surface they head for the sea.

Above: The extraordinary Mata-mata turtle, *Chelys fimbriatus,* of South America. The turtle's shell is irregular and its head and limbs are covered with folds of skin which

undulate in the currents of water to camouflage it. It lies in wait on a river bottom until a fish touches the skin near the mouth. Instantly the Mata-mata's mouth springs open and the fish is swept in.

Below right: Newly hatched leatherback turtles, *Dermochelys coriacea*, on a beach. Leatherbacks are the largest species of turtle and they have the widest range of any of the world's reptiles.

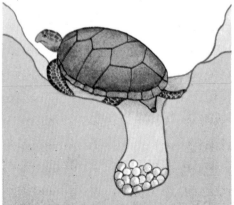

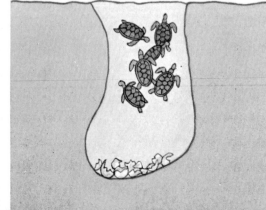

Above and left: Giant tortoises, *Geochelone elephantopus*, from the island of Isabela in the Galápagos archipelago. These creatures were made famous by Charles Darwin after he had visited the islands in the 1830s. The tortoises spend most of their time in the warm dry lowlands of the islands, but they make regular journeys to the volcanic highlands in search of fresh water. The pool in the picture above lies in the crater of an extinct volcano. A curious feature of some local plants is that they germinate much more effectively if the seeds have first passed through the gut of a giant tortoise. The tortoises feed on all kinds of vegetation.

Above: An Indian star tortoise, *Testudo elegans*. Star tortoises rest in the middle of the day when the sun is hottest, being most active in the early morning and late afternoon. Curiously, they still rest at noon even when kept in captivity in cool climates.

Left: The alligator snapping turtle, *Macroclemys temminckii*. It lies with its mouth open and part of its tongue is filled with blood to resemble a worm. A fish that tries to take the 'worm' will be caught instantly.

Below: A newly hatched green turtle, *Chelonia mydas*. Its shell is still curved to fit the eggshell and a yolk ball protrudes from its belly. In 24 hours the shell will be straight and the yolk absorbed.

Below right: A map to show the movement of turtles in the Caribbean from the beaches of Costa Rica where many begin life.

islands, it seems rather odd that islands so very far away should be chosen. The answer to this problem may lie in the antiquity of the group. Possibly millions of years ago the islands were lying only a short distance from the mainland. According to the theory of continental drift the land masses have moved, over millions of years, so possibly the turtles' nesting island gradually and imperceptibly drifted apart from the mainland. To each successive generation of turtles the distance was no more than on the previous visit but over millions of years inches became many miles.

The nesting patterns of turtles vary, but have many common features. The green turtle, *Chelonia mydas*, comes ashore on an incoming tide, using the waves and her paddles to beach as high as possible. After a few minutes rest she uses her front paddles, advancing both of them at the same time, to drag herself forward. The rear paddles acting in unison with the front ones also assist in pushing the turtle forward. The body is never raised clear of the sand but moves forward a few inches at a time by the pushing and pulling of the paddles. At first the female turtle takes frequent rests of several minutes but as she progresses further up the beach these become shorter. On reaching the softer dry sand, she stops and begins to use her paddles to dig into the sand at a chosen spot. After twenty minutes of digging the action of the rear paddles changes, digging more directly downwards and curving like hands to scoop out the sand.

When finished, the egg chamber is pear-shaped with a narrower neck region and a wider chamber below which will house most of the eggs. This egg chamber is around 40 cm (16 in) deep. The eggs are white and resemble table tennis balls; at first they are discharged singly into the chamber but later in twos, threes, or fours, until up to 500 eggs may lie in the chamber. After laying the eggs the turtle fills in the depression with her paddles, and then, with one strong series of flipper movements, toboggans down to the sea.

After several months the eggs hatch. When emerging from the eggs, the young turtles find themselves underground and it takes them several days to dig their way to the surface. Group effort plays an important part in the emergence of young turtles—the movement of the first to hatch stimulates the others to activity. When they near the surface, the leading turtles will stop moving if the sand is warm because to emerge during the day would leave them open to attack from predators. As the sand cools in the night, activity resumes and the lower turtles again respond to the efforts of those above. In this way most of the young from a particular clutch of eggs will break the surface at more or less the same time.

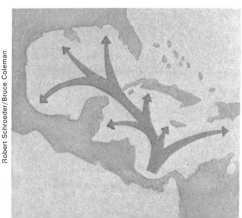

99

Late hatchers, without the benefit of the group effort, are doomed.

Once the hatchlings leave the nest they make rapid progress to the sea. However, even during this short space of time they are preyed upon by crabs, particularly the large ghost crab, and birds. This kind of predatory action on land is nothing compared with the hazards which the baby turtles face on entering the water, from attack by carnivorous fish. Those that survive will one day return to lay eggs of their own.

Crocodiles and alligators

In contrast to the generally placid tortoises and turtles are the group of reptiles familiarly known as crocodiles. Those alive today, formidable enough, are not as big as the crocodiles which lived at the time of the dinosaurs. One, called *Phobosuchus*, the 'terror crocodile', was about 14 m (45 ft) long and most probably preyed on the huge aquatic plant-eating dinosaurs. The present day crocodiles can be divided into three groups: the true crocodiles confined to the warmer parts of Africa, Asia and Australia, the alligators and caimans of North and South America and the long-nosed crocodiles called gharials or gavials from India.

There is one small difference between the true crocodile and an alligator: in crocodiles the fourth tooth of the lower jaw on each side fits into a notch in the upper jaw and is visible when the animal's mouth is closed. In alligators it fits into a pit in the upper jaw. The gharials have long slender jaws, very like a beak and set with small teeth.

The largest crocodile now living is the estuarine crocodile, *Crocodylus porosus*,

CAIMAN

ALLIGATOR

Giuseppe Mazza

found in Asia, Southern China and Southern Australia. Although it is mature and can breed when about three metres (ten feet) long, it continues growing throughout its life. The largest one ever recorded was found in Bengal in India and measured 10 m (33 ft) in length and was nearly 4.2 m (14 ft) in girth at the middle of its body. Unfortunately hunting is widespread and consequently very few estuarine crocodiles reach any great age or size: specimens over six metres (20 ft) long are now very rare. The smallest species of crocodile is a South American caiman, *Caiman palperbrosus*, which barely reaches a length of 1.2 m (4 ft).

All crocodiles are adapted for life in water. The tail is flattened from side to side like an oar for efficient swimming and the nostrils are situated in a small dome or bump on top of the snout so that the animal can breathe when almost completely submerged. They can also spend a long period under the water without breathing: up to 5 hours in the case of the alligator. The teeth are conical

Above: The eyes of a crocodile are located high on the head so that the animal can see what is going on above the water level while still submerged.

Left: An American alligator, *Alligator mississippiensis*, emerging from the water. With the exception of a single Chinese species, all alligators live in North or South America. As in all reptiles, the limbs project from the sides of the body and are therefore not very good at supporting the body weight on land.

P. A. Milwaukee/Jacana

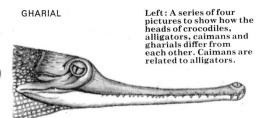

Left: A series of four pictures to show how the heads of crocodiles, alligators, caimans and gharials differ from each other. Caimans are related to alligators.

and pointed, designed for holding prey, not for chewing or cutting it up, so crocodiles have to swallow their food in large lumps. This does not help the digestion processes. Stones are often found in the stomachs of crocodiles, which might assist in digesting the food by crushing and grinding it. This is only a possibility however, since they may just be swallowed by accident.

Like most other reptiles, crocodiles lay eggs. These are laid on land and may be as large as geese eggs. The Nile crocodile, *Crocodylus niloticus*, of Egypt and Northern Africa, buries its eggs in the sand; others, including the estuarine crocodile, make a sort of nest consisting of a heap of water weeds and vegetable debris in which the eggs are buried. This not only helps to keep the eggs hidden, but also maintains them at a constant and fairly high temperature because of the heating effect of the moist, decaying vegetable matter. The mother crocodile guards the nest area until the young hatch out, but does not tend her offspring after they emerge. The nest-building habits of crocodiles are reminiscent of those of birds; indeed, crocodiles are their nearest living relatives.

The emerging crocodiles are miniature adults. They grow rapidly at first, especially if food is plentiful. Alligators, for example, grow about 30 cm (one foot) a year for their first four years of life, achieving sexual maturity after six years when they are around two metres long. Individual alligators and crocodiles are known to have lived for about 45 years, and some may well reach greater ages.

Characteristics of reptiles

All reptiles have a number of features in common. To begin with, like fishes and amphibians, they are all cold blooded, or *poikilothermic*. This means that they have no effective internal mechanism for regulating the body temperature; in conse-

quence it varies widely, depending mainly on the temperature of the environment. When the outside temperature is low, for example at night, a reptile will be very sluggish because the biochemical processes in its body will proceed only slowly.

Reptiles breathe air by means of lungs; they never possess gills like fish or amphibian larvae. The ventricle of the heart is usually only partly divided by a *septum* and, as a result, some mixing of arterial and venous blood occurs. This is an important point of distinction from adult birds and mammals where arterial and venous blood never mix.

The skin of a reptile is comparatively waterproof, being made up of an *epidermis* on the outside and an inner *dermis*. The epidermis forms the scales or scutes (in turtles) which are characteristic of reptiles and distinguish them from amphibians. The scales are composed of dead, horny tissue of which the protein *keratin* forms a large part. They are continually being shed from the surface of the body, either flaking off piecemeal or being sloughed off in one piece as in snakes. This loss is made good by the proliferation of living cells in the epidermis.

A reptile's teeth are shed and replaced throughout its life, instead of there being just one or two sets as in mammals. In some reptiles the replacement of teeth follows an alternating pattern. Between any two functional teeth there is often an empty space. As a new tooth grows in the empty space and begins to function, the teeth on either side of it are shed. This prevents the reptile from losing all its functional teeth at the same time. The teeth are capped with enamel, but its composition is different from that of mammalian tooth enamel.

Reptiles have a well developed sense of sight. The eyes are often brightly coloured, the iris being yellow or red, or sometimes blending in with the camouflage pattern of the rest of the animal. The sense of hearing varies considerably from one reptile group to another. Crocodiles and certain lizards, for example, have fairly keen hearing whereas snakes are almost deaf. Reptiles do not have an external ear and the exposed eardrum is often visible on the surface of the head behind the eyes. Whereas mammals have three bones for conducting sound from the eardrum to the inner ear, reptiles have only one.

Above: Most reptiles lay eggs rather than bear live young, and crocodiles are no exception. This picture shows a young crocodile breaking out of its egg.

Left: A long-nosed crocodile or gharial, *Gavialis gangeticus*, from India. These animals are fish eaters and are not dangerous to man. Another type of gharial, the false gharial, *Tomistoma schlegelii*, lives only in the Malay peninsula and Sumatra. It is more closely related to true crocodiles than to its Indian namesake.

Jen & Des Bartlett/Bruce Coleman

Ron Boardman

Left: The spectacled caiman, *Caiman sclerops*, is common in the northern parts of South America. It rarely grows to more than 2 m (6 ft).

Right: One of the largest crocodiles is the Nile crocodile, *Crocodylus niloticus*. Once common in Africa it is now found only in isolated preserves.

Bavaria

Amphibians

The amphibians were the first group of vertebrate animals to have made a serious attempt at a life on land. Their history is long and complex from a fish-like ancestor to the three groups of modern amphibians, the *Anura* (frogs and toads), the *Urodela* (newts and salamanders) and the *Apoda* (worm-like animals called caecilians).

To trace the origin of the amphibians we must look back over 350 million years to the Devonian period, a time of seasonal drought and wet periods. Prototype amphibians are thought to have arisen from a fish-like ancestor related to the modern coelacanth. These ancient fish had primitive lungs and a skull structure resembling that of later amphibians; they were also probably capable of surviving the periods of drought.

Since the Devonian period many amphibians have evolved and adapted to terrestrial life while others have reverted to a mainly aquatic existence. *Ichthyostega* is the oldest and best known fossil form, resembling a cross between a fish and a salamander. It probably had the five-fingered (pentadactyl) limbs of all higher four-legged animals. *Ichthyostega* belonged to a large group of fossil amphibians called the *Labyrinthodontia*, named from the folded nature of the surface of their teeth. The most successful members of this group were the *Temnospondyli* which grew to a length of up to three metres (ten feet).

Another great branch of fossil forms were the *Lepospondyli*, generally small amphibians with salamander or limbless snake-like forms. Most inhabited the great swamps of the Carboniferous period in areas that now include Europe and North America. There are considerable gaps in our knowledge relating to the evolution of modern forms, but we do know that during the Carboniferous period hundreds of different amphibian forms roamed the swamps and that these

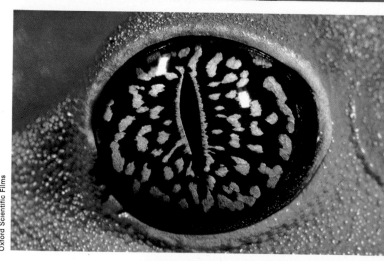

Heather Angel

Above: A tree frog, *Hyla arborea*, resting on the leaf of a *Poinsettia* plant. Clearly visible are the frog's toe pads which enable it to climb trees. Although very obvious in this picture, the frog would normally be well camouflaged by its bright green skin colour against tree foliage. These animals are sometimes found resting in the full glare of the tropical sun. Evaporation of moisture from their body surface helps to keep their bodies at a reasonable temperature.

Right: The eye of a tree frog, *Phyllomedusa trinitatis*. Unlike fish, but like many other land animals, sight is the dominant sense in most amphibians.

Oxford Scientific Films

Right: The mating of common frogs, *Rana temporaria*. The eggs are fertilized by the male (above) as soon as they are laid by the female. A mass of spawn can be seen in the background.

Left: An Argentine horned frog, *Ceratophrys ornata*, is well camouflaged against its background. Unlike most amphibians, these frogs are equipped with biting teeth. Their tadpoles have especially strong jaws and frequently prey on their own kind. The skin of frogs and toads contains poison glands for defence: one of the strongest poisons known comes from a tree frog, *Phyllobates bicolor*. It is used by South American Indians to poison arrowheads.

Jane Burton/Bruce Coleman

H. Rivarola/Bruce Coleman

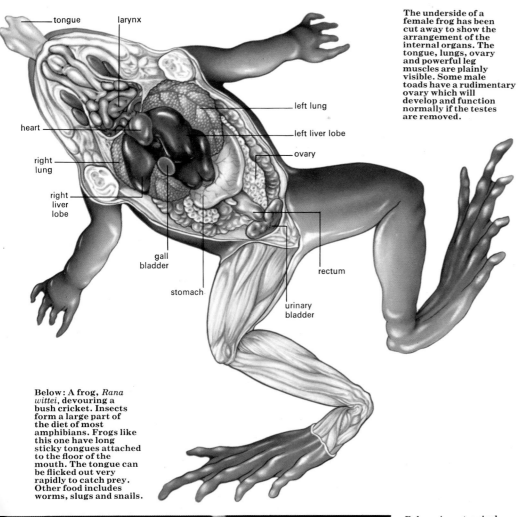

tongue

larynx

left lung

heart

left liver lobe

right lung

ovary

right liver lobe

gall bladder

rectum

stomach

urinary bladder

The underside of a female frog has been cut away to show the arrangement of the internal organs. The tongue, lungs, ovary and powerful leg muscles are plainly visible. Some male toads have a rudimentary ovary which will develop and function normally if the testes are removed.

Below: A frog, *Rana wittei*, devouring a bush cricket. Insects form a large part of the diet of most amphibians. Frogs like this one have long sticky tongues attached to the floor of the mouth. The tongue can be flicked out very rapidly to catch prey. Other food includes worms, slugs and snails.

creatures led easy lives with little competition from other animals and an abundance of fish and insect food.

The change from life in the water to that on land involved relatively few changes in the form and function of amphibians. Apart from caecilians, modern amphibians lost their fish-like scales and developed a soft naked skin that was kept moist to help respiration. This arrangement carried with it the danger of dehydration of the body tissues (water was easily lost by evaporation from the moist skin surface), but provided the amphibians kept to humid regions where the air was already laden with moisture the problem was not a serious one. For effective movement the body was raised off the ground by the development of a sturdy, lightweight skeleton and associated strong muscle systems. The skull lost its stiff connection with the pectoral girdle, giving better mobility. The hind limbs of frogs and toads became well developed for a swimming, and later jumping, habit and in both the anuran (frogs and toads) and urodele (newts and salamanders) groups the pentadactyl limbs became webbed for use as swimming paddles.

Frogs and toads

The anurans are the largest and most widely distributed amphibian group with over 2,500 species. They live in a wide variety of habitats from swamps and marshes to mountain streams and deserts.

Respiration in frogs is effected in three ways. In common with all higher vertebrates, frogs have paired airsacs or lungs. While breathing, the mouth is kept tightly closed and air is sucked in through the nostrils by lowering the floor of the mouth. Air is passed backwards and forwards several times between the lungs and the mouth before finally being exhaled. The skin and the lining of the mouth are also important for respiration. Both areas are richly supplied with blood vessels and are kept moist by secretions of mucous glands.

To help camouflage themselves many amphibians are able to change colour by

Below: A neotropical toad, *Bufo marinus*, calling to attract a mate. Frogs and toads were the first vertebrates to have a larynx and vocal cords. The inflated vocal sac under the mouth of the toad amplifies the sound and enables it to be heard from a distance of a kilometre or more.

Left: A series of diagrams to show how a frog leaps. The power for the jump comes from the well-muscled back legs which push the frog upwards and forwards. On landing, the back legs are once again drawn up against the body and the impact is taken by the front legs. The frog is then ready for another jump.

expanding and contracting three layers of pigment cells in the skin. The skin is composed of several outer layers which are continuously renewed by moulting. It is often thickened as seen in the warty nature of toads. Apart from mucous glands to keep it moist, the skin contains poison glands used for defence. The poisonous secretion of toads contains substances which have a similar effect to the drug digitalis on the human heart.

The life history of the common frog, *Rana temporaria*, shows the change in body form (complete metamorphosis) common to anurans. Males and females congregate near ponds in early spring and sound is an important factor in bringing the sexes together. Both sexes have vocal cords but only those of the male are fully developed. The typical croaking call is produced by vibration of the vocal cords, a pair of folded membranes in the larynx. Prior to mating the male frog develops a horny 'nuptial pad' on its forelimbs which helps give a secure grip on the female when mating. The male grasps the female during the whole period of egg-laying which may last for several days.

The eggs are almost always fertilized externally by the male immediately after being laid and swell up on contact with water. A jelly-like covering acts as a food supply for the young tadpole and also as a protection against predators. The tadpoles differ greatly in form from their parents, they are completely aquatic and in the early stages are vegetarian. In early summer, young frogs emerge from the pond to feed on small insect prey.

While the common frog gives us an example of the typically amphibian dependence on water for breeding, some species have devised more ingenious methods to ensure the survival of the species. Asian tree frogs, *Rhacophoridae*, lay their eggs in a bubble mass of rainwater on leaves overhanging streams and pools, so that on hatching the young fall directly into the water to continue their development. The male European midwife toad, *Alytes obstetricans*, protects the eggs by carrying them in a string

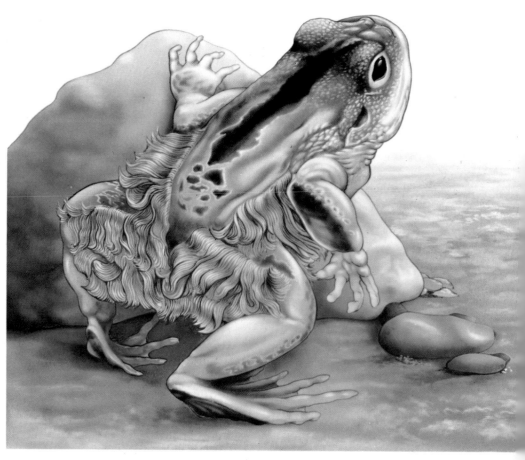

Above: The hairy frog, *Trichobatrachus robustus*. These curious amphibians are found in West Africa and they have small claws on several of their toes. The function of the vascular 'hairs', present only on male frogs, is uncertain. They may be for recognition, camouflage or other purposes.

Heather Angel

Above: A pair of mating toads, *Bufo bufo*. Toads mate in much the same way as frogs, but their spawn is in the form of 'ropes' rather than a disorganized mass.

H. Reinhard/Bruce Coleman

Left: A fire salamander, *Salamandra salamandra*. These amphibians are common in central Europe. They were thought by the ancients to be able to withstand the action of flames. The salamander secretes a milky poison from glands in its smooth skin, and the bright yellow and black markings serve as a warning to potential predators. Fire salamanders give birth to live young.

Right: Pyrenean mountain salamanders, *Euproctes asper*, during courtship.

104

around his legs until just before hatching when he rushes down to a stream to allow the young tadpoles their freedom. In *Phyllobates* of South America, the tadpoles live on their father's back until they reach an advanced stage of development. The Seychelles frog, *Sooglossus*, goes one step further in parental care, for the tadpoles develop into young frogs while still on the father's back. An extreme short cut in the life history is shown by a few species. For instance in the marsupial frog, *Gasterotheca*. eggs are laid in a brood pouch on the mother's back and the young hatch out in a zipper-like fashion from the pouch. The young of the Surinam toad, *Pipa pipa*, emerge singly from honeycomb depressions on the female's back.

These examples show not only degrees of parental care, but also some independence of water for breeding purposes. Frogs and toads that live in the extremely dry conditions of the Australian desert can imbibe so much water after a rainstorm that Aborigines catch them during the dry season to drink their water store. These desert amphibians often spend the heat of the day in deep burrows and are able to breed almost immediately after a sudden downpour of rain. Since the rainy season is short, the embryos develop very rapidly.

Anurans range in length from a few centimetres to the giant goliath frog, *Gigantorana goliath*, of West Africa which measures up to 40 cm (16 in). Oddities of the group include the Borneo flying frog, *Rhacophorus pardalis*, which can glide from tree to tree and the hairy frog, *Trichobatrachus robustus*, of West Africa.

Newts and salamanders

Most of the 450 species of urodeles live in water or else hidden away in mossy retreats or other humid habitats like the rotting stumps of trees, in caves or under stones. They have long tapering bodies with weak legs, and the adult and larval forms differ little from each other. Urodeles are commonly found in mountainous regions with a temperate, moist climate and have their greatest distribution in the Northern Hemisphere.

The most familiar members are the newts which belong to the large group known as true salamanders. Newts have long, laterally flattened tails and often develop crests in the breeding season. Colour plays an important role in breeding and the gaudy nuptial colours of the males are particularly striking. The pattern of courtship varies with the species, but the secretions of 'hedonic glands' play an important role in initiating sexual response in all cases. These glands are located in the skin, especially in the cloaca and tail region. Among the more common European newts, the male deposits a packet of sperms called the *spermatophore* which is taken up by the female's cloaca. Eggs are commonly laid on the leaves of water plants and from these swimming larvae emerge with well developed feathery gills.

One curious phenomenon observed in many of these amphibians is a tendency for larval features to be retained in the adult. This is called *neoteny*. The giant Asian salamanders, *Andrias*, for example, lose their larval gills, but lack eyelids and retain their larval teeth. Still more modified are the mud puppies, *Necturus*, of North America which keep their larval gills throughout life and have very small lungs. Perhaps the most famous example of neoteny is the axolotl, *Ambystoma mexicanum*, found in Lake Xochimilco and a few other cold water mountain lakes around Mexico city. The axolotl hardly ever changes into the adult form in nature, although of course it does reach sexual maturity. It will, however, metamorphose into a salamander under experimental conditions after treatment with thyroid hormone, extract of pituitary gland (the gland that controls hormone activity in vertebrates) or iodine.

Many urodeles represent the last living species of a previously large and widely distributed group. Some 60,000,000 years ago during the Tertiary period, giant salamanders were found over much of Eurasia. Today there are only three living species confined to China and Japan.

Above: Toads moult regularly throughout the summer months. The process takes about 15 minutes and the old skin is eaten, as seen here. Moulting begins with the secretion of a fluid under the outer layer of dead skin which is to be removed. The toad pulls off the old skin by a series of slow deliberate actions.

Below: An alpine newt, *Triturus alpestris*. Like most other tailed amphibians, these newts prefer a temperate, moist climate. They have a well developed sense of smell which operates under water as well as on land. All amphibians are cold blooded—their body temperatures depend on the surroundings.

Below: A male palmate newt, *Triturus helveticus*. The webbed hind feet and slender tail extension are plainly visible. Male and female newts are easily distinguished from each other, particularly during the breeding season. The males are more vividly coloured and have higher crests on their backs.

Right: An axolotl, *Ambystoma mexicanum*. In their natural habitats these amphibians remain permanently in the larval state although they mature sexually. The feather-like external gills are typical of salamander larvae. Axolotls can be induced to metamorphose into salamanders by treatment with iodine.

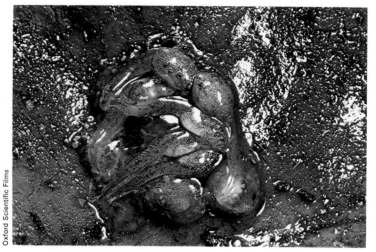

Left: Some frogs have achieved a degree of independence from the water even for breeding. This picture shows young tadpoles of the frog *Phyllobates trinitatis* on a leaf. The tadpoles will eventually be carried on their father's back before being released into a pond or stream.

Below: Five stages in the development of a tadpole. Newly hatched tadpoles have external gills, suckers to help them cling to plants but no eyes. The eyes soon develop and the gills become covered by an operculum. They feed mainly on algae and other plant material. Later the back legs develop and finally the front legs grow out from the gill cavity.

These relics grow up to 1.5 m (5 ft) in length and live on the bottom of fast-flowing streams. They are nocturnal and hunt a wide variety of prey from fish and frogs to smaller invertebrate animals.

Another relic group are the cave salamanders, *Hydromantes*. Although they are found above ground they prefer the damp and constant environment of caves. They move slowly, using their prehensile tails for climbing and hunt soft-bodied invertebrates which they catch with their extremely long tongues. The olm, *Proteus anguinus*, is another cave dweller, but this time aquatic. This blind larval urodele with pale unpigmented skin and orange feathery gills, lives in the underground water systems of Yugoslavia.

The largest urodele family is the *Plethodontinae* containing over 60 per cent of known species. These lungless salamanders are mostly found in North America, especially in the Appalachian mountain chain. Such lungless salamanders range from purely aquatic forms like the larger dusky salamanders to the tree-climbing salamander of California.

These creatures demonstrate that an animal can survive on land even without lungs. They breathe through their moist skin and through mucous covered membranes inside the mouth. To survive in this way it is obviously an advantage for the surface area of the body to be as large as possible for a given body weight, so plethodont salamanders are usually long and slender.

The Congo eels or *amphiumas* form another curious group of urodeles. Their common name is singularly inappropriate since they have no connection with eels and are not found in Africa. All amphiumas live in the south-eastern United States. They have long cylindrical bodies equipped with very small weak limbs, often only a few millimetres long.

3 external gills

2 days

2 suckers

anus

8 days

water to internal gills

operculum covering internal gills

1 month

water from gills

2 months

3 months

Right and below: Tadpoles move through the water in a similar way to fish by side to side movements of the body and tail. Because most of the weight is concentrated in the body rather than the tail, the swimming action is not very efficient. The tail is absorbed in the final stage of metamorphosis.

Caecilians

The apodans are all blind, limbless, burrowing animals and are the least known of the three amphibian groups. They lack both shoulder and pelvic girdles and their long, ringed, worm-like bodies are often scaled. They range in length from several centimetres to the giant *Caecilia thompsoni* which grows to a length of 1.5 m (5 ft).

Caecilians are all confined to tropical and sub-tropical regions of the world, especially Africa and South America. The best known member is the Ceylonese caecilian, *Ichthyophis glutinosus*, a striking blue-black creature with a bright yellow longitudinal stripe. This species shows a curious feature in that parental care is often very well developed. After laying her eggs, the female wraps herself around them until the larvae hatch out. Other caecilians give birth to live young which hatch out from eggs inside the mother. The young larvae feed in the oviduct on 'uterine milk' consisting of oil droplets and sloughed-off cells from the oviduct.

Many amphibians have made a good attempt at a life on land and are not just a precarious remnant of a once more widely distributed group. In habitats like swamps and marshes and mountain streams, they are often quite numerous and have evolved into a variety of forms. However, their survival has often meant evasion rather than total adaption to the more severe conditions of a terrestrial life.

Above: A South American caecilian, *Siphonops annulatus*. Caecilians are found in the same sort of habitat as earthworms and are often confused with them. They can, however, be distinguished from earthworms quite easily by their method of locomotion which is much more like that of a snake.

Right: A caecilian from the Seychelles burrows into the soil. Caecilians are blind: instead of eyes they have special sensory tentacles with which they find their way through the earth and locate their prey. They feed mainly on invertebrates, although larger species may eat snakes or small rodents such as mice.

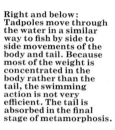
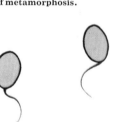

The Big Cats

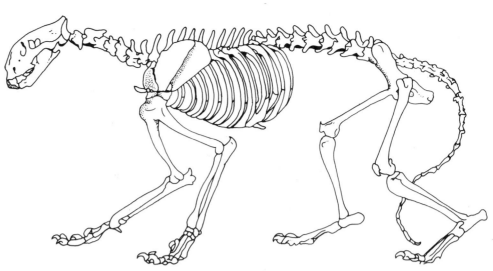

As long as animal life has existed on earth, most animals have eaten plants, leaving the way open for a fiercer minority to become meat-eaters. During the course of evolution a succession of carnivorous animals has appeared, and among the terrestrial mammals the cat family (*Felidae*) of the order *Carnivora* contains in many respects the most highly-developed and efficient carnivores of all.

Like the other members of their order they are descended from the weasel-like miacids that flourished about 50 million years ago, becoming a recognizable group on their own account about 35 million years ago. For most of the time since then there have been two very distinct types of cats, one of which, the sabre-tooths, died out only a few thousand years ago. With their huge fangs—those of the sabre-toothed tiger were up to 20 cm (8 in) long—the sabre tooths are thought to have hunted large plant-eating animals such as rhinoceroses by making slashing attacks.

The other group of cats, the one that survives today, relies instead on stealth. Moving on tip-toe with retracted claws, so that only the soft pads touch the ground, the typical cat approaches its prey silently, before springing, using the powerful muscles of the hind legs and back. The killing weapons are the claws and teeth. Cats have shorter jaws than any other carnivores, and this gives them great biting power. The pointed canine teeth are primarily used in killing, and the large last upper premolars and first lower molars (the *carnassial* teeth) for crushing and slicing the flesh before it is swallowed. Most cats hunt prey smaller than themselves, for there are many more small herbivores than large ones, but the biggest and most impressive cats of all usually hunt prey even larger than themselves.

Above: The skeleton of a tiger, *Panthera tigris*. It has a strong flexible backbone to enable it to pounce swiftly on its prey, and a long body with most of the weight carried by the front legs so that it can negotiate uneven ground and steep inclines with ease. Although tigers and lions look quite different from each other, their skeletons are almost identical and it takes an expert to tell them apart.

Right: A tiger cub. Normally a tigress gives birth to between two and four cubs after a gestation period of 105 days. They are born in a secluded den and are at first blind and helpless. Full maturity is not reached until the animals are more than three years old, but they learn to fend for themselves long before this.

Below: A sabre-tooth, *Machairodus lapidens*, which lived in the early Pleistocene epoch, less than 2,000,000 years ago. Sabre-tooths were members of the cat family but did not belong to the same sub-family as modern cats.

ZEFA

The big cats make up the genus *Panthera*, and apart from their size resemble each other in various ways. Unlike the smaller cats they have eyes with round pupils, and their larynxes or voice boxes are flexibly joined to the skull.

This may seem to be rather an unimportant anatomical detail, but it has important effects on sound production. Small cats yowl, but big cats roar, small cats can purr almost continuously, but when big cats purr they must pause for breath between each reverberation. Finally, in relation to their size the big cats have even larger heads than the small ones.

The first big cats evolved about a million years ago, as fossils from southern Europe and China prove. It may be that the arrival of this genus was a major cause of extinction of the sabre-tooths, for members of both groups hunted large prey, and may therefore have been in competition with each other. Travelling by land bridges, often temporary, which linked the major land-masses the big cats invaded Africa, the islands of south-east Asia, and (passing through North America) South America.

There were never very many species of big cats, but until man as a hunter com-

world distribution of tigers

Left: Tigers are much less common than they once were. Not only has their jungle habitat been cleared for cultivation in many places, but the animals themselves have been hunted for their skins and for 'sport'. Sometimes tigers become man-eaters and have to be hunted and destroyed, but this is relatively rare. Man-eaters are usually injured animals which can no longer catch their normal prey; the injury is often a gunshot wound or a porcupine quill lodged in one foot. A single man-eater has been known to kill more than 100 people in the course of its career.

Right: A cheetah, *Acinonyx jubatus*, feeding on the carcass of a Thomson's gazelle.

Below: The cheetah is the fastest of all mammals. It has a highly flexible backbone which allows the powerful back muscles as well as the leg muscles to be used in running. Hoofed animals such as zebras and antelopes have much more rigid backbones than cheetahs and rely on their leg muscles for running.

Jacana

Left: The most distinctive feature of the tiger is its striped coat which blends in well with the strong shadows of the trees and grass in its jungle homeland. Tigers range from South-East Asia to Siberia, and their prey varies accordingly. Russian tigers hunt roe deer, elk, musk deer and sometimes wolves or bears, whereas in tropical Asia tigers pursue deer of other species, nilgai (large antelopes), wild boar and even young elephants. Throughout their range tigers will take domestic animals when they can.

Right: Unlike most members of the cat family, tigers are not afraid of water and are strong swimmers.

P. Castel/Jacana

peted with them, in some cases exterminating their prey, every major part of the world except for Australasia and some remote islands, had its own big cat population. For example, there were lions in Europe until only a few thousand years ago. The lion *Panthera leo*, was the biggest cat of Europe, western Asia, and Africa, being replaced by the tiger, *Panthera tigris*, in more eastern regions of Asia. Over much of the Old World these two species coexisted with the leopard, *panthera pardus*, which, being slightly smaller and a better climber, was adapted for hunting different prey and was therefore not in competition with them. In the mountains of central Asia the snow leopard, *Panthera uncia*, was best adapted for the conditions, and the jaguar, *Panthera onca*, was the only

member of the group to find its way to America, where it lived in the warmer and more forested regions.

Human activity has whittled down the original ranges of the big cats. Not only have the lions gone from Europe, but more recently they have also become extinct in what was then Palestine and North Africa. Almost all surviving lions now live in Africa south of the Sahara Desert, but a few still live in the Gir Forest of north-east India.

Not all wild members of the same species are the same colour: the colour of lions' manes is very variable, ranging from black to tawny, and in both leopards and jaguars dark individuals are not uncommon in some parts of the world. These are very dark brown with black spots, and at a quick glance appear to be

plain black. A 'black panther' is simply a dark-haired leopard. Similarly, 'white' tigers, which have dark stripes and blue eyes are merely a paler version of the usual colouring. Like red hair in humans, these variations sometimes appear naturally in the wild.

Lions and tigers are the biggest members of the genus, tigers being slightly bigger than lions and can weigh up to 200 kg (440 lb) or more. Leopards and snow leopards are only a little shorter than the biggest cats, but much of their length consists of a long tail, useful in balancing on overhanging branches, and 45 kg (100 lb) is a good weight for either animal. Jaguars are superficially similar to leopards, and only a little shorter in overall length. However, they have shorter tails and are much more heavily

Above: A jaguar, *Panthera onca*, with its prey—in this case a domestic goat. Jaguars are the only large cats of the Americas, and they hunt deer, peccaries and some of the huge rodents of tropical America such as the sheep-sized capybara. The home range of a single jaguar may extend over 500 sq km (190 sq miles) or more.

Below: The clouded leopard, *Neofelis nebulosa*, hunts such prey as deer and wild pigs in the forests of South-East Asia.

built, weighing about 90 kg (200 lb). Being the only big cats of tropical America, they fill the ecological niches occupied in the Old World by both the lion or tiger and the leopard, and this may be the reason why jaguars are intermediate in size. Ecologically speaking, they are a compromise.

Most cats live and hunt on their own, and the majority of the big cats are no exception. Sometimes more than one individual of species such as the tiger are seen together, but these are almost certainly pairs during their brief courtship, or part of a growing family. There is no certain proof that any of the big cats defend fixed territories against other members of their own species, but it seems probable that they do, for all of them make scent marks using both dung and urine, and also scratch on trees or the ground. This sort of behaviour looks very much like territorial demarcation. Certainly a large carnivore must range over a wide area for it must not deplete the local population of prey animals faster than they can reproduce or it will eventually run out of food. Individual leopards range over an area of roughly 22 sq km (8 sq miles), and tigers range over about 65 sq km (25 sq miles). On scantier evidence the ranges of both jaguars and snow leopards are thought to be even larger.

Lion families

The lions of the grasslands of eastern and southern Africa live in groups known as prides whereas other big cats are solitary animals. This seems to be an adaptation to their environment, for of all the big cats lions are the only ones to live where their prey species occur in large herds. In order to outwit the combined vigilance of the herd, lions co-operate, making combined rushes, or lying in ambush for their prey. Because prey is usually numerous, the territory occupied by a pride is not particularly large—perhaps 33 sq km (13 sq miles). Although lions are the only big cats which are easy to observe in the wild, it is only very recently that detailed studies have been made of their social behaviour by zoologists working on the Serengeti Plain of Tanzania.

A typical pride consists of two or three adult males, perhaps twice as many mature lionesses, and their young. Before they become mature, at between 2 and 3 years old, the adolescent males

109

Giuseppe Mazza

Above: The leopard, *Panthera pardus*, is an expert climber. It hunts antelopes, monkeys (including baboons), hyraxes and large rodents, often wedging the remains of a kill in the fork of a tree to protect it from hyenas, jackals and other scavengers. Leopards live in Africa and southern Asia and, as with other big cats, old or injured animals occasionally become man-eaters.

Right: The snow leopard, *Panthera uncia*, has the longest fur of all cats for it inhabits the cool plateaux and mountain slopes of central Asia. It ranges over a wide area, hunting small deer, mountain goats, ground squirrels and some domestic animals.

Below: A lion, *Panthera leo*, splashes through a shallow pool. This is an African lion, recognizable by its thick mane. A few hundred lions also live in north-east India: they are a different race of the same species and have noticeably shorter manes than their more numerous African cousins.

Above: A lioness with her cub. Lions are the only cats of the genus *Panthera* to live in family groups consisting of males, females and cubs. This is probably an adaptation to life on the open plains where prey animals live in large herds. Tigers, leopards and jaguars are solitary animals of the forest and bush.

Jacana

Above right and right:
Within a pride of lions
hunting is normally
carried out by the
females, who kill
zebras, wildebeests and
other antelopes. Related
lionesses form the
permanent core of the
pride, for the males are
ousted every few years
by stronger males from
outside, thus ensuring
an influx of new blood.

and some of the females too are expelled by the adults. The females that are allowed to remain become part of the pride, but the others must live more solitary, less successful, and probably short lives. The young males wander in company, hunting on their own account, and growing powerful. When they are adult two or more of them will move in on another pride, take on the reigning males one at a time and kill or expel them, taking over the pride as their own. They kill the young cubs and, probably as a result of shock, any of the lionesses that are pregnant tend to lose their litters. Later the new males mate with the lionesses and sire their own cubs—in this way their social system is perpetuated and an influx of strong new blood ensured.

This life-style is very different from that of tigers, but nevertheless the two largest species of cats are quite closely related. In zoos hybrids between lions and tigers have been bred. They are called 'ligers' if a lion is the father and 'tygons' if a tiger is the father. Beyond this, the fact that the geographical ranges of the two species do not overlap indicates that they are both filling the same ecological niche—that of the strongest, and fiercest of predators.

Cheetahs

The cheetah, *Acinonyx jubatus*, is in many ways the most distinctive member of the otherwise rather homogeneous cat family. It is taller than a leopard, measuring about 90 cm (3 ft) at the shoulder, and nearly as long but is very lightly built weighing only about 54.5 kg (120 lb). Unlike those of the leopard and jaguar, the cheetah's spots are not grouped into rosettes, but are scattered singly all over the sandy-brown coat. Alone among the cats the adult cheetah is unable to retract its claws.

Other cats hunt by pouncing on the prey from close range, but the cheetah which is able to reach a speed of up to 100 kph (62 mph), catches its prey by sheer speed. However it has no stamina, and can maintain high speeds only over a few hundred yards or metres.

Cheetahs live in grasslands and semideserts of southern Asia and Africa. In many parts of their range, especially in Asia, they are now very rare. They hunt small, fleet-footed antelopes such as the Indian blackbuck and Thomson's gazelle of East Africa, and are usually most active early in the morning and in the evening. Either they stalk their prey, using the sparse cover that is available

before launching the attack from some dozens of metres away, or else they move towards the prey first at a walk, then a trot, and then a full-blooded gallop.

Living in herds, the prey species are watchful for such an attack, and usually stay well away from cover that could conceal a cheetah. If a sprinting cheetah succeeds in catching its prey (and often it does not), it bowls the animal over with its paws, and bites into the throat in order to kill.

Clouded leopards

Although smaller than some so-called 'small' cats, the clouded leopard, *Neofelis nebulosa*, is regarded as an intermediate species between the smaller cats and the big cats. Anatomically it possesses features of both major groups of cats in almost equal parts. It purrs like a small cat, and has neither round pupils (typical of big cats) nor vertical slit-like ones (like small cats), but horizontal oval ones. In relation to its size it has longer canine teeth than any other living cat. It lives in the forests of South-East Asia from Nepal to southern China and Sumatra, hunting quite large prey species, including deer and wild pigs—it has even been known to attack man.

111

Pandas, Raccoons and Badgers

The weasels and their relatives, which together make up the family *Mustelidae*, have the short legs and long muscular bodies which were typical of the remote ancestors of the carnivores. Although this shape is a primitive one it can, with just a little modification, be adapted to the varied life-styles of the small to medium-sized species that make up the family.

The typical weasels hunt through thick cover, sometimes pursuing their prey into burrows beneath the ground. The more heavily built badgers dig their own burrows. Martens chase squirrels through the treetops, catching their prey by a combination of speed and agility. With the addition of webbing between the toes, otters can swim fast enough to catch fish. It is not surprising that members of this family are successful in all parts of the world that they have been able to colonize: they are found in every continent except Australasia.

Mustelids are more closely related to dogs than to the specialized carnivores of the cat family. Like dogs they have relatively long jaws containing rows of molar and premolar teeth—typically three teeth of each type on either side of both the lower and upper jaws. Their eyesight is only fair, but they have keen hearing and an excellent sense of smell. They have five digits on each limb, and the claws are often partially retractable.

Females are usually appreciably smaller than males, and have a fixed breeding season. In some species the ovum, fertilized during mating, does not immediately implant itself on the wall of the uterus and start to grow. Instead it only becomes implanted after a delay of some months, making the gestation period very long—nearly a year in the case of some martens. A few mustelids, such as weasels and polecats, may have two litters in the same year, but most have only a single litter usually consisting of about four young. Sea otters generally have only one young one at a time.

Weasels and badgers

The *Mustelidae* is divided into five subfamilies, the first of which contains the most typical members of the family including the weasels, polecats, minks, ferrets and stoats of the genus *Mustela*, and the longer-tailed, arboreal martens of the genus *Martes*, about 30 species in all. Many members of the group inhabit cool climates of northern Europe, Asia, and America. Being small, long and slender their bodies do not hold heat well, and so the mustelids of northern climates have superbly soft, dense fur. It is no accident that some of the most expensive and sought-after furs used in the fashion trade come from members of this group. Like other mammals of cool climates, many mustelids grow especially thick winter fur and for this reason the early fur-trappers of the Canadian north used to ply their trade in winter.

Left: A stoat, or ermine, *Mustela erminea*, with its prey. Stoats hunt a wide variety of small animals, including insectivores, rodents, rabbits, birds, lizards and insects; only rarely do they eat any plant material. Stoats are territorial animals, marking stones, tree stumps and other prominent features in their home ranges with a strong-smelling secretion from scent glands to warn off their rivals. They move quickly, stopping from time to time to survey their surroundings, sometimes standing up on their hind legs.

Right: A spotted skunk, *Spilogale putorius*, performs a 'handstand' before spraying its scent at an enemy.

Right: The wolverine, *Gulo gulo*, is the largest member of the weasel sub-family. It lives in northern Asia and North America where it feeds mainly on carrion, eggs and insects. It is an efficient predator, especially in the winter months when it can move noiselessly across the snow, but it usually hunts only when carrion is scarce. The wolverine can successfully tackle prey as large and strong as elks and lynxes.

Below: A female polecat, *Mustela putorius*, with her young. The babies are born in early summer after a pregnancy of six weeks and are weaned at one month. By the end of the summer they will be fully grown.

Frank Lane

S. C. Bisserot

Frank Lane

The largest of the weasels is the wolverine or glutton, *Gulo gulo*, of northern pine forests and tundras, which weighs about 18 kg (40 lb). It has long dark brown fur with unique water-repellent qualities. For this reason the fur is used to line the edges of the hoods of Eskimos' parkas. The wolverine normally feeds on lemmings, although it occasionally also kills reindeer. It owes its reputation for gluttony to its habit of using its powerful scent-glands to mark uneaten kills, thus seeming to spoil the meat that it cannot immediately eat. Its smaller relatives feed mainly on rodents and birds: the European polecat, *Mustela putorius*, has a well-deserved reputation for raiding chicken runs. Members of the subfamily are common in Europe, Asia and North America, but also occur in

Hans Reinhard/Bruce Coleman

Below: One of the most familiar mustelids is the Old World badger, *Meles meles*. It is active mainly in the evening and at night when it searches for fruit, roots, insects and other small animals. Badgers live in dens, or *setts*, which consist of numerous chambers and tunnels, with several entrances.

Right: An African clawless otter, *Aonyx capensis*, devouring a fish. This species differs from most other otters in having no claws and only very short webs between the fingers. This makes it considerably more skilful at grasping prey and other objects in its front paws than other species.

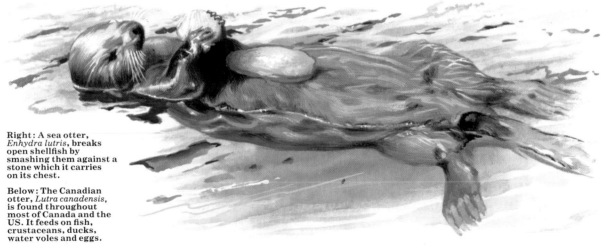

Right: A sea otter, *Enhydra lutris*, breaks open shellfish by smashing them against a stone which it carries on its chest.

Below: The Canadian otter, *Lutra canadensis*, is found throughout most of Canada and the US. It feeds on fish, crustaceans, ducks, water voles and eggs.

South America and in Africa, where one of them, the zorilla, *Ictonyx striatus*, has paralleled the evolution of the skunks in its black and white coat and defense behaviour.

Placed in a sub-family of its own is the ratel or honey badger, *Mellivora capensis*, of Africa and southern Asia. This species is best known for its relationship with the indicator bird, which postures and chatters in order to lead the ratel to wild bees' nests. The ratel, heavily built and strikingly marked in black and grey, rips open the nest with its claws and feeds on the honey, incidentally providing food for the birds. This is a good example of *symbiosis*, a partnership between two species from which both benefit.

The badgers and the slightly smaller ferret badgers of southern Asia make up

another sub-family which contains eight species. They are heavily built and usually eat both animal and plant food. For example, the common badger, *Meles meles*, of the woodlands of Europe and temperate Asia, which weighs about 13 kg (29 lb) and spends the day in extensive burrows, feeds on berries, roots, bulbs and acorns as well as invertebrates and mammals of up to the size of a rabbit. In North America it is replaced by a slightly smaller species, *Taxidea taxus*, which prefers open sandy plains.

Skunks and otters

The nine species of skunks are found only in the Americas, and make up the fourth sub-family. They too feed on a wide variety of plant materials as well as invertebrates and rodents. Presumably it is because they are among the least fierce of the carnivores that they have evolved their remarkable defensive system. Like many other mammals, mustelids have special scent-glands, which have primarily evolved as a means of signalling to other members of their own species. Like other glands in the skin, these glands tend to release their odour when the animal is under stress.

The paired scent-glands of the skunk, situated beneath the tail on either side of the anus, have become modified to serve as weapons of defence in situations where the animal feels threatened, and the scent itself has become virtually a poison gas. Armed in this way, and giving warning of their deterrent by means of bold black and white markings, skunks are quite fearless and rarely flee from potential enemies. If they are threatened they emphasize their markings by means of special displays: the spotted skunk, *Spilogale putorius*, of Central and North America performs handstands as a threat. Only if this does not deter the enemy is the secretion of its tail glands discharged, being squirted with considerable accuracy for up to 3.6 m (12 ft). Starting as a liquid, it rapidly becomes a poisonous and foul-smelling vapour. No enemy would willingly face an angry skunk twice.

The fifth mustelid sub-family contains the 18 species of otters. These have very thick fur which, even when the otter is swimming, always retains plenty of trapped air, forming a warm and flexible diving suit. In addition to the webbed feet, the powerful tail, which is horizontally flattened, is also used in swimming. Otters live near lakes and rivers, and sometimes on estuaries and sea coasts, in most parts of the world.

The Eurasian otter, *Lutra lutra*, occurs from Britain to North Africa and Sumatra, and is in many respects typical of the group. It weighs up to about 15 kg (33 lb) and feeds on invertebrates including crayfish, fish, frogs and small aquatic birds. The largest of the otters is the giant otter, *Pteronura brasiliensis*, of South America, which may be up to 2.2 m (7 ft) long and weigh 24 kg (54 lb). The rarest is the sea otter, *Enhydra lutris*, from the north Pacific which has been hunted almost to extinction for its fur. Sea otters live in groups on remote coasts, feeding on sea urchins, molluscs, crabs, fish and sea weed, and often swimming lazily on their backs.

Raccoons

The raccoon family, *Procyonidae*, is found only in the Americas. It contains 16 species, and its members are much more alike than those of the weasel family. Like mustelids and dogs, raccoons have long jaws, usually with four premolar teeth and two molars in each corner of the mouth. They have moderately long legs with five toes on each foot, and are usually plantigrade, the soles of the feet making contact with the ground at each step. The best-known member of the family is the North American raccoon, *Procyon lotor*, which lives in woods and forests, usually not far from water. The favourite food of this species is the fresh water crayfish.

The North American cacomistle, *Bassariscus astutus*, has a shorter nose and larger ears than the raccoon. It lives in woods and on dry, rocky hills, and is an efficient predator, catching small rodents

Above: A North American raccoon, *Procyon lotor*, searching for food near the edge of a lake. It will eat almost anything, from leaves and grass to snails, small mammals, fishes, crayfishes and occasionally birds. The habit of searching for food underwater with its fore-paws is retained in captivity: zoo animals place food items into water and then go through the motions of searching for them. This behaviour has led to the popular misconception that the raccoon washes its food.

Right: A ring-tailed coatimundi, *Nasua nasua*, from Brazil. Coatis spend much of their time on the forest floor searching for food, but seek refuge in trees when danger threatens.

with great skill. The coatimundis, *Nasua*, have long, pointed noses and live in the forests and bush of Central and South America. They travel in troops, poking their noses into the soil and into crevices in the bark of trees as they search for food. The most arboreal member of the family is the kinkajou, *Potos flavus*, which inhabits tropical forests and has a prehensile tail. It is nocturnal, and feeds primarily on fruit, using its long tongue in order to extract the pulpy flesh. The olingos, *Bassaricyon*, are very similar, but are unable to cling by means of their tails.

Pandas

The precise relationships of the two living species of pandas are still the subject of much argument among zoologists. When the giant panda, *Ailuropoda melanoleuca*, was first discovered on the remote, bamboo-covered plateaus of China by Père David, a French missionary, it was very understandably described as a black and white bear. Later, after a detailed examination of its anatomical features, it was classified as one of the raccoons. This was not such a startling change as it might appear to be, for the raccoons and the bears have evolved from the same ancestors, and a large raccoon will inevitably look bear-like. Today some zoologists once more believe that the giant panda rightly belongs to the bear family. It is no wonder that many experts, seeking to answer the problem of classification, place the pandas in a family of their own, the *Ailuropodidae*.

The giant panda's closest living

Below: The kinkajou, *Potos flavus*, is an expert climber and is the only member of the raccoon family to have a prehensile tail. Feeding mainly on fruit, such as wild fig, guava and mango, it occupies much the same ecological niche as the New World monkeys. It is, however, active at night rather than in the day.

Right: The lesser panda, *Ailurus fulgens*, lives in mountain forests and bamboo thickets from Nepal to western China. It is a nocturnal animal and feeds on bamboo shoots, grasses, fruit and occasionally insects and small mammals. When attacked the lesser panda defends itself efficiently with its long sharp claws.

Right: The giant panda 'Chia Chia' eating bamboo shoots at London Zoo. Giant pandas, *Ailuropoda melanoleuca*, have never been very common because they can thrive only in cool mountainous regions where bamboo is abundant. Today they live in the western part of Szechwan province in western China at altitudes of between 1,500 and 4,000 m (5,000 to 13,000 ft). In spite of their restricted distribution giant pandas are probably not in danger of extinction because the Chinese government conserves them with care.

Left and below: The curious 'playing' behaviour of the giant panda makes it a popular, if rare, zoo animal.

relation is undoubtedly the red panda, *Ailurus fulgens*, which looks much more like a raccoon than a bear. It is long-tailed and arboreal and lives in Asia on forested slopes of the Himalayas. The red panda is mainly active at dawn and dusk, when it feeds on lichens, acorns, and bamboo shoots. It spends much of the day sleeping either in the fork of a tree or in a hollow tree. Weighing only about 5 kg (11 lb) it is much smaller than the giant panda, but has the same pigeon-toed walk.

The giant panda eats a variety of foods, including some small animals, but the bulk of its diet consists of bamboo shoots which are like large, tough, woody grasses. It holds the shoots by means of a long wrist bone that works rather like a thumb. Its teeth are powerful, the molars having flattened crowns designed to crush and chew bamboo. Giant pandas need bulky bodies in order to be able to hold enough of their rather unpromising diet, and they weigh about 135 kg (300 lb). Despite their weight and their short tails, they can climb quite well, if rather clumsily, and climbing is their main defence against predators such as wolves.

It was not until the 1930s that giant pandas first appeared in zoos, and in the early 1970s they became instruments of diplomacy as the Chinese government presented pairs of them to zoos in Japan, the US, France and England. So far giant pandas have never bred in zoos outside their native continent, but the probability that they will soon do so is good. The female panda suckles her one or two young sitting up and holding them in her arms in a manner rather like that of primates.

Seals, Walruses and Sea Cows

Seals, sea lions and walruses are aquatic mammals belonging to the carnivore suborder *Pinnipedia*. This suborder is divided into three families: the true or earless seals, *Phocidae*, the eared seals, *Otariidae*, and the walruses, *Odobenidae*. The pinnipeds evolved from terrestrial carnivores but it is not known exactly when the transformation took place. Although fossil remains of seals from each of the three modern families have been discovered (dating from the Miocene epoch some 20 million years ago) they are from animals which already closely resemble their modern relatives. Many zoologists believe that the true seals have a separate ancestry from the eared seals and the walruses: they suggest that true seals evolved from a creature resembling an otter while the other two families had a bear-like ancestor.

Modern pinnipeds are very well adapted for an aquatic existence. Their bodies are streamlined and the digits of both front and hind limbs are fused together to form paddles or flippers for swimming. Although able to spend considerable lengths of time at sea, all seals must come ashore, on to land or ice, in order to breed. A female normally gives birth to a single calf which is suckled on land from one or two pairs of nipples which are hidden from view in pouches on the underside of her body.

True seals

The true seals have no obvious external ears. Their bodies and limbs are covered with a pelt of short, coarse hair which is moulted annually. The hind flippers are directed backwards, beside the tail, and are no use at all when the creature is moving on land. In the water the hind flippers spread out sideways like the tail-flukes of a porpoise and are used to propel the seal forwards while the front flippers are used for steering. True seals are, at best, rather awkward on land, moving forward by a series of wriggling jerks involving muscular contractions of the whole body.

The largest of the true seals are the elephant seals of which there are two species. The southern elephant seal, *Mirounga leonina*, is a huge animal found in Antarctic waters. A large bull may be as much as 7.6 m (25 ft) long and weigh up to three tonnes. The cows are about half this size. Breeding colonies, called 'rookeries', form each year on many Antarctic islands. The cows arrive at the rookeries in September and shortly after this each gives birth to a single calf. The bulls begin arriving in October for the next mating season and each one takes possession of a 'harem' of cows. Rival bulls are constantly fighting over the ownership of the largest harem and the losers of these fights are often severely wounded. During the 19th century, elephant seals were hunted almost to extinction for the sake of their blubber which was processed to yield an oil.

True seals are most numerous in the Antarctic and the crab-eating seal, *Lobodon carcinophagus*, is particularly abundant.

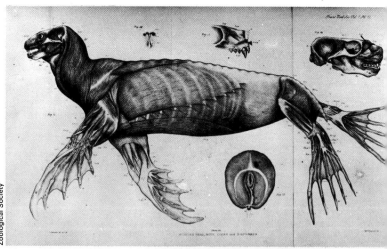

Right: This early anatomical illustration of a sea lion shows how the creature's outer muscles are arranged. Movement through the water is effected by flexing the body as well as moving the flippers.

Below: A herd of walruses, *Odobenus rosmarus*, lying on a rocky shore on the coast of Alaska. These creatures are much less common than they were a century ago having been hunted by man for their skin, meat and blubber. Apart from man, they have few enemies for they can defend themselves very effectively with their huge canine teeth. Polar bears and killer whales occasionally take young walruses, but rarely molest adults.

116

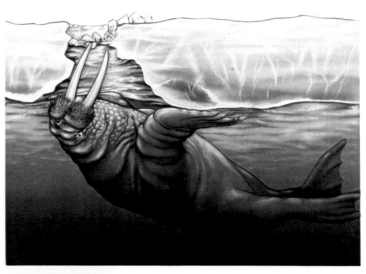

Left: A young walrus supports itself on one of its front flippers. Walruses, like sea lions, have quite well developed front limbs and can move about surprisingly rapidly on dry land.

Right: Walruses spend much of their time feeding beneath the pack ice, and they use their tusks to prevent breathing holes from freezing over. Walruses also use their tusks, which are enlarged upper canine teeth, to help haul themselves out of the water.

Below: The dugong, *Dugong dugon*, is found around the coasts of the Red Sea and the Indian Ocean as far east as northern Australia.

Rex Features

Allan Power/Bruce Coleman

Erik Pabst

A survey in the early 1970s estimated the total population of these seals at between two and five million animals. It is a slender and fast moving seal with an unusual method of feeding. Whereas the majority of seals feed on a variety of fishes, cephalopods and crustaceans the crab-eating seal feeds only on a type of small, free-swimming shrimp, known as *krill*. When feeding the seal swims into a shoal of krill, takes in a mouthful of the shrimp-filled water and then squeezes the water out between its cheek teeth which are specially shaped to trap the shrimps within the seal's mouth. Weddell's seal, *Leptonychotes weddelli*, is another inhabitant of the Antarctic pack-ice. It is larger than the crab-eating seals and is capable of underwater dives of prodigious depth and duration.

Around the British coastline there are only two resident species of seal, the larger of these being the grey seal, *Halichoerus grypus*. An adult bull may be over 2.7 m (9 ft) long. Grey seals are gregarious and large rookeries exist on various rocky islands and beaches around Britain. Breeding takes place in the autumn, and the pups grow extremely quickly, doubling their size and weight within a week of birth. The pups are born with a shaggy coat of white fur which is moulted when they are weaned at about three weeks. At this early age the pups are deserted by their mothers and must thereafter fend for themselves. The other resident British seal is the common or harbour seal, *Phoca vitulina*, a small seal about 1.7 m (5.5 ft) long. Common seals are monogamous and less gregarious than grey seals. Breeding takes place in mid-summer on offshore sandbanks and secluded beaches.

Eared seals

The eared seals are divided into two sub-families—sea lions, *Otariinae*, and fur seals, *Arctocephalinae*—and they differ from true seals in having small but distinct external ears. Their hind flippers, as well as providing the main propulsive force in the water, can also be brought forward sideways to help the animal move about on land. The front flippers are larger and more supple than those of true seals and they can be flapped together underwater to provide some propulsion as well as providing steering power. On land the front flippers support the forward part of the body and are used as true walking legs. Eared seals are a great deal more mobile on land than true seals.

Steller's sea lion, *Eumetopias jubatus*,

Below: Bull elephant seals, *Mirounga angustirostris*, fight for the possession of females on the Pacific coast of Mexico. Elephant seals are so called because the nose of the male is long and pendulous and can be inflated with air to form a proboscis reminiscent of an elephant's trunk.

Right: A sea lion about to eat a fish. The majority of sea lions are found in the southern oceans where fish are plentiful, but a few species live in the Northern Hemisphere. The Californian sea lion, *Zalophus californianus*, for example, inhabits the rocky coastal areas of the US West Coast.

James Tallon/NHPA

Far left: An encounter between sea lion cows during the breeding season. At this time of year each of the older bulls takes possession of a harem of about 15 cows, and there is much rivalry both between cows and bulls.

Left: A sea lion uses its rear flippers for grooming as well as for swimming.

Right: A female harp seal, *Payophilus groenlandicus*, resting on the ice. Harp seals are members of the family *Phocidae* and they are found in the North Atlantic. Their fur, particularly that of pups, is much prized by hunters, and because they spend so much time on the ice they make easy targets.

is one of the largest species of seal, adult males reaching a length of more than 3 m (10 ft) and a weight of one tonne. Each summer many thousands of these sea lions migrate to the Aleutian Islands to breed, the adult bulls arriving first, in early May, to establish territories. Pregnant females are the next to arrive and almost immediately each one gives birth to a single calf. The calves of sea lions are suckled by their mothers for a great deal longer than those of true seals; weaning is rarely completed in less than two or three months.

The Californian sea lion, *Zalophus californianus*, is a smaller, more agile species which inhabits the rocky coastal areas of California. This is the sea lion commonly seen in zoos and circuses around the world. It is a playful and intelligent animal and it appears to have a natural talent for performing tricks which require a fine sense of balance.

In their habits fur seals closely resemble their relatives the sea lions. The Alaska fur seal, *Callorhinus ursinus*, is found in the northern Pacific and breeds only in the fog-bound Pribilov Islands of the Bering Sea. At the height of the summer breeding season as many as two to three million seals congregate at the Pribilov rookeries. There are several other species of fur seal belonging to the genus *Arctocephalus* from the Southern Hemisphere.

The walrus

The walrus, *Odobenus rosmarus*, is the sole representative of the family *Odobenidae*. It has features in common with both true seals and eared seals although it is more closely related to the latter. Like true seals, walruses have no external ears, but they use both front and hind flippers when walking on land like the eared seals. The walrus inhabits the shallow Arctic coastal waters of the Atlantic and Pacific oceans, always living close to land or ice. Adult males reach a length of 3.7 m (12 ft) and weigh up to 1.5 tonnes, while the females are somewhat smaller and slimmer. Walrus skin is enormously thick and wrinkled and adults are almost completely hairless. In both sexes the upper canine teeth are greatly enlarged to form tusks which, in old males, may reach a length of 76 cm (30 in). Walruses feed mainly on shellfish, the tusks being used when feeding to rake the shellfish up off the sea-bed. Once inside the mouth they are crushed between massive cheek-teeth and the soft contents are sucked out and swallowed. Walruses breed during April and May.

Jacana

The bulls are polygamous and use their tusks as formidable weapons when fighting for possession of the females; old bulls are invariably heavily battle-scarred. Young walruses are not fully weaned until the end of their second year, probably because they are unable to feed properly until their tusks have grown.

Sea cows

Although sea cows are aquatic mammals and superficially resemble seals in many respects, they are quite unrelated and belong to a different order, the *Sirenia*. Indeed, the closest living relatives of sea cows are elephants. The order *Sirenia* is extremely ancient and sea cows were widespread in the oceans of the world as far back as the Eocene epoch some 40 to 50 million years ago. The order is divided into two families: the manatees, *Trichechidae*, and the dugongs, *Dugongidae*.

Sea cows are completely aquatic and they die very quickly if they become stranded on land. They are shy, slow moving creatures and they are entirely herbivorous, feeding on various water plants and sea-weeds. Their bodies are bulky and the tail is flattened horizontally to form a broad paddle, or 'fluke', which is used to propel the animal through the

Above: A herd of South African fur seals, *Arctocephalus pusillus*. Fur seals have a thick coat of soft waterproof underfur beneath their coarse outer hair, and this distinguishes them from their relatives the sea lions. Fur seals were once vigorously hunted for their fur, but today hunting is strictly controlled.

Below: A female hooded seal, *Cystophora cristata*, with her pup. The hooded seal is closely related to the elephant seal and it inhabits the drifting ice floes of the Arctic. Like elephant seals, the male hooded seal can inflate its nostrils with air to form a large bulbous air-sac or hood.

Fred Bruemmer

Fred Bruemmer

Left: A leopard seal, *Hydrurga leptonyx*, pursues a penguin off the coast of Antarctica. Penguins form a major part of the diet of the leopard seal, along with fish and the young of other seals. Penguins are notably reluctant to enter the water when leopard seals are patrolling nearby. When a leopard seal catches a penguin it shakes it vigorously and then swallows it complete with feathers and skin. Leopard seals get their name from their spotted markings. They are true seals, belonging to the family *Phocidae*. They are the only pinnipeds to feed on warm-blooded prey. Most seals feed exclusively on fish and invertebrates such as squid.

water. The hind limbs have disappeared completely and the front limbs are small and oar-shaped. The eyes of sea cows are very small and their faces are curiously grotesque because the upper lip is huge and mobile and adorned with a fringe of stiff bristles. The skin of the sea cow is thick and tough and beneath it is a layer of fat or blubber which helps to insulate the animal from the cold.

There are three species of manatee: the Florida manatee, *Trichechus manatus*, which is found in small numbers around the Gulf of Mexico and the Caribbean, the Amazonian manatee, *Trichechus inunguis* from the northeastern coast of South America and in the rivers Amazon and Orinoco, and the West African manatee, *Trichechus senegalensis*, which is very rare and occurs along the tropical west

coast of Africa. Manatees vary in length from 1.8 to 4 m (6 to 13 ft) and weigh from 270 to 900 kg (600 to 2000 lb). They are slate grey or black in colour and the huge upper lip is deeply divided in the centre into two prehensile halves which can be moved independently when gathering food into the mouth. The tail fluke is smooth and rounded and the flippers are sufficiently supple to be helpful in collecting food. The flippers are equipped with short nails and the body has a sparse covering of short hairs.

There is one living species of dugong and one species which became extinct within the last 200 years. The dugong, *Dugong dugon*, is found around the coasts of the Indian Ocean. Dugongs are slightly smaller than manatees and are more highly adapted for aquatic life. The

upper lip has no cleft in it and the tail fluke has a deep indentation in the centre. The clawless flippers are less supple than those of manatees and are no use in feeding. The body is completely hairless and male dugongs have two short tusks in their upper jaws.

Steller's sea cow, *Hydrodamalis stelleri*, an extinct member of the dugong family, was first discovered in the cold Bering Sea in 1741 by the German naturalist Steller. It was a huge animal which grew to a length of 7.6 m (25 ft). Its skin was curiously rough and bark-like and instead of teeth it had horny plates on the inside of its mouth which it used to chew the seaweed on which it fed. Within 17 years of their discovery, the Steller's sea cows had been completely exterminated by hunters and traders.

Whales

Of all the mammals, both living and extinct, whales are the most perfectly adapted to an aquatic way of life. So perfect is this adaptation that, until comparatively recent times, naturalists mistakenly classified them as fish. Belonging to the order *Cetacea*, they are descended from four-legged, terrestrial mammals, although there is some uncertainty as to precisely which early mammals were their true ancestors. The change from terrestrial to aquatic habitat probably took place in the Palaeocene epoch some 65 million years ago.

Whales have streamlined, fish-shaped bodies and they lack a proper neck as a result of shortening or, in some cases, joining of the neck vertebrae. The body tapers smoothly towards the tail which is expanded out horizontally on both sides to form two flat, pointed tail flukes which provide the whale with propulsive power when they are beaten up and down in the water. Cetaceans show no trace of hind limbs and the front limbs have evolved to become smooth paddle-shaped flippers which are used for balancing and steering. Most whales have a dorsal fin positioned on the midline of the back which varies considerably in size and shape depending on the species.

Like all mammals, whales breathe air. Air is inhaled and exhaled through a special nasal opening known as the blow-hole which is situated on the highest point of the head behind the snout.

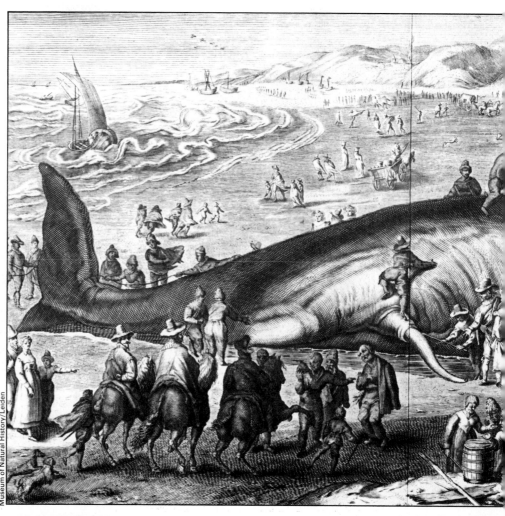

Museum of Natural History/Leiden

P. Morris

The position of the blowhole allows the whale to breathe when only a small portion of its head and back are above the surface of the water. The blowhole has a characteristic shape for each species, and a few of the larger whales have two blowholes instead of the more usual one. Air is exhaled from the blowhole explosively, producing a blow or spout. The spout consists of mucus and water which forms as the whale's breath condenses in the air. The whale's windpipe is completely separated from its throat or pharynx so that it can open its mouth under water and breath at the same time.

The openings of the female's reproductive organs lie in a narrow slit on the underside of the body in front of the anus. The nipples are hidden in recesses on each side. When suckling, the nipples

Above: A Dutch engraving dating from about 1600 shows a stranded male sperm whale, *Physeter catodon.* The artist was clearly more interested in showing the size of the creature, which is slightly exaggerated, than in anatomical accuracy, for the eye (which is too large) and the flippers are wrongly positioned.

Right and far right: Sections through the skin of a dolphin and skin from a human palm. The dolphin's skin is perfectly smooth to reduce water resistance, and the dark cells (1) show through the outer transparent layer (2). It lacks the ridges (3) and sweat glands (4) which are typical of human skin.

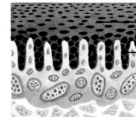

Above: A pilot whale, *Globicephala scammoni,* from the Pacific Ocean. These animals are toothed whales and they live in herds of 100 or more individuals, feeding on fish and marine invertebrates, notably cuttlefish. They belong to the same subfamily as the killer whale and can grow to a length of 8.5 m (28 ft).

Right: The white whale, *Delphinapterus leucas,* is a close relation of the narwhal, and it is found in the oceans of the Northern Hemisphere. Although preferring Arctic waters, white whales are sometimes found along the coasts of northern Europe. The creature's blowhole and broad tail flukes are plainly visible in this picture.

P. Morris

Right: A dolphin drives itself through the water by beating its tail flukes up and down with its powerful body muscles.

are protruded and milk is rapidly injected by the female directly into the calf's mouth. Suckling is rapid and takes place while both cow and calf are fully submerged. In the male the testes are internal and the penis lies beneath the abdominal skin in an almost coiled form. Beneath the skin, the whale's body is completely encased in an envelope of thick fat or blubber. For hundreds of years whales have been hunted by man for the sake of this blubber which, once refined, gives rise to a commercially valuable whale oil. Whale flesh is used in the manufacture of pet foods and is eaten by humans in some countries.

The whales are divided into two sub-orders: the baleen or whalebone whales, *Mysticeti*, which include the right whales, rorquals and humpback whales, and the toothed whales, *Odontoceti*, which include the sperm whales, beaked whales, narwhals, dolphins and porpoises.

Toothed whales

The *Odontoceti* or toothed whales are generally smaller than the whalebone whales and they have only a single blowhole. Toothed whales feed on fish, squid and cuttlefish, and one species, the killer whale, also feeds on sea birds, seals and

other whales. The behaviour of toothed whales is better known than that of whalebone whales because many of the smaller species are kept and studied at marine parks and oceanariums around the world. They are gregarious, playful animals and communicate with each other by means of clicks, whistles and quacking sounds.

Many, if not all, of the toothed whales are able to navigate in the dark by echolocation: the whale emits a pulse of ultrasonic clicks and then listens to the echoes of these clicks reflected off nearby objects. The pattern and quality of the returning echoes gives the whale detailed information about its surroundings and enables it to hunt for food in total darkness. As far as is known, whalebone whales cannot navigate by echolocation.

The sperm whale, *Physeter catodon*, is by far the largest of the toothed whales, adult males growing to a length of 18 m (60 ft). The females are considerably smaller. Each tooth is about 20 cm (8 in) long and weighs about 2.7 kg (6 lb). Sperm whales have a characteristic, domed forehead containing a large organ filled with a waxy substance called *spermaceti* which was once highly valued as an industrial lubricant and was also used in the manufacture of candles. The purpose of the spermaceti-producing organ is unknown but it may be involved in echolocation. Sperm whales were extensively hunted for their spermaceti and blubber, and in the days of sailing ships and hand-thrown harpoons the capture of these whales was a dangerous business. Unlike most other whales, sperm whales have been known to attack whaling boats, either ramming them

Below: A series of photographs showing the birth of a dolphin. Whales are born tail first, unlike most large mammals, and because they are born underwater they do not attempt to breathe at once. Only when the mother has nosed her newborn calf to the surface does it fill its lungs with air.

Below right: Bottle-nosed dolphins, Tursiops truncatus, are familiar performers at oceanariums throughout the world. They seem to delight in co-operating with their trainers and soon learn to perform the most remarkable tricks. They grow to a length of 3.6 m (12 ft) and come from the North Atlantic.

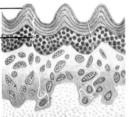

Below: Like all other whales, killer whales, Orcinus orcas, mate by swimming alongside each other belly to belly. Killer whales are the only cetaceans which regularly tackle warm-blooded prey such as dolphins, seals and penguins. Packs of 40 or more killer whales have even been known to overcome baleen whales.

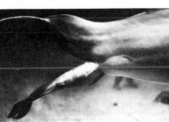

Rex Features

Rex Features

Francisco Erize/Bruce Coleman

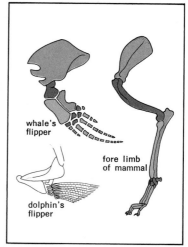

Left: The whale's flipper has the same construction as a land mammal's fore limb, with adaptations. In the dolphin's flipper the size of the major bones has been reduced, while the 'hand' has become longer. The digits are completely enclosed in fibrous tissue.

Right: Whalebone whales eat small planktonic shrimps called *krill*. After drawing in a mouthful of sea water and krill (above), it lowers its whalebone plates to form a huge sieve (the *baleen*) through which the water is expelled, trapping the krill (below). It then collects the krill with its tongue.

whale's flipper

fore limb of mammal

dolphin's flipper

Rex Features

Left: An Amazon river dolphin, *Inia geoffrensis*, is caught for an aquarium. It has a longer snout and smaller eyes than its salt-water cousins.

Above left: A black and white dolphin, *Cephalorhynchus commersoni*, skims the surface of the southern ocean off the coast of Argentina.

with the snout or splintering them like matchwood between their massive jaws.

The narwhal, *Monodon monoceros*, is a peculiar, small whale inhabiting Arctic waters. Adult narwhals have only two teeth in the upper jaw, and in the male one of these teeth, usually the left one, is enormously enlarged to form a long, straight, spirally twisted horn or tusk which projects to a length of 2 m (6.5 ft) from the whale's snout. Although many suggestions have been made, it is not known how the narwhal uses its tusk.

Dolphins and porpoises

The dolphin family contains many species of small toothed whales. The largest of these is the killer whale, *Orcinus orca*, which grows to a length of 9 m (30 ft), has a striking black and white coloration and a very tall dorsal fin. Killer whales have about 50 sharp, conical teeth and are, as their name suggests, fierce predators. Their reputation as man-eaters, however, is probably undeserved for in captivity they have proved to be surprisingly gentle and co-operative.

The true dolphins are among the fastest of marine animals and are capable of reaching a speed of 25 knots in pursuit of the fish on which they feed. Dolphins usually travel around in large schools, sometimes containing hundreds of animals. They are natural acrobats and in the wild they frequently jump high out of the water when playing. Schools of dolphins often accompany ships at sea, positioning themselves at the front of the ship where they ride the bow-wave like surfers. They seem to enjoy this activity immensely and jostle each other for the best positions for wave riding.

Dolphins are curiously friendly towards humans and there are a few authenticated cases of dolphins attempting to rescue drowning swimmers by swimming underneath them and pushing them towards the surface. They will behave in the same way with injured members of their own species. In captivity, no dolphin, however severely provoked, has ever been known seriously to attack its trainer. In the wild, dolphins attack and kill sharks without hesitation and in the breeding season the males sometimes injure each other in fights, so there is little doubt that they could kill or maim a human if they wished to do so.

Many small toothed whales, dolphins included, have relatively large and complex brains and there seems to be little doubt among scientists that these are highly intelligent animals. Some zoologists who have studied dolphins firmly maintain that they must have a language of their own which is suffiiciently complex to allow them to convey complicated instructions to each other. If this is true then dolphins must have an intellectual level comparable to man's and far above that of our nearest living relative, the chimpanzee which is highly intelligent, but has no language of its own.

The common porpoise, *Phocaena phocaena*, is one of the smallest whales, measuring 1.5 to 1.8 m (5 to 6 ft) in length. It is found in the North Atlantic and is one of the most familiar whales to be found along the coasts of Europe. Occasionally porpoises enter the mouths of large rivers, such as the Seine and the Thames, and they may travel upstream for several kilometres.

Whalebone whales

The most characteristic feature of a whalebone or baleen whale is its enormous mouth equipped with rows of whalebone plates which are used to strain food from the water. Each strip of whalebone is made up of thousands of long hairs which have grown together to form a single rigid plate with a fringe of stiff bristles

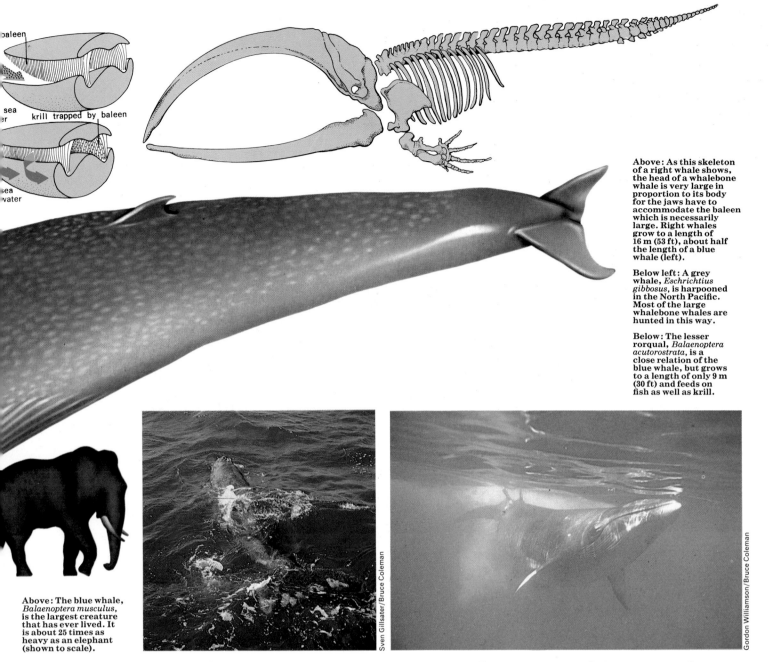

baleen

sea water

krill trapped by baleen

sea water

Above: As this skeleton of a right whale shows, the head of a whalebone whale is very large in proportion to its body for the jaws have to accommodate the baleen which is necessarily large. Right whales grow to a length of 16 m (53 ft), about half the length of a blue whale (left).

Below left: A grey whale, *Eschrichtius gibbosus*, is harpooned in the North Pacific. Most of the large whalebone whales are hunted in this way.

Below: The lesser rorqual, *Balaenoptera acutorostrata*, is a close relation of the blue whale, but grows to a length of only 9 m (30 ft) and feeds on fish as well as krill.

Above: The blue whale, *Balaenoptera musculus*, is the largest creature that has ever lived. It is about 25 times as heavy as an elephant (shown to scale).

Sven Gillsater/Bruce Coleman

Gordon Williamson/Bruce Coleman

projecting from the end. There may be hundreds of individual plates within the jaws of a single whale. The plates are rooted at their bases to the inside of the upper jaw and can be raised when the animal has its mouth closed to lie along the roof of the mouth. When the whale is feeding the plates are lowered to form a dense barricade, called the *baleen*, at the entrance to the mouth. The whalebone whales are filter-feeders and they use their baleens as gigantic sieves to extract shrimp-like organisms called *krill* from the water. After feeding, a large whale may have as much as ten tonnes of krill in its stomach.

Surprisingly little is known about the behaviour of whalebone whales. Most of them are migratory, spending the winter in tropical and temperate waters and migrating to the poles in summer, those in the Northern Hemisphere wintering in the arctic and those in the Southern Hemisphere in the Antarctic. Though occasionally observed on their own, these whales are sociable animals and are usually seen in pairs or small groups called *pods*. When migrating some species form huge schools of more than a thousand individuals. To communicate with each other, certain species produce

an extraordinary 'song' made up of a series of peculiar squeals, grunts and moans. Many species migrate to specific areas in order to breed. Calves are born after a gestation period of about 11 months and are suckled by their mothers for from four to seven months depending on the species. Their rate of growth is astonishing: a whale calf may double its weight within the first week of life.

Right whales are unusual in having no dorsal fin and, unlike other whalebone whales, the right whale has no grooves on the underside of its throat. The mouth is a curious shape with the upper jaw being strongly arched and containing up to 600 plates of whalebone, each with a maximum length of 3.6 m (12 ft). Right whales formed the basis of the earliest whaling industries, indeed they are thought to have got their name simply because early whalers considered them the 'right' whales to hunt. They are unable to swim very fast and were successfully pursued and killed from rowing boats. The Greenland right whale or bowhead whale, *Balaena mysticetus*, is now very rare but still occurs in the Atlantic west of Greenland. It is dark grey in colour and grows to a length of 18 m (60 ft).

Rorqual whales are usually more slender and streamlined than right whales. The mouth is smaller and less grotesque, the back is equipped with a dorsal fin and there are conspicuous grooves on the throat. It is believed that these grooves enable the throat to expand when the whale is feeding so that a greater volume of water can be taken into the mouth. Until the advent of motorized whaling ships and harpoon guns, the rorqual whales were virtually unmolested by man because they are too swift to be pursued by a rowing boat. In this century, however, they have been the subject of a terrible slaughter and many are in danger of becoming extinct.

The blue whale, *Balaenoptera musculus*, is the largest of the rorquals and is also the largest animal which has ever lived. Blue whales sometimes reach a length of 33 m (110 ft) and a weight of 130 tonnes. Once widespread throughout the world, these whales are now exceptionally rare having been hunted almost to extinction by the whaling industry. Many scientists believe that the population of blue whales is now so drastically reduced that it has no hope of recovery and that the species will inevitably disappear in the near future.

Lampreys, Sharks and Rays

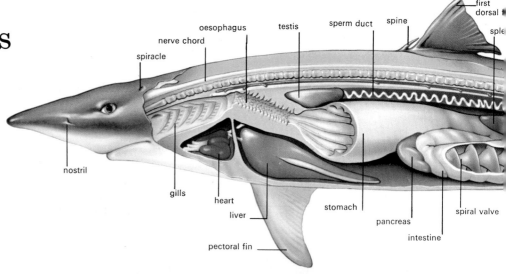

spiracle · nerve chord · oesophagus · testis · sperm duct · spine · first dorsal · sple · nostril · gills · heart · liver · stomach · pancreas · intestine · spiral valve · pectoral fin

The earliest vertebrates of which we have reasonably detailed knowledge were fresh-water fish, known as *agnathans*, which lived well over 300 million years ago. While not totally dissimilar from modern fish in form, these primitive fish lacked bony jaws. Most were flattened from the back of their bodies to the front, and lived near the river or lake bed. Almost certainly they fed on small organic particles which they found on the ooze and mud.

The living descendants of these fish are known as *cyclostomes*—like their ancestors they are jawless. Their skeletons are made of cartilage, they have long slender bodies and look rather like eels. There are two groups of cyclostomes, the hagfish and the lampreys.

Lampreys and hagfish

Hagfish live only in temperate or cold sea water. By day they bury themselves in the sea bed, emerging to feed at night. They are blind, for their eyes are covered with pigmented skin, but each of them has a single, very efficient nostril which helps them to find the dead or dying fish, as well as invertebrates such as ragworms and shrimps which live on the sea bed—on which they feed. A hagfish also has finger-like feelers around its mouth.

Like their relatives, the lampreys, hagfish have no scales and instead their skin is protected by a copious secretion of slime. For respiration they have between six and fourteen pairs of gill-slits each, but their relatives the lampreys always have seven pairs. Another important difference between the two groups is that adult lampreys have well-developed eyes. The heart of both hagfish and lampreys is a very simple structure being a mere muscular thickening of a curved part of the main artery.

All lampreys breed in fresh water and the sexes are separate. (Although not all invertebrate animals have separate sexes, it is always the case among vertebrates). Both sexes gather in swift-running water and, using their mouths, make a simple nest by moving the stones. The males then fertilize the eggs while the females spawn, and the eggs are buried in the sand by the movement of the parents' bodies. After about 20 days each egg hatches as a larva, called an *ammocoete*, which lives for about five years before metamorphosing into an adult.

The lamprey larvae are in many ways like their distant relative, the invertebrate chordate *amphioxus*. They bury themselves and feed by taking water in at the mouth and passing it through the pharynx where mucus traps the small planktonic food particles. Cilia on the wall of the pharynx pass the mucus together with the food to the simple, uncoiled gut for digestion. This is very similar to the feeding of amphioxus, although in the lamprey larvae the water current passes in at the mouth and out of the gills as a result of muscular action—a fish-like procedure—rather than by ciliary action.

Some kinds of lampreys spend their

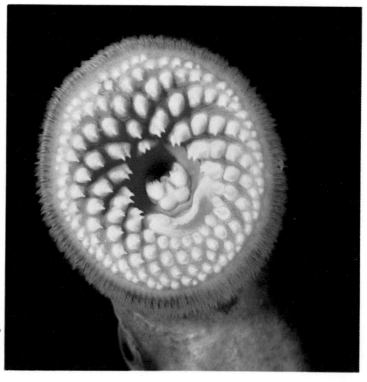

Heather Angel

Below and left: A sea lamprey, *Petromyzon marinus*, clinging to a host fish and a close up of its sucker. Like the earliest vertebrates, lampreys do not have jaws. They are usually parasitic, feeding on the body tissue and blood of a host fish. The sucker is equipped with rows of hooked teeth surrounding the central mouth opening. Within the mouth can be seen a tongue carrying two larger teeth for tearing away the flesh of the host. Around the edge of the sucker is a circular lip. The lamprey's sucker is extremely powerful and it is almost impossible for a fish to dislodge the parasite. In the end the host usually dies from loss of blood or tissue damage.

Right: A nurse shark, *Ginglymostoma cirratum*. These animals are found in the shallow coastal waters of warm seas. Indeed they often lie in such shallow water that their dorsal fins break the surface. They reach a length of about two metres (six feet). As in many sharks the upper lobe of the tail fin is larger than the lower one.

Seaphot

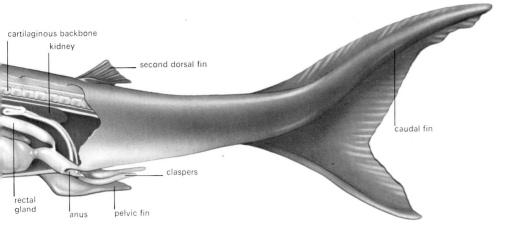

cartilaginous backbone
kidney
second dorsal fin
caudal fin
claspers
rectal gland
anus
pelvic fin

adult lives in the sea, migrating into rivers only to breed, while others spend their entire lives in fresh water. Most are parasitic, and have rounded, sucker-like mouths. They cling on to the host fish with their teeth, feeding on its muscle and blood. Anticoagulants in the lamprey's saliva prevent the blood of the host fish from clotting as the parasite feeds. They will attack a variety of fish including mackerel, cod and salmon, and marks left by lampreys have even been found on the skin of whales.

Although they are sometimes caught for human consumption while they are migrating, the chief economic significance of lampreys lies in the damage they can do to commercial fisheries. The best-known case concerns the lampreys which entered the Great Lakes of North America through newly dug canals and, in a very few years, so decimated the population of lake trout and other fish that a formerly valuable fishery became worthless. Despite their primitive features the cyclostomes are evidently still a force to be reckoned with.

Cartilaginous fish

The best known cartilaginous fish are the sharks, dogfish, skates and rays which all belong to one subclass, the *Elasmobranchii*. Despite the fact that they are often grouped together with bony fish, cartilaginous fish form a distinct class on their own, little more resembling bony fish than the bony fish themselves resemble amphibians. Like hagfish and lampreys they have skeletons made up of cartilage rather than hard bone.

Although not as strong as bone, cartilage is lighter and it is strong enough to provide support in the water where buoyancy makes large animals almost or completely weightless. Another characteristic of most of these fish is the *spiracle*, an opening behind the eye leading to the gill system. Drawing at least part of the oxygenated water required for respiration through the spiracle is particularly helpful to a flat-bodied fish like a skate or ray. Their mouth, being on the under surface of the body, would supply sandy or muddy water to the delicate gills if it was used for breathing. Elasmobranchs have separate gill slits opening directly on to the body surface. There are usually five pairs of gill slits but no gill cover, or *operculum*.

The entire body surface including the fins of sharks and the other cartilaginous fish is covered in pointed scales. In structure, these scales are very similar to the teeth of other vertebrates, containing a pulp cavity and nerves. This is not surprising, for the elasmobranchs' teeth are simply specially adapted scales round the mouth. Other vertebrates, including man, are descended from the same ancestors as the elasmobranchs, and it is these teeth which we have inherited. In the case of mammals, the teeth are the only scales that we retain.

Sharks and dogfish

Sharks and dogfish belong to the order *Selachii* and they are perhaps the most typical of the cartilaginous fish. There are some 200 different species all of which are good swimmers with streamlined bodies. But even with their light cartilaginous skeletons they are slightly heavier than the water in which they swim and so have the same problem as aeroplanes;

Above left: A reef shark partly cut away to show the internal body structure. The animal has a skeleton made of cartilage. The backbone encloses a notochord and, above the notochord, is a spinal chord. The brain is protected by a case called the cranium, a feature typical of vertebrate animals. The gill slits are used for respiration, and oxygenated water is supplied through the mouth and through openings in the body wall called spiracles. The intestine is fairly short and shaped in the form of a spiral.

Left: A large wobbegong shark, *Orectolobus maculatus*, is well camouflaged against the sea bed. The animal has a wide, flat head fringed with skin flaps which look like seaweed and break up the body outline.

Below: A tiger shark, *Galeocardo cuvieri*. These animals are found along the coasts of warm seas where they reach a length of about 4.5 m (15 ft). They feed on almost anything, even rubbish from rivers, and they can be a threat to swimmers.

Ben Cropp

Flip Schulke/Black Star

125

John X. Sundance/Jacana

Keystone

Ron Taylor/Transworld

Left: Sharks are among the most successful predators in the sea. Three characteristics contribute much to their success: sharp biting teeth, mobility and an efficient nervous system. The long thin teeth of these sand sharks, *Carchariidae*, are plainly visible.

Right: A series of diagrams to show how a shark moves through the water by sideways movements of the body.

Below: The birth of a shark. The embryo develops in the sea protected by a horny case secreted by a special gland in the mother. The young of some sharks reach an advanced stage of development in the oviduct of the female and are born live.

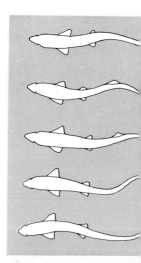

they must use power to stay up. Their bodies are somewhat flattened at the front, and thick-based immobile pectoral fins project from each side like stubby delta wings. The whole front end of the body thus works like an aeroplane's wing to provide 'lift' as the animal moves through the water.

A few kinds of selachians have evolved mechanisms enabling them to float weightlessly. For example, the huge oily livers of the basking sharks, *Cetorhinus maximus*, act as buoyancy organs, for oil is lighter than water. The sand tiger shark, *Carcharias taurus*, swallows air and uses its own intestines as water wings. Most sharks and dogfish, however, must either keep swimming or sink, and some, like the leopard shark, *Triakis semifasciata*, of the Pacific Ocean, just keep swimming endlessly, day and night, as automatically as we breathe. Others, such as the dogfish, *Scyliorhinus canicula*, which provide us with 'rock salmon', live in shallow seas and spend much of their time lying on the bottom.

For the predatory shark, being unable to hang suspended in the water means that after it has homed in on its prey, it is unable to keep still and take a leisurely bite—it would sink before it could do so. Instead it must keep swimming, biting as it passes. However, this does not seem to be much of a disadvantage since sharks are among the fiercest and most successful predators in the sea.

Not all selachians are hunters. Dogfish, for example, are scavengers and the huge basking sharks, which may be up to 12 m (40 ft) long, swim only sluggishly and feed on plankton which they strain from the water using projections of the gill skeleton known as gill rakers. However, in warm and tropical seas there are a number of fierce predatory sharks. The great white shark, *Carcharodon carcharias*, is greatly feared along the coasts of Australia. A relatively small specimen 4.5 m (15 ft) long can quite easily bite a man in half. The largest great white sharks reach a length of up to 12m (40 ft) and weigh about three tonnes. Among

other species which are dangerous to man are the great blue sharks, *Prionace glauca*, the tiger shark, *Galeocardo cuvieri* and the mako, *Isurus oxyrinchus*.

Sharks usually hunt alone, but they will sometimes attack in packs especially if there is blood in the water. When attacking humans, sharks seem to single out a victim, often a bather, and then completely disregard all others who may be in the vicinity.

Sharks in action

Defensive measures adopted by swimmers in shark-infested seas have varied over the years. At one time it was thought sensible to thrash about in the water, using noise to frighten the sharks away. This is definitely a mistake. During the Second World War the American forces in the Pacific used shark repellent tablets which, by dissolving in the water, were thought to ward off sharks. These tablets had psychological value, helping struggling swimmers to keep their spirits up, but are now known to have had little effect upon the sharks. Presumably where the tablets failed, dissatisfied customers did not return to complain.

Modern research on the sharks' senses reveals that they have very good hearing. They often feed on wounded or unhealthy fish, which swim clumsily, making a noise in the water as they do so. Homing in on the sound, sharks then use their efficient noses to pick up such clues as traces of blood in the water. When they are very close indeed to their prey their inefficient eyes, able to see only in black and white and incapable of seeing detail, guide them for the last few feet.

Above: A great blue shark, *Prionace glauca*. This animal feeds mainly on herring, mackerel and tuna, but will attack almost any other animal including other sharks and man. It is an open sea fish and is therefore only rarely a danger to bathers. Blue sharks sometimes damage fishing nets in an attempt to reach the catch.

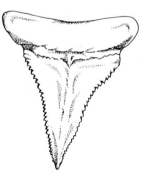

Left and above: A great white shark, *Carcharodon carcharias*, and a drawing of one of its upper teeth. White sharks feed on animals as large as dolphins and sea lions, and they are reputedly the fiercest of all sharks.

Right: Whale sharks, *Rhincodon typus*, are completely harmless to man and, as this picture indicates, they are not at all shy. They are reported to reach lengths of up to 18 m (60 ft) but this one is only 10 m (34 ft) long. Like basking sharks, whale sharks feed on plankton. They are found in the warmer parts of most oceans.

Ben Cropp

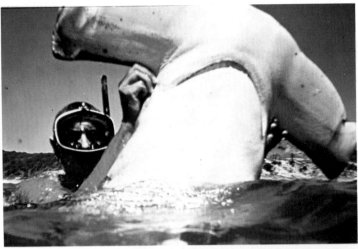

Left: A hammerhead shark, *Sphyrna*. The animal's eyes are carried on the two opposite ends of the hammer-shaped snout. Unlike most sharks, hammerheads do not have spiracles.

Below: A giant manta ray, *Manta birostris*, flaps its way through the water. Mantas can have a 'wingspan' of as much as 7 m (23 ft) and reach a weight of two tonnes. They swim along with their mouths held wide open to catch small fish and crustaceans. Mantas are sometimes seen to leap right out of the water, landing back on the surface with a slap that can be heard from a distance of a mile or more. This behaviour may be an attempt to dislodge parasitic crustaceans.

Transworld

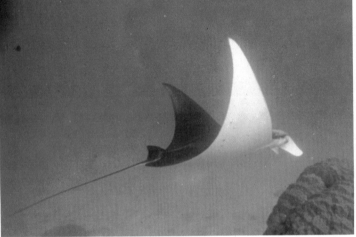

Okapia

Above: A chimaera, *Chimaera monstrosa*. Although they have skeletons made of cartilage, these fish are quite unlike other cartilaginous fish. There are four covered gill slits and the upper jaw is firmly joined to the cranium. At the front of the first dorsal fin is a sharp spine which is highly poisonous.

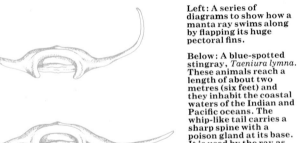

Left: A series of diagrams to show how a manta ray swims along by flapping its huge pectoral fins.

Below: A blue-spotted stingray, *Taeniura lymna*. These animals reach a length of about two metres (six feet) and they inhabit the coastal waters of the Indian and Pacific oceans. The whip-like tail carries a sharp spine with a poison gland at its base. It is used by the ray as a defensive weapon and can cause severe injury and prolonged illness in man: the spine often breaks off and remains in the wound. Their flattened bodies and back markings equip rays for life on the ocean floor. They feed mainly on invertebrates such as mussels and snails.

Allan Power/Bruce Coleman

Even the fiercest of sharks do not always attack. Their moods are difficult to predict. The fact that attacks by sharks on humans have tended to increase in recent years has much more to do with changes in human behaviour than that of the sharks. Skindiving in warm waters provides sharks with tempting targets. In cooler waters, such as those around Britain's coasts, man-eating sharks are not found.

Skates and rays

Skates and rays belong to the order *Rajiformes*. In structure they are very similar to sharks, but they are even more flattened, with wing-like pectoral fins merging smoothly with the sides of the body. This flattened shape enables the animal to lie on the sea bed without being seen and also helps in swimming. Rays can glide through the water in much the same way that paper darts fly through the air. Some, like the thornback ray, *Raja clavata*, found along the Atlantic coasts of Europe feed on shrimps and other crustaceans, while the huge manta ray *Manta birostris*, flaps its way through the surface waters of the Atlantic feeding on plankton. The sawfish *Pristis pectinatus*, of tropical seas, kills fish for food by flailing its long toothed snout from side to side.

Rays usually avoid predators by remaining concealed on the sea bottom, but they are often well equipped to protect themselves if attacked. Electric rays are capable of delivering a severe electric shock to any potential assailant, and the mechanism is also used to disable prey. The most common of these animals is the eyed electric ray, *Torpedo torpedo*, found in the eastern Atlantic and the Mediterranean. Stingrays have poison spines which can inflict deep wounds and break off to remain in the attacker's body. In man such an injury is extremely painful and can lead to an illness lasting many weeks.

The guitar fish, *Rhinobatos rhinobatos*, looks rather like a combination between a ray and a shark. The front part of the body is flattened like that of a ray, but the tail is fairly thick and carries fins like a shark's tail. The animal is found in the eastern Atlantic and in the Mediterranean living in shallow coastal waters. It feeds on invertebrates which live on the sea bed and can therefore cause considerable damage to oyster beds.

Unlike most bony fishes, sharks, dogfish, rays and skates produce relatively few eggs. These are fertilized inside the mother's body, and in a few cases the eggs are retained inside the mother's body until they emerge as live young. In most species, however, the large yolky eggs are laid in a horny egg-case. When empty these are sometimes washed ashore to be picked up by holiday makers who call them 'mermaids' purses'.

Chimaeras

The chimaeras or ratfishes are also cartilaginous fish, but they are placed in a subclass of their own, the *Bradyodonti*, because they differ from elasmobranchs in a number of ways. In particular, the upper jaw is fixed firmly to the cranium. They have flattened, grinding teeth, feed on small fish and invertebrates, and never attain any great size. Although they are found throughout the world, there are only about 25 living species of chimaeras. Unlike their larger relatives they are weak swimmers.

Rays, like sharks and dogfish, belong to the sub-class *Elasmobranchii*. They have skeletons of cartilage, not hard bone, and their separate gill slits open directly on to the body surface.

130

The Primates

An Orang-utan family. Offspring are
usually born one at a time, after a
gestation period of 8 to 9 months,
average weight at birth being 3.3lbs.

Old World Monkeys

The monkeys of Africa and Asia belong to the same infraorder, *Catarrhina*, as the great apes and man himself. Although some of them can walk upright on their hind legs for short distances they generally walk on all fours. They have flattened nails on all fingers and toes, and, like all primates except tree shrews, they are able to grasp objects between the thumb and forefinger. Many Old World monkeys have long tails to help them balance when moving through the trees, but these are never prehensile as they are in many African monkeys. Also, the nostrils of Old World monkeys are closer together than they are in their American cousins.

All monkeys and apes are thought to have originated from a family of lower primates, the *Omomyidae*, which inhabited Europe and North America in the early Tertiary period some 60 million years ago. Descendants of these creatures migrated southwards, probably about 50 million years ago in the Eocene epoch, from North America to South America and from Europe to Africa and southern Asia. The two groups thus became geographically separated and evolved along slightly different lines to produce the zoologically distinct New and Old World monkeys we know today.

The African and Asian monkeys are

divided into two families, the *Cercopithecidae* which includes the macaques, baboons, guenons, drills and mandrills, and the *Colobidae* which includes the colobus monkeys, the proboscis monkey and the langurs. Man has been attracted by monkeys from the earliest times, the obvious resemblances to humans making them particularly fascinating. Two species of baboon were regarded as sacred by the ancient Egyptians and one of them, *Papio anubis*, still bears the name of their god of the dead, Anubis. Monkeys have always been popular research animals. As long ago as the second century AD the Greek physician Galen dissected baboons and other monkeys in the hope that he would learn about human anatomy.

Macaques

Macaques are found in southern and central Asia from India to Japan. They are heavily built monkeys reaching a maximum weight of about 13 kg (29 lb), and their fur is usually a yellowish brown colour. Like many Old World monkeys they have conspicuous pads of hard, hairless skin on the buttocks which develop after puberty and are often reddish in colour.

One of the best known macaques is the Barbary ape, *Macaca sylvana*, which gets its misleading name from the fact that, like the true apes, it has no tail. Living in North Africa and Gibraltar, it is the only macaque to be found outside Asia. Whether it was introduced to Gibraltar by man or whether it has always been a resident there is uncertain, but fossil remains of similar monkeys have been found in various parts of Europe. They live in family troops and are quite bold even in their North African habitat where they frequently raid gardens and fields. This behaviour has, not surprisingly, made them unpopular with the human population and they are killed as pests in some regions.

Another well known macaque is the rhesus monkey, *Macaca mulatta*, from northern India, China, Burma and Thailand. Their true homes are the forests of

Above: Rhesus monkeys, *Macaca mulatta*, enjoy the protection of a temple at Kathmandu, Nepal. Grooming, as seen here, is an important activity for most monkeys; it not only rids them of parasites but also serves as a constant reminder of social position—high ranking animals receive the most attention.

Below: The pig-tailed macaque, *Macaca nemestrina*, from South-East Asia is one of the largest macaques. The males have longish muzzles and look rather like baboons. This particular animal, from Singapore, has been trained to shin up coconut palms and pick the fruits for its human masters.

Mark Boulton/Bruce Coleman

Ivan Polunin

The barbary ape (below) is protected in Gibraltar, where a legend dating from French and Spanish attacks of 1779 prophesises that if the apes leave the Rock then the British will lose it.

Right: With its arms and legs outstretched and its tail curled upwards behind it, a silvered leaf monkey, *Presbytis cristatus*, prepares to land on a tree in western Malaysia. These monkeys move with great agility when they are disturbed, covering as much as 10 m (33 ft) with a single leap.

both lowland and highland areas, but nowadays they have become adapted to, and even seem to prefer, man-made environments. In some parts of India, where monkeys are protected by religious laws, only about 15 per cent of the total rhesus monkey population lives in the forest, the remaining 85 per cent preferring villages, cities, temples and other human habitations.

Of all monkeys, the rhesus monkey is most commonly seen in zoos. It has played a vital role in medical research for many years, the most important contribution being the identification of the rhesus factor, a blood characteristic which occasionally appears in both rhesus monkeys and man. The unborn offspring of a rhesus negative mother and a rhesus positive father has a high risk of being stillborn because antibodies in the mother's blood tend to destroy the red corpuscles in the blood of the foetus if the latter should prove to be rhesus positive. Nowadays, thanks to research on rhesus monkeys, this dangerous condition can be detected early and the child's life saved by a blood transfusion.

Baboons and mandrills
The baboons, *Papio*, are a group of ground-dwelling monkeys from Africa. They are heavily built animals, reaching a maximum weight of about 50 kg (110 lb), and have well developed teeth, the canines being exceptionally long and pointed. As well as the usual plant diet, baboons eat eggs and small animals. One of the baboon's chief enemies is the leopard, and although the predator usually overcomes its prey in the end, this is by no means always the case. Large male baboons can defend themselves very effectively and will often drive off a marauding leopard; there are even cases of leopards being killed by baboons.

Baboons are active in the day and they spend much of the time in open grasslands close to herds of antelopes and zebra where they feed and groom each other. As well as keeping them free from parasites, grooming is an important social

Above: A troop of baboons on the move. The dominant males travel at the centre of the troop with the main group of females and young. Acting as a guard for this central group are the remaining adult males and females. The juveniles travel at the edge of the group but retreat inwards when danger threatens.

Right: When a dominant male baboon encounters rivals he 'yawns' to display his teeth. Because the size and condition of his teeth, particularly the canine teeth, are a good indication of his physical strength, the 'yawning' threat is a clear demonstration of his high social standing in the troop.

W. H. Muller/ZEFA

activity and is an indicator of a particular animal's rank: a dominant male will be groomed more frequently than other members of the troop. At night, when predators like hyenas and leopards are active, baboons climb trees for security, and several of the males take it in turn to keep watch throughout the night.

The mandrill, *Mandrillus sphinx*, is another large African monkey. It comes from the rain forests of central West Africa and is easily recognized by its extraordinary face: its long nose is covered by reddish skin and is flanked on either side by patches of pale, often bluish skin which have longitudinal grooves running along them from the eyes to the nostrils. The creature's buttocks are also hairless and brightly coloured. These areas of pigmented skin act as threat

Left: The mandrill, *Mandrillus sphinx*, is easily recognized by its bizarre face markings. Although it lives in the equatorial rain forests of West Africa, it spends most of its time on the ground searching for roots, fallen fruit, insects and frogs. It uses the same 'yawning' threat display as the baboon (above).

Below: A southern black-and-white colobus monkey, *Colobus polykomos*, from the coast of East Africa. At the beginning of this century colobus monkeys were shot in large numbers for their fur, and they became quite rare in some places. Nowadays their chief enemies are leopards and eagles.

Natural Science Photos

signals to other mandrills for they become markedly more vivid when the animal is excited. They probably also play an important role in attracting mates. Like baboons, mandrills spend the day on the ground, climbing trees at night to sleep. They live in small troops and feed on a variety of plant and animal food. Of similar appearance and habits but less vividly coloured is the drill, *Mandrillus leucophaeus*, also from West Africa.

Guenons

Almost every region of Africa south of the Sahara is inhabited by one or more species of guenon monkey. Although most species are residents of the central African rain forests, some guenons are more at home in open country. Guenons are slender animals with long tails and they have well marked and often brightly coloured coats. One of the most common guenons is the vervet or green monkey, *Cercopithecus aethiops*, which prefers savannah to forest. Having greenish-grey fur, vervet monkeys live in small troops and are quite bold, approaching other animals and even tourists without apparent concern.

Like all monkeys, guenons breed throughout the year, one or, rarely, two

Ivan Polunin

Left: Guenons, genus *Cercopithecus*, can be distinguished from each other by their facial markings. Shown here are (1) the owl-faced guenon, *C.hamlyni*; (2) DeBrazza's monkey, *C.neglectus*; (3) the vervet monkey, *C.aethiops*; (4) the mona monkey, *C.monas*; and (5) the crowned guenon, *C.pogonias*.

There are often differences in colour and marking between the adults and young of the same guenon species. This may serve to prevent young animals from being attacked by the adult males (who tend to be aggressive) by making them easily distinguishable from other members of the family troop.

Below: The odd-looking proboscis monkey, *Nasalis larvatus*, is a native of the island of Borneo. Adult males have huge, bulbous noses which are important secondary sexual characteristics: in the breeding season females select the males with the largest noses. The females have short, turned-up noses.

Bruce Coleman

young being born after a gestation period of about seven months. For the first weeks of its life the baby guenon clings to its mother's abdomen using its tail as well as its arms to help it hold on. This ability to grasp with its tail, so common among American monkeys, is soon lost as the young animal grows. By the time it is two months old the baby guenon is very active and eating its first solid food, and by four months it is fully weaned. It becomes sexually mature at the relatively advanced age of four years.

Colobus monkeys

These are the only leaf monkeys (members of the family *Colobidae*) to inhabit the African continent—they live in the equatorial rain forests south of the Sahara. There are four species of which the southern black-and-white colobus, *Colobus polykomos*, is perhaps the most striking. Its coat is mostly black but there are areas of long white hair on the tail, the flanks and the face. Although it is not a true brachiator (an animal which uses only its arms when moving through the trees) like the gibbons of South-East Asia, the black-and-white colobus is very agile and it does use its arms and hands more than many other monkeys as it moves from branch to branch. This probably explains its lack of thumbs, for these digits appear to hinder brachiation.

Colobus monkeys live high in the forest canopy where they feed on leaves. Unlike that of most other monkeys (except leaf monkeys) the colobus's diet is restricted almost entirely to leaves and shoots; surprisingly it eats very little fruit. To cope with their unpromising diet of leaves, colobus monkeys as well as the other leaf monkeys have compartmented stomachs rather like those of ruminants such as cattle or sheep. In the first two stomach compartments bacteria begin the digestion process by breaking down the cellulose in the leaves into smaller, more manageable carbohydrates. These compounds then pass to the gut proper for normal enzymic digestion.

Langurs and proboscis monkeys

The langurs of the genus *Presbytis* are the most common of the Asian leaf monkeys. They are slender, long-limbed monkeys which inhabit the forests of India, South-East Asia and southern China. Langurs have long tails which no doubt help them to balance as they jump from tree to tree. In fact langurs and the other leaf monkeys are not so restless as most Old World monkeys, but they nevertheless move with great agility when they need to, and can cover 10 m (33 ft) or so with a single jump.

One of the most remarkable leaf monkeys is the proboscis monkey, *Nasalis larvatus*, from Borneo. It is a large, strong monkey immediately recognizable by its long nose. An adult male may reach a length of 76 cm (30 in) from its nose to the base of its tail, and its large, bulbous nose may be 10 cm (4 in) long. Proboscis monkeys spend most of their time in the mangrove forests feeding on buds and leaves. They are reputed to be excellent swimmers. Closely related to the proboscis monkeys are the snub-nosed langurs, *Rhinopithecus*, from China and Tibet and the pig-tailed langur, *Simias concolor*, from Sumatra. These leaf monkeys also have long noses, but not so long as that of the proboscis monkey.

Gibbons and Orang-utans

Of all living animals the true apes are the most closely related to man. As well as having large brains and being highly intelligent, they have the same number of teeth as we do and they lack tails. Nevertheless, in spite of these similarities, the relationship between apes and man must not be overstated: we are not descended from them. We should regard ourselves rather as cousins, for we are both descended from common ancestors who lived in the Miocene epoch, some 25 million years ago. Since that time the true apes and man have evolved along different lines, and it is therefore a mistake to think of apes simply as less perfect versions of ourselves. They are as highly adapted for their way of life as we are for ours.

All of the surviving apes live in or near the tropical forests of the Old World. The gorilla and chimpanzees live only in Africa, and the orang-utan and gibbons in Asia. Of these four groups of apes the gibbons are set rather apart from the others. Not only are they smaller, ranging in height from about 38 to 91 cm (15 to 36 in) when standing erect, but also, like the Old World monkeys, they have on their buttocks leathery patches which are useful when sitting on the tops of branches. The gibbons are therefore usually classified in a family of their own, the family *Hylobatidae*, which means 'tree walkers'.

Gibbons

On the ground gibbons are the only non-human primates which move only on their hind legs. Their arms are so long that in this erect posture their knuckles sometimes touch the ground and are used in rather the same way as crutches. The arms are often held rather awkwardly

Below: The gibbon's lightly-built skeleton reflects its arboreal existence. Its arms are long and its hands act as hooks as it swings from branch to branch.

Bruce Coleman

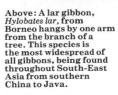

Above: A lar gibbon, *Hylobates lar*, from Borneo hangs by one arm from the branch of a tree. This species is the most widespread of all gibbons, being found throughout South-East Asia from southern China to Java.

Left: A lar gibbon resting at the top of a tree. Gibbons have dense fur which they keep spotlessly clean and free of parasites by constant grooming. Having such thick coats they can thrive in surprisingly cold climates. Several European zoos keep gibbons in outdoor enclosures or on islands in the middle of lakes for much of the year.

Right: The siamang, *Symphalangus syndactylus*, from Sumatra and the Malay peninsula is the largest and strongest of the gibbons. Siamangs produce a loud and characteristic 'song' at dawn and dusk. The sound is amplified by the creature's throat sac and probably denotes the ownership of territory. Siamangs are considerably less agile than the true gibbons of the genus *Hylobates*.

Norman Tomalin/Bruce Coleman

P. Morris

Below: The most obvious features of the human skeleton, when compared with that of a gibbon, are the larger skull, longer legs, shorter arms and wider pelvis.

Above: A gibbon can move through the forest very swiftly by swinging hand over hand from one tree to the next. This mode of progression, using the arms rather than the legs, is called *brachiation*, and is typical of the apes.

Left: A large male orang-utan like this one may weigh as much as 150 kg (330 lb). The huge cheek flaps are seen only in males and appear after the animal has reached maturity.

Below: Orang-utans, *Pongo pygmaeus*, live in the forests of Borneo and Sumatra. Although they come from the same part of the world as the gibbons, they are in fact more closely related to the gorillas and chimpanzees of equatorial Africa. Now on the brink of extinction in the wild, orangs were once quite common throughout eastern Asia. Their remains have been found in excavations as far north as Peking. In the last few thousand years orangs have become smaller—early remains show that orangs as large as gorillas once lived on the Asian mainland.

P. Morris

Okapia

clear of the ground when the animal runs. However, wild gibbons spend almost all their time in trees, and when they run along branches on two legs, grasping with their opposable big toes, their arms are extended as balancing organs. More often gibbons climb by *brachiation*, swinging on their long arms beneath the horizontal branches. The length of their arms is an adaptation to this mode of progression, and usually they swing hand over hand, although sometimes both arms are used in unison. They are capable of leaping across gaps up to 9 m (30 ft) wide, and can cover 3 m (10 ft) with a single reach of the arms. In gripping the branches the four fingers of each hand are held together and used as grappling hooks. The thumbs are small and are not brought into play. Moving fast and at considerable heights above the ground, it is not surprising that gibbons sometimes miss a hand-hold and fall. Usually they are saved from injury by the lower branches which act as safety nets, but injuries do occur from time to time. Sampling of some wild populations has shown that about one gibbon in three has suffered from a broken limb at some time in its life. Like the other apes, gibbons cannot swim.

The study of the behaviour of wild primates and especially apes is a popular branch of zoological science. The early hope that these studies would throw light on aspects of human behaviour has been fulfilled only in part. It seems that behaviour evolves more rapidly than anatomy, and in their behaviour wild apes differ much more than they do in bodily form. For example, the behaviour of gibbons, first studied in the wild in the 1930s, is in some ways more like that of many birds than that of other mammals. This is not as remarkable as it seems for gibbons, like many birds, live in the trees of dense forests, and have had to overcome much the same problems. Adult gibbons live in monogamous pairs. Each pair defends a territory and, being unable to see the neighbouring pairs, does so primarily by means of vocal signals, uttering loud, ringing and whooping calls. These carry over long distances, and are directly comparable to bird-song. Each pair of gibbons is accompanied by up to four of their young of differing ages, but on reaching maturity at perhaps six years of age the young are driven from the group.

Females give birth to usually only a single young one after a pregnancy of about 200 days. Like other young primates, young gibbons are at first almost completely helpless, able only to suckle and to cling to the mother's breast as she moves through the trees. At night the family sleeps huddled together, sitting erect on branches, with their limbs tucked up against their bodies. Early in the morning there is a burst of noisy territorial defence, and then the group moves round the territory feeding on leaves, buds, fruits and some insects. Some species also eat small birds, which they snatch from the air with remarkable dexterity. When drinking, gibbons usually dip their hands into the water, and then lick the moisture from them. As with other primates, part of the day is spent in social grooming. How long gibbons live in the wild is not certain, but in zoos many individuals have lived for more than 20 years.

137

Above: The social behaviour of the orangs is quite unlike that of the other great apes. Females and juveniles live in small, widely scattered groups, each keeping to its own home range, while adult males travel, mostly on their own, through a large territory visiting the various groups it contains. Pictured here is a group of young animals in a Sumatran forest. The territorial males father some but not all of the young. Less mature and less assertive males also visit the females when opportunity offers.

Left: A young orang. Like human babies, newborn orangs are almost completely helpless. They are suckled for between three and four years, but are fed some pre-chewed solid food from an early age.

Below: A female orang stands erect and carries her baby in her arms.

In appearance individuals of the typical gibbon genus, *Hylobates*, vary considerably. Even within a single species the thick, shaggy fur of some individuals may be black and that of others brown or silver-grey. The six species are therefore not easy to distinguish. Most often seen in zoos is the lar gibbon, *Hylobates lar*, found throughout South-East Asia, which can be identified by the white fur on the hands and feet and round the face. The hoolock gibbon, *Hylobates hoolock*, of Assam, Burma, and south-western China has prominent white eyebrows and an especially penetrating call. The smallest of the gibbons is *Hylobates klossi*, which is found only on the Mentawai Islands, off the west coast of Sumatra.

Orang-utans

Although it is the only Asian representative of the great ape family, *Pongidae*, the orang-utan, *Pongo pygmaeus*, is more closely related to the gorilla and chimpanzees than it is to the gibbons. Orangutan means 'old man of the woods' in the Malay language, and in facial appearance orangs are the most like humans of all the apes.

Fossil remains of orangs are widely distributed in southern China and Malay-

sia, but in historic times the species has been found only in Borneo and Sumatra. Even in these islands they are now rare, and the total population numbers only a few thousand. The populations of the two islands are very similar in appearance, both having the same reddish brown, rather sparse hair, but there are differences. Sumatran orangs are on the average slightly larger, while male Bornean orangs have larger cheek flaps. For these and other reasons the two races are regarded as separate sub-species. The present rarity of orangs is chiefly the result of man's destruction of their native forests, both for timber and to make way for plantations. Also, orangs are too often caught as zoo specimens and pets, although this is now illegal. Attempts are now being made to conserve them in the wild: illegally caught young orangs are being rehabilitated for release in the wild, and reputable zoos no longer seek wild-caught specimens, having learned to breed their own orangs. However, economic pressures for forest destruction are strong, and the survival of the orangutan is by no means certain.

The forests in which orangs live are usually dense, with some very tall trees and little or no undergrowth, and the forest floor is often swampy. Orangs are found in the trees at all heights, and at night they sleep in nests of branches and leaves about 20 m (66 ft) above the ground. The same nest is occupied for only a few nights before a new one is built elsewhere. The ability to make nests appears to be at least partly instinctive. When it rains they cover themselves with large leaves. Orang-utans mainly feed on fruit, especially that of the durian tree, which is their staple diet from August to December, but they also eat some leaves, seeds, bark and birds' eggs.

The gestation period is between eight and nine months, and almost always only one young is born at a time. The average weight at birth is 1.5 kg (3.3 lb) and the young orang clings tightly to its mother with its long arms. It may suckle for several years, but grows up at almost twice the speed that humans do. Orangs can breed when they are about seven years old, and are full-grown at about ten years. More information is needed, but it seems likely that the potential lifespan is comparable to that of chimpanzees and gorillas, about 30 or 40 years.

Although orangs can move with surprising speed when they want to, their movements are normally slow and deliberate. Compared with chimpanzees they appear to be slow and introverted, so it is often believed that they are less intelligent than chimpanzees. There is however, no firm foundation for this view for most of the scientific intelligence testing that has been carried out on apes has been on chimpanzees, whose seeming fondness for showing off makes them cooperative, at least when they are immature. Orang-utans are certainly very intelligent: their brains are about as large as those of chimpanzees, being up to 450 cc (27 cu in) in volume. In captivity orangs show greater mechanical aptitude than chimpanzees do, being able to undo nuts and bolts that would fool a chimpanzee. They use their hands with great dexterity, but because their palms are long, the rather short thumb is less useful than the human thumb for many purposes.

Bruce Coleman

Okapia

The Sumatran orang-utan (below), lighter coloured than its Bornean relatives, is seriously threatened with extinction. As long ago as 1964 it was estimated that only 100 still existed on Sumatra.

Gorillas and Chimpanzees

gibbon   orang-utan   gorilla   chimpanzee

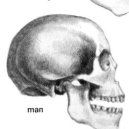

man

Popularly known as the great apes, the chimpanzees and gorillas, together with the orang-utan of South-East Asia, make up the family *Pongidae*. Of all primates these are the most closely related to man, whom they resemble in having no visible external tail, and in their well developed brains. Within the family the chimpanzees and gorillas, which live in Africa, are more closely related to each other than to the orang-utan, having diverged from a common ancestor perhaps seven million years ago.

Both chimpanzees and gorillas have the long arms associated with the arm-swinging method of climbing (*brachiation*) best seen in the gibbons of Asia, but because they are so large and heavy, adult chimpanzees and gorillas rarely brachiate for long. Gorillas spend most of their time on the ground, and chimpanzees spend only about half of their time in trees. One expert, Adriaan Kortlandt, has argued that the immediate ancestors of the chimpanzee were even more terrestrial, living in the African grass-lands from which they have since been driven by mankind. This is far from certain. We know only that when chimpanzees were first discovered by Europeans they were living in the African forests.

Gorillas

The gorillas' reputation as savage monsters is entirely without foundation. They are shy vegetarians. During the day the dominant male leads the troop through a home range which has a total area of about 39 sq km (15 sq miles). Home ranges are not defended against other groups of gorillas—if two troops happen to meet, the adults usually ignore each other, although the juveniles may mix together briefly. This cool behaviour is typical of gorillas and reflects their aloof, introverted personalities.

The dominant male is allowed to rest in the most comfortable places, and gets the first choice of the food available without appearing to assert his massive authority. Only rarely, in defence of the troop against the gorilla's only serious enemy, man, or very occasionally when confronting rivals, does he launch into his threat display, hooting, rising on to his hind legs, beating his chest with his hands, and finally charging. Even then he is not very likely to attack; usually the charge is a bluff, and stops short of the intruder. More often at the first hint of danger the troop silently moves off, avoiding confrontation.

Such shy animals are difficult to observe in the wild and so, no doubt, a great deal remains to be discovered about gorillas' behaviour. As far as we know they are purely vegetarian, feeding on leaves, stems, bark, roots and fruit. Some of their favourite foods, for example, are stringy stems with about the consistency of celery. Like most other primates they eat quite a wide variety of foods, but are fussy as to which part of it they accept: before eating they examine their food carefully, pulling it apart, and

Below: A lowland gorilla. Gorillas are vegetarians and they spend much of their time feeding on shoots, leaves and the pith of stalks and branches. Because their food is so low in nutritional value, they have to eat a large quantity each day. Although they are good climbers, they generally remain on the ground.

Bottom: In the wild, gorillas live in groups like this one of about 15 animals. Led by a large silver-backed male, the group consists mainly of adult females with their young, juveniles and one or two other adult males. On reaching maturity most males leave the family group. These are mountain gorillas.

Above and right: The human cranium is larger and more rounded than that of any ape, for it has to accommodate a brain whose volume is about 1,500 cc. The brain sizes of gorillas, chimpanzees and orang-utans are about 500, 400 and 450 cc respectively. Man's weaker jaw accounts for many other differences.

Jacana

Bruce Coleman

Left: A large male gorilla in typical surroundings. Because they feed on bushes and small trees, gorillas prefer to live near the edge of the rain forest where the sunlight can penetrate. Whereas felling trees for timber often provides an ideal habitat for gorillas, wholesale clearing of the forest for cultivation reduces their range.

Below: The male gorilla's threat display can take a number of forms. Usually it begins with a series of hooting sounds and culminates in a chest-beating performance, but a variety of other gestures may intervene. Only very rarely is the threat display followed by a genuine attack.

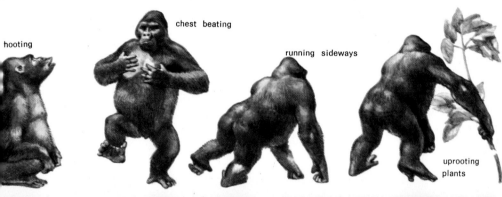

hooting

chest beating

running sideways

uprooting plants

rejecting any discoloured parts.

Gorillas sleep in nests, but even when tall trees are available these are constructed near the ground. Male gorillas, having nothing to fear from predators, usually make their nests in low bushes or even on the ground. An adult male gorilla standing on its relatively short hind legs may be up to 1.8 m (5.9 ft) tall, and has an arm span of up to 2.75 m (9 ft). Large males may weigh up to 275 kg (605 lb), but this is exceptional. The creature's head is particularly massive because it includes a tall bony ridge on top of the skull to which the powerful jaw muscles are attached. These give the gorilla a very strong bite used primarily to tear through the hard stems of some plants to get at the softer pith inside. Adult male gorillas are larger than the females and can be recognized by the greyish-white fur on their backs.

Females and juveniles climb more often than adult males do. No doubt the gorilla's ancestors were smaller and more arboreal than their modern descendants, for, apart from their size, they are well adapted for climbing, with long, grasping digits, opposable thumbs and big toes, long arms which are potentially useful for brachiation and good binocular vision. The ability to judge distance is essential to an active climber.

Gorillas have a discontinuous distribution in equatorial Africa. The western lowland gorilla inhabits forests of Cam-

Left: Like humans, chimpanzees use a whole range of facial expressions to indicate their emotions. This animal, with its gaping mouth and jutting upper lip, is expressing frustration. Chimpanzees also communicate with other group members by a variety of hoots and grunts, and, to some extent, by touch.

Below: Chimpanzees spend more time in trees than do gorillas. Every evening the adults build nests like the one shown here to provide protection from predators. The nests are made of bent and woven branches covered with a bed of smaller branches and leaves. They may be as much as 30 m above the ground.

Giuseppe Mazza

excitement

elation

eroun, Gabon, and western Zaire. Nearly 1,000 miles to the east, the eastern lowland gorilla inhabits forests from the Lualaba or upper Congo River to the foothills of the mountains beyond. Here on the slopes of the Virunga volcanoes and the mountains bordering Lake Kivu lives the mountain gorilla. These three populations differ slightly from each other in features of the skull and in certain other ways— mountain gorillas, for example, have slightly longer, thicker fur.

However, most zoologists now agree that there is only one species, *Gorilla gorilla*, and that the various forms are only subspecies. Lowland gorillas live in dense forest, preferring areas where fallen trees or rivers break the upper canopy, allowing the sunlight to encourage thick undergrowth, which is a rich source of their food. Mountain gorillas prefer more thinly wooded valleys where ferns and creepers abound. Sometimes they venture above the tree-line in search of bamboo shoots.

The gestation period of the gorilla is about nine months. At birth baby gorillas are even more helpless than those of most other primates. For the first month of life they cannot even cling to their mother, but have to be cradled in her arms. At three

months a baby gorilla may start to ride on its mother's back, and at six or seven months it can walk and climb on its own. However, the bond with the mother remains very strong until, three or four years later, she has another youngster. In the rate at which they mature, gorillas resemble chimpanzees. More data is needed, but it seems likely that they have a potential life-span of 40 or more years.

Chimpanzees

There are two main kinds of chimpanzees. The commoner of these, *Pan troglodytes*, is widely distributed in tropical Africa, and several different races or subspecies have been described. However, all chimpanzee populations are rather variable in appearance, and these differences are not very important. The most distinct of all chimpanzees is the pygmy chimpanzee, the only form to be found south of the Congo River. This is regarded by many authorities as a separate species, *Pan paniscus*. The pygmy chimpanzee is less heavily built than the common chimpanzee, which weighs up to 50 kg (110 lb) or more, adult females being almost as large as males.

Chimpanzees are far from being specialized feeders. In mature rain forests they

feed mainly on fruit, when it is available, although they also eat leaves and bark. In more open savannah woodland they make up for the smaller supply of vegetable foods by eating insects, and sometimes by hunting and eating other mammals, such as small antelopes. In some parts of West Africa chimpanzees have colonized rubbish dumps outside towns, where they feed on scraps.

Chimpanzees have developed a remarkable technique for obtaining termites, a popular item of diet. Picking a small twig or grass stem they remove all its side branches, and poke it into a termites' nest. Angry termites seize the intruding object with their jaws, and cling to it as the twig is withdrawn. The chimpanzee then pulls the twig through its lips, removing the termites. This action looks highly intelligent, but there is some evidence to suggest that it is purely instinctive. If they are given a slender twig, zoo-bred chimpanzees need little encouragement to poke it into holes, and also draw it through their lips.

One interesting aspect of this behaviour is that in preparing the twigs for use chimpanzees are essentially making tools. They also do this when crushing dry leaves before using them to soak up

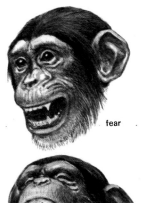

fear

sadness

Left: Some common chimpanzee expressions.

Right: A female pygmy chimpanzee with her baby. Like the other apes, chimpanzees reproduce only slowly because the females cannot conceive while they are lactating. Since the female will nurse her young for between two and three years, she can produce only one (occasionally two) offspring every three years or so. The gestation period is between seven and eight months. This particular species, *Pan paniscus*, is found in equatorial Africa, south of the Congo River. The more common species, *Pan troglodytes*, is found throughout central and western Africa, from Senegal to Tanzania.

Tierbilder Okapia

Tierbilder Okapia

Above: Chimpanzees in captivity are enthusiastic painters, and their efforts resemble the early works of human children. They seem to have a rudimentary sense of symmetry for their compositions on paper are usually fairly well balanced. They rarely paint only down one side of the paper.

Below: The most significant difference between man and his nearest relatives, the apes, is his much greater mental capacity. The ability to learn and remember things made language possible and paved the way for logical thought. These spectators are watching a chess championship in the USSR.

Marc Riboud / John Hillelson Agency

water for drinking. This means that man is not unique as a toolmaker, and the attempts that were made a few years ago to use toolmaking ability to place man apart from all other animals are not based on fact. The truth is that no absolute distinction can be made between man and all other animals.

Chimpanzees are certainly intelligent. Experiments to determine intelligence have all been carried out with young chimpanzees, for adults are aggressive and uncooperative, and young animals learn more quickly than old ones. Once young chimpanzees have learned that by standing on a box they can reach higher objects—even such an obvious fact has to be learned—they swiftly put their knowledge to good use in obtaining fruit which is otherwise out of reach. Behaviour of this kind enables them to solve problems which could never be solved by instinct alone, and produces flexible behaviour which can be adapted to meet a variety of situations.

In the wild chimpanzees live in large, loosely-knit groups. About 80 animals may occupy an undefended home range of between 20 and 78 sq km (8 to 30 sq miles). They move equally well through the trees or on the ground, where they walk on all fours, touching the ground with the backs of their knuckles. Adult males travel further than the others, acting as scouts for the main party. When they find a tree laden with ripe fruit their drumming and loud hooting calls attract other chimpanzees from up to 3 km (2 miles) away to join in the feast. On these occasions chimpanzees belonging to neighbouring troops mix without hostility. Large males have high status,

and are treated with deference, but within the troop there is no rigid 'pecking order'. When conflicts arise between individuals they are usually solved when one of the individuals concerned moves off to join another troop.

The chimpanzee's essentially peaceable disposition is not even disturbed when the females come into breeding condition, as they do every month or so. At this time females have swellings in the region of the genital organs. They are promiscuous, and may mate with several males in succession. The gestation period is usually between seven and eight months, and at birth the young chimpanzee weighs about 1.9 kg (4.2 lb). For the first two years of life it is completely dependent upon its mother, but as it grows older it is supported by other members of the troop.

By playing with other juveniles it exercises its body, learns about its surroundings and, probably most important of all, becomes socialized and learns how to get on with other members of its species. Until about six years of age the young chimpanzee never goes far from its mother, but it then becomes more independent and, especially if it is a male, may begin to go off with other chimpanzees for increasingly lengthy periods. Chimpanzees are sexually mature at about 8 years, full-grown at about 12 years, and may live for 40 or more years unless they fall victim to a predator. Apart from man the chimpanzee's greatest enemy is the leopard. When threatened by such a predator, chimpanzees arm themselves with missiles and sticks, and confront it aggressively, the combined strength and resourcefulness of the troop being their main defence.

143

During 50 million years of evolution the African Elephant's upper lip has become a trunk, and its tusks hugely extended in the search for food.

Index

Page numbers in *italics* indicate illustrations in addition to text matter on the subject.